GEOLOGY UNDERFOOT ALONG COLORADO'S FRONT RANGE

Lon Abbott and Terri Cook

2012
Mountain Press Publishing Company
Missoula, Montana

First Printing, August 2012

All photographs and illustrations by authors unless otherwise credited.
Cover art: Original painting *Coming Home* by Dona Abbott

The Geology Underfoot series presents geology with a hands-on, get-out-of-your-car approach. A formal background in geology is not required for enjoyment.

Library of Congress Cataloging-in-Publication Data

Abbott, Lon, 1963-
Geology underfoot along Colorado's Front Range / Lon Abbott and Terri Cook.
pages cm. — (Geology underfoot)
Includes bibliographical references and index.
ISBN 978-0-87842-595-2 (pbk. : alk. paper)
1. Geology—Front Range (Colo. and Wyo.)—Guidebooks. 2. Front Range (Colo. and Wyo.)—Guidebooks. 3. National parks and reserves—Colorado—Guidebooks. I. Cook, Terri, 1969- II. Title.
QE92.F7A23 2012
557.88'6—dc23

2012021387

PRINTED IN HONG KONG

P.O. Box 2399 • Missoula, MT 59806 • 406-728-1900
800-234-5308 • info@mtnpress.com
www.mountain-press.com

Dedicated to the many people who saved Lon's life in Eldorado Canyon in May 2008 and who assisted with his recovery.

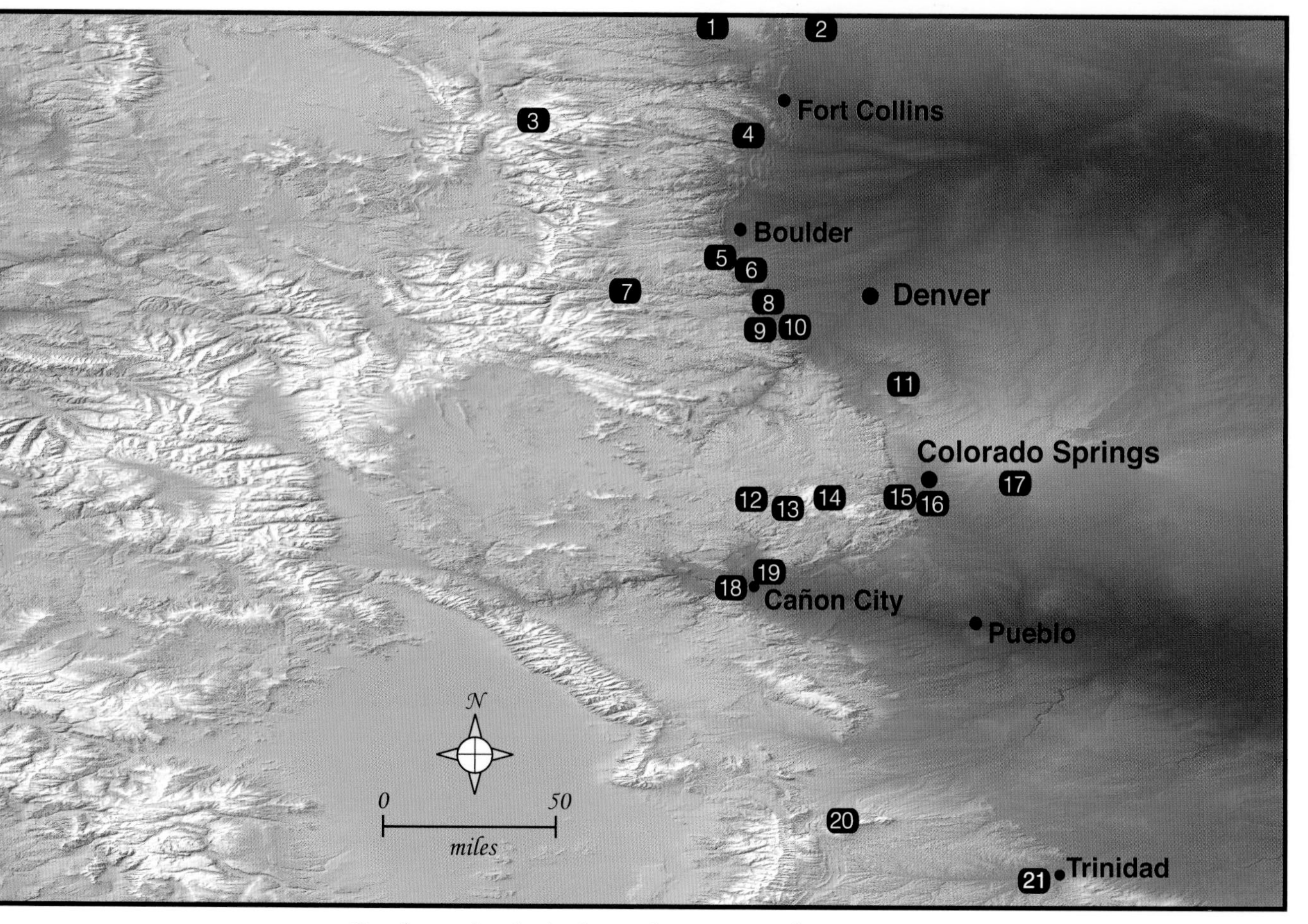

Sites featured in this book. Numbers correspond to vignettes.

Contents

Preface

The scenery along Colorado's Front Range is breathtaking. The area owes its grandeur in large part to its extraordinary geologic diversity. Thanks to that diversity, as well as the fact that the Front Range has more earth scientists per capita than just about any place on the planet, its geology has been poked, prodded, and studied throughout the 150 years since geologists first laid eyes on it. Thanks to that exhaustive study, we know a great deal about the area's fascinating geologic history. And yet the more we learn, the more questions crop up. Not only is Front Range geology beautiful, it is also puzzling. This book is a guide to twenty-one noteworthy sites along the Front Range and to the extraordinary events that have sculpted its spectacular scenery over the last 1,800 million years. We endeavored not only to tell the area's geologic story as scientists know it today, but also to highlight areas of scientific disagreement or uncertainty. Numerous scientists, including many Front Range residents, are working vigorously to fill in the gaps in our knowledge of this area's geologic evolution. The rocks will reveal new information to those scientists who develop novel techniques and who think in refreshingly creative ways. We look forward to learning and sharing those new stories as they unfold.

Each of the twenty-one vignettes is a self-contained story, yet together they constitute a biography of the Front Range through the vastness of geologic time. For the reader who wishes to trace the Front Range's remarkable evolution, we compiled a table with which you may follow vignettes chronologically, transforming your travels through the region into a journey through time. Additional sources of information listed at the back of the book enable you to delve deeper into any of the topics.

The story of Earth is told in the language of rocks. A crucial piece of this vocabulary is the theory of plate tectonics. If you're not familiar with the theory's concepts, we urge you to first read vignette 7, which discusses plate tectonics in the context of the formation of the Front Range's crust.

Unless we say otherwise, dirt roads we send you on may be bumpy or dusty, but they should be passable in good weather in a passenger car with normal clearance. In wet weather, and especially in winter, some roads become impassible or are closed by the authorities. Check road conditions locally, prepare, and don't go if in doubt. In remote areas mentioned in this guide, no services are available, so make sure you have a good spare tire and plenty of water, gasoline, food, and warm clothes. And always exercise extreme caution clambering around on rocks and near cliff edges.

We are indebted to a number of people who helped this project come to fruition. We thank Cheryl McCutchan, who painted "The Last Supper" specifically for this project and provided excellent color advice for figures. Bob Anderson, Leonard Ewy, Ed Heffern, Kirk Johnson, Alan Lester, Herb Meyer, Peter Molnar, and Sara Neustadtl shared their considerable scientific and editorial expertise, greatly enhancing the content of several chapters. We thank Kirk Johnson at the Denver Museum of Nature and Science, James Balog, the Denver Public Library, and Herb Meyer, Conni Jo O'Connor, and Lindsay Walker at Florissant Fossil Beds National Monument for permission to use their paintings and photographs. We are particularly indebted to Vince Matthews at the Colorado Geological Survey for sharing his deep knowledge of Front Range geology during his helpful review and to James Lainsbury for his deft editorial hand throughout the manuscript revision process.

TIME	EVENT	VIGNETTES
19th century–present	Mining of metals and diamonds; radioactive contamination; and flash floods.	1, 4, 6, 7, 13
2.5 Ma–10,000 years ago	Pleistocene ice ages—sculpting of Front Range by glaciers; alternating aggradation-incision on Plains.	3, 6
5 Ma–present	Erosion excavates Laramide Rockies to create modern topography, caused by a pulse of uplift or climate change.	2, 8, 12, 20
28 Ma	Rio Grande Rift extension begins in Colorado.	13, 18, 20
35–5 Ma	Laramide Rockies buried in their own debris and in volcanic ash from Ignimbrite Flare-up.	2
37–24 Ma	Rocky Mountain Erosion Surface forms; Ignimbrite Flare-up happens.	2, 3, 8, 11, 12, 13
55 Ma	Climate warms during PETM event.	17
67–53 Ma	Laramide orogeny raises Front Range in two pulses and is accompanied by igneous intrusions that form the Colorado Mineral Belt.	2, 7, 8, 13, 16, 17, 20
65.5 Ma	Asteroid impact in Yucatan, Mexico, wipes out 70 percent of Earth's species, including dinosaurs.	21
100–70 Ma	Western Interior Seaway rises and falls.	9, 10, 19
150 Ma	Front Range consists of lowland inhabited by dinosaurs; supercontinent Pangaea breaks up, delivering volcanic ash to region.	9, 10, 19
260–250 Ma	World's biggest mass extinction occurs; Front Range region is an arid tidal flat.	9
280 Ma	Sand dunes envelop Front Range region.	9, 16
315–300 Ma	Assembly of Pangaea raises Ancestral Rockies.	5, 9, 16
500–320 Ma	Quiet interlude with deposition of limestone and sandstone in shallow seas and coastal environments.	1, 15
616 Ma	Intrusion of diamond pipes.	1
1,080 Ma	Intrusion of Pikes Peak granite; supercontinent Rodinia is assembled.	14
1,450–1,400 Ma	Intrusion of extensive granite; northeast-trending shear zones develop.	3, 7
1,650–1,600 Ma	Collision between growing North American continent and another series of volcanic island arcs during Mazatzal orogeny.	7, 18
1,700 Ma	Erosion of uplifted mountains deposits material that becomes Coal Creek quartzite.	5
1,780–1,700 Ma	Formation and amalgamation of volcanic island arcs that collide with proto–North American continent during Yavapai orogeny.	7, 18

Timeline of major geologic events in the Front Range's history and the vignettes that explore them. Ma = millions of years ago.

Geology of Colorado's Front Range

Colorado's Front Range is renowned for its majestic mountains. But what makes it geologically noteworthy is the tremendous physiographic contrast—one of the continent's most abrupt—between the Great Plains and the Rocky Mountains. The area's magnificent landscapes beckon residents and visitors alike to experience their stunning beauty, and the rocks record vivid tales of mountain ranges raised, torn down, and rebuilt again; mighty floods and mightier glaciers that sculpted the beauty we enjoy today; volcanic eruptions that dwarf the biggest any human has ever experienced; and the plants and animals that have called Colorado home.

As you travel the Front Range's main roads and byways, you can trace its awe-inspiring evolution from a nondescript patch of ocean floor to its present splendor. Here we briefly narrate this epic, providing an overview to place the geologic features you observe in each vignette in the broader context of the Front Range's vast 1,800-million-year history.

Earth, along with the rest of the solar system, coalesced from star dust 4,600 million years ago. Because geologists must deal with such large sweeps of time, they have, based on the fossil record, divided and subdivided Earth's history into increasingly shorter time intervals, from eons to eras to periods. They have radiometrically dated the rocks of each time slice in order to place a numerical age on the boundary between the slices. There are three eons: the Archean and Proterozoic, collectively referred to as the Precambrian, and the younger Phanerozoic, which is split into three eras. These eras are further subdivided into periods, which are, in turn, comprised of several epochs. We frequently refer to the period in which a rock formed and, for the more recent rocks, its epoch, so the accompanying geological timescale will serve as a handy companion while you read. Basic understanding of the theory of plate tectonics is essential to understanding much of Earth's geologic story. If you are unfamiliar with its concepts, please read vignette 7 before proceeding.

For the first 2,800 million years of Earth's existence, the patch of ground that would become the Front Range was a nondescript scrap of barren seafloor composed of dense oceanic crust destined for obliteration in a subduction zone. Hence, no rock record from the Archean eon remains for the Front Range. That all changed about 1,800 million years ago, during the Proterozoic eon, when a series of volcanoes developed over a subduction

The geologic timescale.

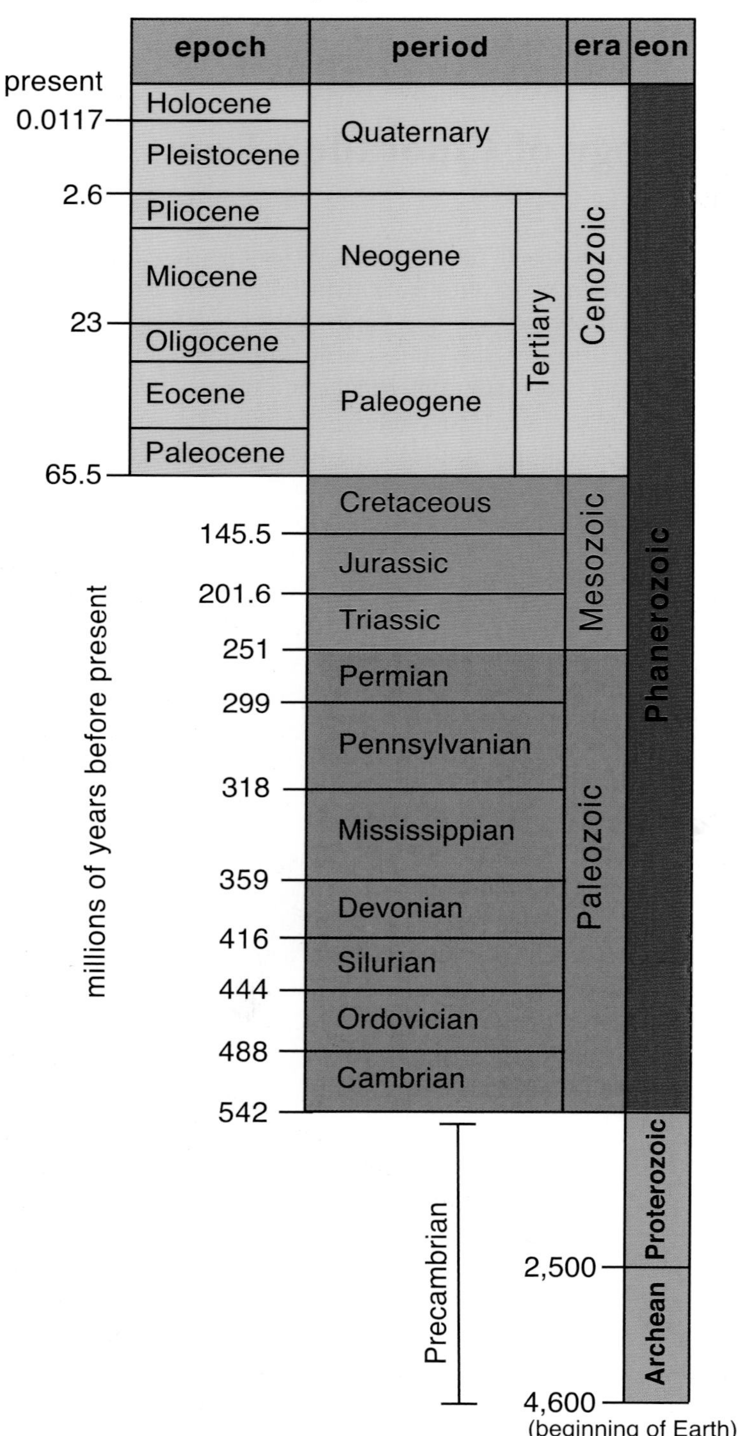

zone and forged (erupted) Colorado's first durable continental crust, consisting of a tangle of mountainous volcanic island chains reminiscent of today's Southeast Asian archipelagos. Vignette 7 narrates the birth of this continental crust, which became the Front Range, and you can examine a cross section of it that will take your breath away at the Royal Gorge (vignette 18).

One island chain after another viciously collided with the embryonic North American continent, like bugs smashing into a windshield, as the subduction zones gobbled up the oceanic crust that separated them from North America. These collisions, which occurred between about 1,780 and 1,700 million years ago, ultimately extended the continent's width 300 miles and raised a series of mountain ranges that stretched along the continent's new coastline, from northern Arizona through Colorado to Nebraska and beyond. The building of mountains by tectonic plate convergence is known as an orogeny. This series of collisions, known regionally as the Yavapai orogeny and locally as the Colorado orogeny, was the first of many to leave its mark on the Front Range. The crust forged during the Yavapai orogeny floors all of northern and central Colorado and forms many of the Front Range's high peaks and foothills. You will glimpse it during your travels in vignettes 3, 4, 7, 8, 9, and 18.

As these coastal mountains were raised, erosion (and possibly normal faulting) began to tear them down, reducing them to pebbles and sand. This debris was deposited in a series of local basins and buried deeply enough to be metamorphosed into a very durable quartzite. Small patches of this 1,700-million-year-old quartzite are scattered across the state, and you can examine one such outcrop in the depths of Eldorado Canyon in vignette 5. Another chain of volcanic islands smashed into the continent between about 1,650 and 1,600 million years ago, adding to North America the real estate stretching from southern Arizona through northern New Mexico and southern Colorado. Colorado evidence for this second orogeny (the Mazatzal orogeny) is strongest in the modern Sangre de Cristo Mountains, which lay near the continental margin at that time (vignette 18).

After all this tectonic excitement, things quieted down until between 1,450 and 1,400 million years ago, when a series of large granite plutons were injected into the old suture zones along which the volcanic island chains had been welded onto North America. This episode of granite emplacement stretched far beyond the boundaries of Colorado, and it has greatly puzzled geologists because the granitic magmas welled up within the continental interior, not along a continental margin, as is more typical. Geologists have long thought the granitic magma welled up thanks to stretching of the crust in a northwest-southeast direction, but recent work indicates that instead the continent was enduring compression in that direction along with strike-slip faulting. This event is known as the

Berthoud orogeny, and it may have been triggered by the collision of a microcontinent with North America, this one forming the land we know today as southeastern New Mexico and the Texas panhandle. A series of major faults, called shear zones, developed at that time, running along the old crustal weaknesses formed in the earlier collision zones (vignette 7). The 1,400-million-year-old granites are prominent in Rocky Mountain National Park (vignette 3) and on Mt. Evans (vignette 7).

North America endured another turbulent period about 1,100 million years ago when it collided with another continent. Known as the Grenville orogeny, this continental collision put the finishing touches on a global supercontinent known as Rodinia. The brunt of this collision fell on what was then coastal North America, which stretched from Austin, Texas, to Alabama and northward to New York's Adirondack Mountains. But this collision was so massive that the continent's interior was not immune. A likely modern analogue is the collision forming the Himalayas, the effects of which are felt far into the interior of Asia. There a rift, in which Siberia's Lake Baikal nestles, has formed behind the Himalayas. During the late Proterozoic, North America was home to a comparable rift, which stretched from Lake Superior to Kansas. Colorado was spared that level of tectonic violence, but it, too, seems to have stretched in an east-west direction, facilitating the intrusion of the state's largest single granite batholith. This granite forms the rock of America's mountain, Pikes Peak (vignette 14).

Earth contains a tremendous amount of internal heat that must be released, much like the warmth that builds up if you exercise while wearing a parka. Like good parkas, supercontinents trap that internal heat, causing it to build up and ultimately form rifts that tear the continent apart. The destiny of all supercontinents, then, is to break up, and that is exactly what happened to Rodinia about 750 million years ago. Australia and Antarctica, which had formerly been western North America's neighbors, were ripped away, and the ancient Pacific Ocean grew in their wake. This separation was accomplished along a rift that lay (in modern coordinates) along a north-south line running from Salt Lake City to Las Vegas. Although Colorado was at the periphery, it was nonetheless rent by a series of north-south-oriented normal faults. These faults formed zones of weakness in the crust that would be reactivated repeatedly in the years to come, thereby strongly influencing Colorado's topography right up to the present. The first noteworthy Front Range geologic feature to exploit such a zone of weakness was a string of explosive volcanoes, known as kimberlite volcanoes, which erupted 616 million years ago along a north-south line running from northern Larimer County to Boulder. The diamonds some of these explosions brought to the surface were the first in North America to be commercially mined (vignette 1).

The Proterozoic was a tumultuous time for Colorado, but as the curtain came down on the eon Colorado settled into a relatively quiet period dominated by extensive erosion of the mountains raised during earlier tectonic episodes, which ultimately exposed the mountains' deeply buried granite and metamorphic roots. The Front Range of 510 million years ago consisted of a nearly flat plain lying near sea level. As the Paleozoic era dawned, during the late Cambrian period a shallow sea crept over Colorado from the west. Although rocks from the early Paleozoic (dating from the Cambrian through the Mississippian periods) are absent from much of the Front Range, they are prominent in the Colorado Springs area, where you can go spelunking in caves etched out of limestone deposited during the Ordovician period (vignette 15). During the Devonian period, a new series of kimberlite volcanoes welled up along the same north-south crustal weakness as their predecessors, bequeathing the state with yet more diamonds (vignette 1).

Because oceanic crust is dense enough to subduct and continental crust is not, it is inevitable that as soon as one supercontinent disintegrates another begins to form. Just over 300 million years ago, during Pennsylvanian time, Rodinia's successor, Pangaea, was born as Earth's continents once again coalesced. The orogeny that completed its assembly raised a continuous chain of mountains running from the Appalachians through the Ozarks and into north Texas. From there the chain bent northward, running through New Mexico and Colorado. Because the Colorado–New Mexico range rose in approximately the same location occupied by the modern Rockies, it is known as the Ancestral Rockies. Why the Ancestral Rockies formed, with their north-south orientation, is a puzzle to geologists because the continent-continent collision, and the other mountains it created, was oriented east-west and occurred far from Colorado. The preexisting weaknesses that Proterozoic tectonic events inscribed into Colorado's crust likely played a role, but scientists are still probing the details behind the uplifting of this ancient range.

Although why the Ancestral Rockies rose has geologists scratching their heads, their former existence is clearly recorded. You will be able to reconstruct this chapter of Front Range history while examining the sediment shed from this former range in vignettes 5, 9, and 16. Although Colorado lay at tropical latitudes when the Ancestral Rockies rose, the globe was in the grip of a major ice age. Scientists have long wondered how cold the globe was and how close to the equator the ice reached. Evidence recently gathered along the Front Range suggests that temperatures at the equator periodically plunged below freezing even at low elevations (vignette 16), indicating the globe may have been even colder than scientists previously suspected.

During the Permian period, Colorado's climate became increasingly arid. Rivers draining the Ancestral Rockies, which by then had been eroded down to mere hills, periodically dried up. Sand dunes migrated across the landscape (vignettes 9, 16). As the Paleozoic era gave way to the Mesozoic 251 million years ago, the sea crept back over the Front Range, which consisted of a vast tidal flat that lay baking under a scorching sun. The heat and aridity likely led to rapid evaporation along many of the region's tidal estuaries, just the sort of harsh conditions necessary for bacterial mats to thrive in the hypersaline lagoons (vignette 9).

The Mesozoic also marked the end for the supercontinent Pangaea, which began to split apart during the Triassic period along seams that eventually formed the modern continents' boundaries. Pangaea's breakup inaugurated the Atlantic Ocean. As the ocean grew, North America moved west and impinged on the Pacific. The oceanic crust flooring the Pacific Ocean began to subduct under North America's west coast, forming a volcanic mountain chain that stretched along North America's west coast for the next 200 million years. By the Late Jurassic, Colorado consisted of a vast lowland plain crisscrossed by sluggish, meandering rivers draining that distant volcanic range. Ash that was belched from the volcanoes settled over the plain, where it was stirred into the river muds (vignette 9). Dinosaurs, the dominant group of land animals during the Jurassic, lived and died along these rivers, and occasionally their remains were fortuitously fossilized. The Front Range is so well-endowed with a rich assemblage of Jurassic dinosaur remains that it became the front line in an unseemly scientific feud known as the Bone Wars (vignettes 10, 19). Despite its childish foundations, this "war" between two eminent paleontologists bequeathed to science an exceptionally rich trove of information on the life and times of dinosaurs, with Front Range fossils playing a starring role.

During the succeeding Cretaceous period (145.5 to 65.5 million years ago), a vast inland sea crept westward across Colorado. The Front Range occupied the western shoreline of this Western Interior Seaway 100 million years ago (vignette 9), and dinosaurs migrated along the so-called dinosaur freeway, a long, sandy beach that stretched from Boulder to Tucumcari, New Mexico (vignettes 10, 19). As sea level continued to rise, the coast migrated westward to Grand Junction and later into Utah and Arizona, drowning the Front Range beneath several hundred feet of seawater. The mudstone and limestone deposited in this seaway are visible at stops in vignettes 2, 6, 8, 9, and 10.

The Mesozoic era literally ended with a bang 65.5 million years ago when a killer asteroid collided with Earth, gouging out a 110-mile-wide crater in Mexico's Yucatan Peninsula and extinguishing 70 percent of all species, including the dinosaurs. Colorado's Raton Basin is one of the best places on Earth to see the clay layer that marks this catastrophic event (vignette 21).

At about the same time (during the interval between 75 and 43 million years ago), vigorous tectonic activity returned to the Front Range in the form of the Laramide orogeny. Driven by compression resulting from unusually low-angled subduction off the California coast, the Rocky Mountains were born (vignettes 2, 5, 8, 9, 16, 20). Like the orogeny that produced the Ancestral Rockies before it and in nearly the same location, the Laramide orogeny occurred unusually far from a plate boundary, making it a particularly puzzling mountain building episode. Not only was the Laramide orogeny itself odd, so too was the pattern of igneous activity associated with it. Because the North American plate converged with a northeasterly moving plate during the orogeny, one would expect a chain of volcanoes to form perpendicular to the plate boundary—northwest to southeast in this case. Instead, the only igneous activity that accompanied the orogeny was a northeast-southwest-trending belt of plutons that developed from Boulder to Durango, perpendicular to the expected trend. Abundant mineral-rich fluid accompanied the magma, leaving behind rich deposits of gold, silver, lead, zinc, molybdenum, and other precious metals, deposits collectively called the Colorado Mineral Belt (vignettes 7, 13).

The sediment shed off the Laramide Rockies accumulated across the adjacent Great Plains, where we can examine it at places like Green Mountain (vignette 8) and Paint Mines Interpretive Park (vignette 17). The uplift of the Rockies changed local climate, fostering one of the world's first rainforests. Global climate was changing as well, and the legacy of a particularly intense bout of heat, whose characteristics potentially contain lessons about our climatic future, is on display at the Paint Mines (vignette 17).

The Laramide compression finally subsided around 43 million years ago. Erosion quickly tore at the mountains, subduing their topography and creating a widespread erosion surface geologists have christened the Rocky Mountain (or Late Eocene) Erosion Surface (vignettes 2, 8, 11). That surface would soon be buried in a pile of volcanic debris when an extraordinary volcanic episode, known as the Ignimbrite Flare-up, swept across the American West beginning about 37 million years ago. The flare-up was one of the biggest episodes of high-silica volcanism the planet has ever witnessed, and during it seventeen of the forty biggest-known volcanic eruptions occurred between Colorado and Nevada (vignettes 11, 13). One eruption set in motion a fortuitous confluence of circumstances that preserved one of the best assemblages of fossilized insects known anywhere on Earth (vignette 12). The volcanoes belched so much material that they buried the Great Plains in 1,500 feet of ash (vignette 2). Most geologists suspect the Ignimbrite Flare-up was caused by a change in the angle—from shallow to steep—of the same subducting slab that had uplifted the Rockies. Details, however, are sketchy, and the flare-up must be added to a long list of Front Range geologic events whose ultimate causes remain shrouded in mystery.

The Ignimbrite Flare-up spans a time period during which the tectonic stresses affecting Colorado were shifting from east-west compression, which uplifted the Rockies, to east-west extension. The result of this shift to extension is the Rio Grande Rift, a major rift valley composed of a series of north-south-oriented valleys that splits the state's highest mountain ranges right down the middle. The San Luis Valley and upper Arkansas River valley (vignette 18) are the most prominent portions of the rift in Colorado. Large volumes of magma were erupted in the rift valley and along its flanks (vignettes 13, 20).

The Laramide Rocky Mountains were slowly buried in their own debris and abundant volcanic ash derived from the Ignimbrite Flare-up. Between 17 and 5 million years ago an episode of vigorous erosion occurred in what was left of the Laramide Rockies, triggering the deposition of coarse sandstone and conglomerate across the Great Plains. The material shed from the Rockies at that time forms the enormously important Ogallala Aquifer, the main source of water for thousands of farms across the Midwest from Nebraska to Texas. The Front Range at that time consisted of little more than a long, gradual inclined plane that merged seamlessly with the Great Plains at its eastern foot (vignette 2).

The Rockies we know today began to take shape during the last 5 million years, when a period of vigorous erosion began, excavating thousands of feet of sedimentary rock (vignettes 2, 20). Because the old Laramide ranges consist of hard granite and metamorphic rock rather than soft sedimentary rock, they have resisted this erosional onslaught far better than have the Great Plains. The Laramide Rockies have therefore reemerged from the sedimentary blanket that covered them. As the elevation difference between the Great Plains and Rockies has increased, so has the erosive power of the rivers draining the mountains. These newly invigorated streams have carved innumerable deep gorges into the mountain flanks. The Royal Gorge is the deepest and most precipitous one along the Front Range (vignette 18).

Geologists agree that this recent pulse of erosion has occurred and that it has exhumed the Laramide Rockies to produce the scenic grandeur characterizing the Front Range today. But they vigorously debate its cause. A welt of warm mantle material underlies Colorado. It is this warmth that likely supports the state's unusually high elevations. If the warmth is a recent phenomenon, as many geologists believe, it likely caused uplift and triggered the erosion. Other geologists, in contrast, believe the mantle became warm earlier in geologic time and that the erosion is due, instead, to recent global climate change. This is yet another Front Range puzzle whose solution awaits the development of new scientific techniques and fresh insights. See vignettes 2 and 12 for a thorough discussion of this controversy regarding when the Front Range reached its current elevation.

Global climate has been cooling over the last 34 million years. About 2.5 million years ago that cooling crossed a threshold that allowed massive ice sheets and mountain glaciers to form in the northern hemisphere for the first time in hundreds of millions of years. Earth's temperature has been poised near that threshold ever since, meaning that slight, periodic changes in Earth's orbit have repeatedly, and cyclically, pulled the planet's temperature above and below that threshold. The ice sheets and mountain glaciers have responded to that fluctuation by alternately growing and shrinking throughout the Pleistocene ice ages. The periodic growth and decay of mountain glaciers up to 25 miles long and 2,000 feet thick has sculpted the Front Range's spectacular scenery, most dramatically in renowned Rocky Mountain National Park (vignette 3). Although the Great Plains were not covered in ice, the periodic melting and freezing of the mountain glaciers triggered wild fluctuations in the water and sediment loads of the rivers traversing them. The result has been the carving of a stairway-like flight of river terraces that are the most prominent feature of the Plains' interface with the Rocky Mountain foothills (vignette 6).

The Pleistocene ice ages were the most recent major geologic event to affect the Front Range, but changes continue to this day. A combination of topography and climate makes the Front Range particularly vulnerable to flash floods, a fact made tragically apparent on the night of July 31, 1976, when a 20-foot-tall wall of water roared down the Big Thompson Canyon, sweeping 144 people to their deaths (vignette 4). Other changes are the result of human activities, such as radioactive contamination created from the manufacture of nuclear weapons (vignette 6) and pollution due to the exploitation of the region's rich resources (vignettes 1, 7, 13).

As a result of its long and tumultuous geologic history, the Front Range is a land of exceptional geologic diversity. That diversity has bequeathed to it an unsurpassed beauty that is enjoyed daily by the millions of people who live in and visit the Front Range. We hope you find this book a worthy companion as you explore the Front Range's world-famous destinations and well-kept secrets, conversing with the rocks as they recount remarkable stories etched in stone.

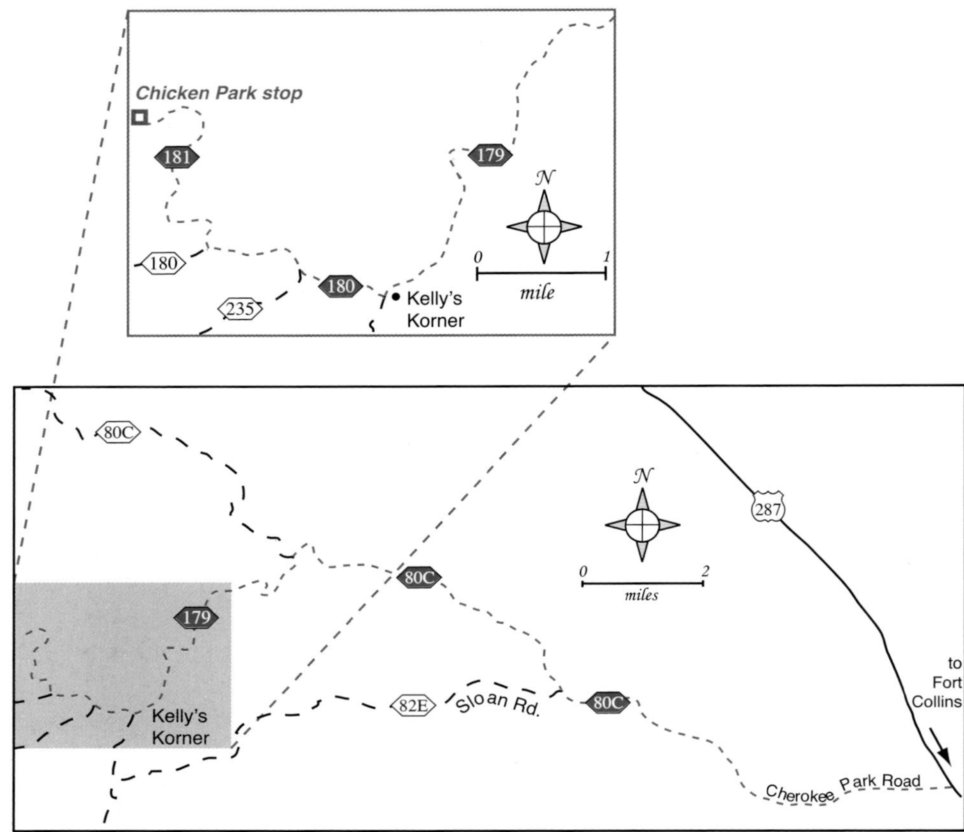

GETTING THERE: Although most Colorado diamond pipes lie on private land, a cluster in Chicken Park, northwest of Fort Collins, is publicly accessible. From Fort Collins travel north on US 287 to its junction with County Road 80C. Marked by a sign to Cherokee Park, the 80C turnoff lies 3 miles north of the turnoff to Red Feather Lakes and 100 yards south of milepost 370. Reset your odometer here. Follow 80C for 14.2 miles, then turn left onto County Road 179. Follow this for 5.8 miles, then turn right onto County Road 180, where a homemade sign announces Kelly's Korner. After 1.6 miles, you reach a junction with County Road 181, which is often closed in winter and early spring. The roads to this point have been good gravel, but 181 is rutted dirt. When it's not too muddy, cautious drivers in 2-wheel-drive vehicles can negotiate it. Turn right (north) onto 181. After 1.6 miles you'll have to open a gate; be sure to close it behind you. After 0.1 mile the road enters Chicken Park meadow. After another 0.4 mile, you can park at the meadow's edge by a solitary metal fence post near the first grove of pine trees immediately north of the road.

1

COLORADO DIAMONDS—IT'S NO HOAX!
Diamond Pipes along the Front Range

Colorado was already home to many swashbuckling, anything-goes mining camps by 1872, the year the soon-to-be state figured prominently in a mining hoax of such monumental proportions that it threatened to shake the very foundations of our nation's economy. Before it could visit such calamity on the country, the Great Diamond Hoax of 1872 was thwarted thanks to the efforts of the man who would, seven years later, be appointed the first director of the U.S. Geological Survey: Clarence King. Given this sordid history of Colorado diamond prospecting, there were understandably many skeptics when, in 1975, Colorado State University geology professor Malcolm McCallum discovered diamonds in Colorado. This time, the verifiable evidence for the diamonds' presence was so overwhelming that, within a year, the state was hosting North America's first commercial diamond mine. Colorado will never rival South Africa as a world diamond center, but the presence of so-called diamond pipes in the state is intriguing, and the rock fragments found within them provide fascinating glimpses into several chapters of the state's geologic history about which we know little else.

In the summer of 1872, San Francisco, the de facto mining capital of the United States, was abuzz with rumors of a massive diamond strike. Two prospectors, Philip Arnold and John Slack, were strutting around town showing off a sack of diamonds and other gems they had collected on their secret mining claim located somewhere in the American West. Many profitable gold strikes had been made throughout the West in the previous two decades, and word of a massive diamond discovery in 1870 in Kimberly, South Africa, was still reverberating, so the mining establishment was hungry for news of the next big thing. Arnold and Slack's goal in flaunting their gems was to attract the interest of one or more wealthy investors. They succeeded when William Ralston, president of the Bank of California, paid them \$360,000 cash and \$300,000 worth of stock options for their claim. This is a handsome amount even today, but in 1872, when the U.S. gross national product (GNP) was 2,500 times smaller than today, $660,000 was a princely sum. With diamond fever sweeping the U.S. mining and financial worlds, American financiers were loathe to be left behind and quickly ponied up millions of dollars to stake their own claims to the bonanza. Because the country's economy was already in a fragile state (the global Long Depression was just beginning) and because in reality no such diamonds existed, the threat to the U.S. economy was very real. Many historians believe that if the United States had squandered a significant percentage of its GNP on this hoax, it would have dealt a crippling blow to America's economic ascendency, in which it soon surpassed Great Britain to become the world's biggest economy.

By pure chance, in October 1872, Samuel Emmons, a member of Clarence King's federal expedition to survey the geology along the country's 40th parallel, struck up a conversation on a train with one of Ralston's associates, who was returning from an examination of Arnold and Slack's mystery diamond claim. Piecing together the clues, Emmons and King deduced that the claim must lie in northwestern Colorado, near the 40th parallel at a spot now called Diamond Peak. King was obviously troubled that he evidently missed such a major discovery in an area he had just surveyed. He immediately hastened to Diamond Peak, and sure enough, on November 3 he and his team discovered diamonds and other precious stones there. However, the wave of excitement that initially swept the party was soon tempered by several troubling revelations. First, precisely twelve rubies accompanied each diamond they discovered. How could nature be so discerning and regular in its distribution of these gems? Next, the party discovered amethysts, emeralds, sapphires, garnets, and spinels with the diamonds. These various stones form in completely different geologic environments and are never found together. The final piece of evidence that the team had unearthed a hoax was the discovery of a cut diamond, which absolutely had to have been planted (in the mining vernacular, "salted") at the site. King rushed to San Francisco to alert William Ralston that he had been duped. Thanks to the shrewd detective work of one of the country's leading geologists, a U.S. economic crisis was narrowly averted. King was rewarded for his efforts in 1879 when President Rutherford B. Hayes established the U.S. Geological Survey, the first official U.S. government scientific research agency, and appointed King as its director.

Throughout the remainder of the nineteenth and for much of the twentieth century, numerous discoveries of metal ores and precious gems added further luster to Colorado's already impressive reputation as a place to seek mineral wealth (vignettes 7, 13). But during that entire time, no hint of a real diamond discovery was made. Then, in 1964, Malcolm McCallum discovered a small pod of a rare volcanic rock called kimberlite within a

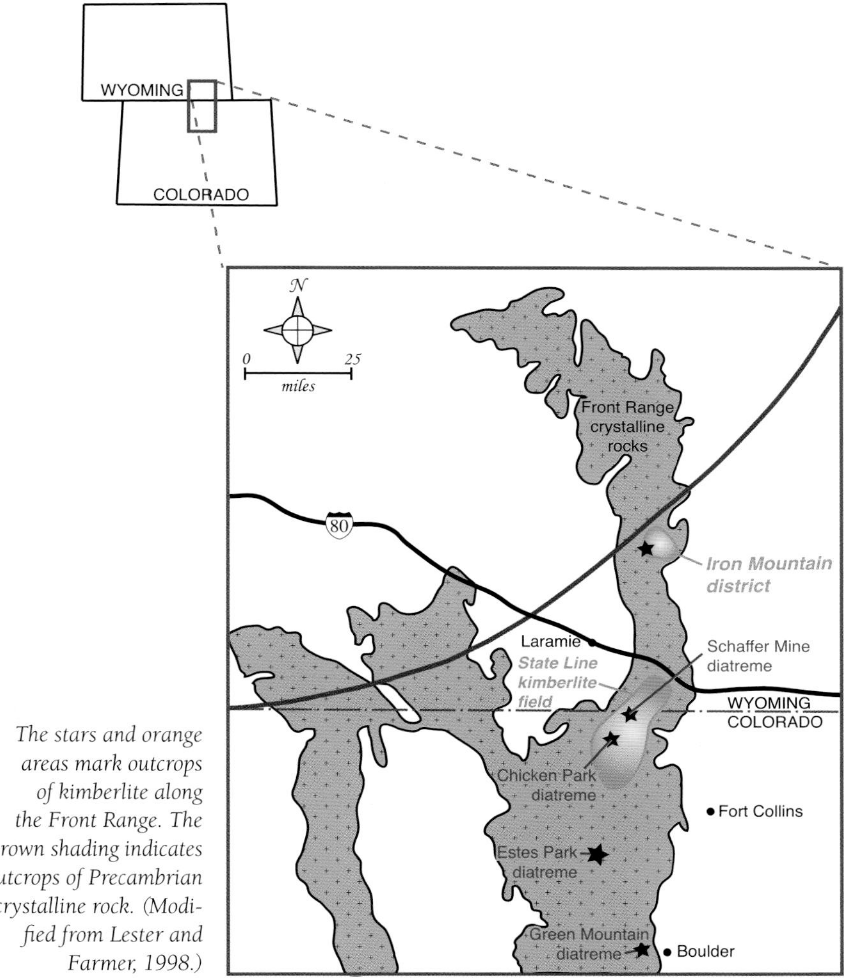

The stars and orange areas mark outcrops of kimberlite along the Front Range. The brown shading indicates outcrops of Precambrian crystalline rock. (Modified from Lester and Farmer, 1998.)

vast expanse of 1,400-million-year-old granite along Sloan Road, just a few miles east of Chicken Park, and later diamonds within it.

Kimberlite is named for Kimberly, South Africa, the location of a mammoth 1870 diamond strike. Unlike northwestern Colorado's first "find," the Kimberly strike was no hoax, and to this day it remains the richest diamond field on Earth. Kimberlite is a chemically unusual igneous rock that hosts jagged blocks of various other rock types (forming a rock called volcanic breccia). Because such blocks are not part of the magma that crystallized as the kimberlite, but rather were ripped from the volcano's walls, they are called xenoliths (foreign rocks). Diamonds can be found embedded within those xenoliths or in the kimberlite itself.

Diamonds are nothing but pure carbon, chemically identical to the graphite in your pencil lead save for one crucial difference: in graphite the carbon atoms are arranged in two-dimensional sheets, not unlike the individual pages in a ream of paper. Diamonds are carbon that has been squeezed at absolutely titanic pressures, forcing the atoms to rearrange themselves into a three-dimensional framework that is clear, is the hardest-known natural substance, and refracts light in such a way that it sparkles with dazzling brilliance. The pressures necessary to effect this amazing metamorphosis occur naturally in only two places: at the site of a big asteroid impact or deep in Earth's mantle. Brazil's tiny, smoky-colored diamonds are thought to have formed due to an asteroid impact, but almost all other known diamonds formed more than 90 miles below the surface, in the mantle. Rock from such great depths reaches the surface in only one way: through the rapid rise of magma during the eruption of kimberlite.

Kimberlite eruptions are so violent they rip rocks off the walls of the conduits through which the magma passes, forever entombing the foreign rocks in the cooled magma. The resulting volcanic breccia fills the vertical conduit that supplied magma to the volcano. Such breccia-containing conduits are called diatremes. Xenoliths in many diatremes were derived from

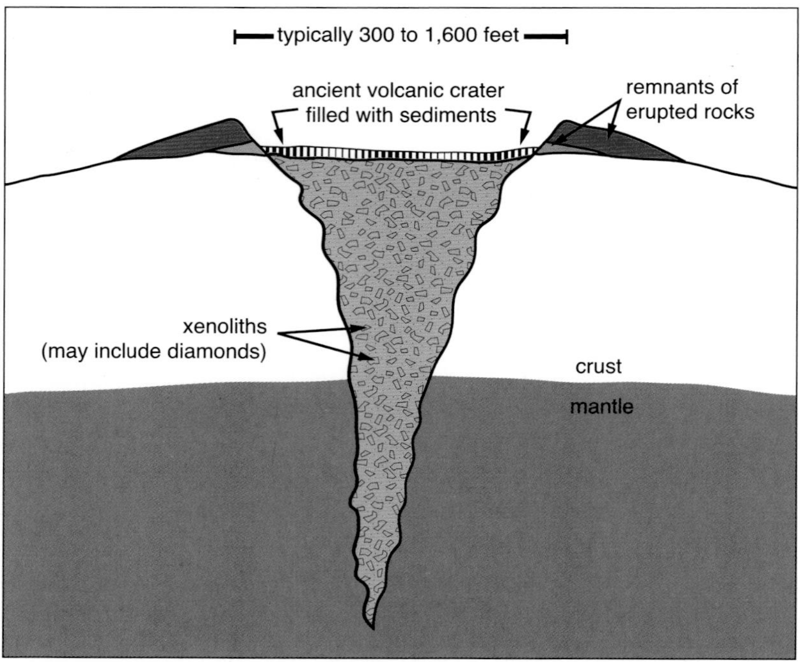

Kimberlite diamond pipes, the primary source of diamonds around the globe, are the remains of great volcanic conduits whose magma sources lay 90 to 120 miles below the surface. Xenoliths of mantle rock are forcefully torn from the conduit walls and carried upward with the magma. Both the solidified magma and xenoliths can contain diamonds. (Modified from Colorado Geological Survey, 1999.)

the mantle, so they potentially contain diamonds. Because diatremes are pipe shaped, those containing diamonds are often called diamond pipes. Since the Kimberly discovery, many other kimberlite diamond pipes have been found around the globe.

Had the kimberlite magma risen gradually through the Earth, the slow drop in pressure would have caused the diamonds' carbon atoms to spontaneously rearrange themselves back into graphite, so the very presence of diamonds attests to the rapid rise of the magma to the surface. Geologists believe that kimberlites rise from a depth of 90 to 120 miles in a mere five to twenty hours, at an ascent rate of 6 to 18 miles per hour! The only plausible driving mechanism for such a rapid ascent is that the magma was loaded with dissolved gas, the pressure of which propelled the magma. As the magma neared the surface the gas expanded, driving the magma up even faster, quite possibly at rates up to a couple hundred miles per hour. No one has ever seen a kimberlite volcano erupt, but the geologic characteristics of uneroded diamond pipes corroborate the incredible violence of these rare events.

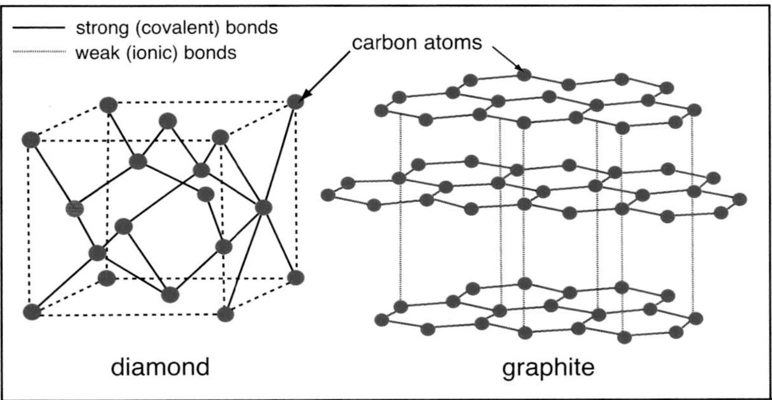

Though graphite and diamonds have the same chemical composition, the arrangement of the carbon atoms into different frameworks accounts for their radically different properties.

Geologists have discovered four kimberlite pipes full of diamonds at Chicken Park. Kimberlites are often highly fractured, and the many low-silica minerals they contain are highly susceptible to chemical weathering. For these reasons, some kimberlites lack good rock outcrops, instead forming unobtrusive low spots in the topography. Because trees don't like the chemistry of the soils that mantle kimberlite, poorly exposed diamond pipes commonly manifest themselves as oval-shaped meadows. Such vegetational detective work is particularly critical in order to locate the Chicken Park diamond pipes because prospectors excavated the tops of the pipes

The easiest-to-locate Chicken Park diamond pipe forms a meadow ringed by pine trees. A few kimberlite boulders lie in the meadow.

with backhoes and then filled them back in. The easiest of the pipes to find is the one closest to the road, about 70 yards southeast of the fence post where you parked. Locate the first break in the grove of aspen trees to the right (southwest) of the prominent granite knob that stands south of Chicken Park. From the fence post walk south, nearly perpendicular to the road, and over a tiny topographic hump to the break.

The pipe consists of an oval-shaped, grassy meadow, measuring about 20 by 30 yards, that is almost completely ringed by pine trees, some of which stand next to low granite outcrops. No outcrop exists in the meadow itself, but if you examine the dirt piles constructed by the area's burrowing rodents, you will see small chunks of a dark, fine-grained rock that is clearly not granite. This is the kimberlite, delivered to the surface straight from the Earth's mantle! At the far side of the meadow, close to the trees that define the diamond pipe's southern border, the backhoe-wielding prospectors partially excavated five kimberlite boulders, the biggest one about 1.5 feet long. The boulders all consist of a dark, greenish gray matrix of microscopic crystals with a few larger, visible crystals that sparkle in the sun.

Among the minerals contained in this kimberlite are green olivine and red garnet. Embedded in the boulders are angular, green and reddish brown chunks, many of which are encircled by a weathering rind of white or light green minerals. These chunks are small xenoliths, pieces of the mantle and lower crust that were entrained in the fast-rising kimberlite magma.

Although it is not uncommon for kimberlite to contain diamonds, it took eleven years after the 1964 discovery of the Colorado kimberlite pipes to notice that they in fact contain diamonds. The discovery was made quite accidentally, when a technician at the U.S. Geological Survey in Lakewood was grinding a xenolith on a lapidary wheel in order to create a thin section (used to analyze the minerals of a rock). Lapidary wheels are made of extremely hard material in order to withstand hundreds of hours of rock grinding, but somehow this sample left deep grooves in the grinding plate. After concerted effort, a tiny diamond less than 1 millimeter long was discovered. This set off a flurry of exploration. Soon many more diamonds were found, and to date over 130,000 diamonds have been removed from what has come to be known as the State Line kimberlite field, which comprises more than one hundred kimberlite deposits stretching in a line along the Front Range foothills from Boulder's Green Mountain to Iron Mountain in Wyoming's central Laramie Mountains. The largest diamond found was

Due to its dark color, the Chicken Park kimberlite is readily distinguished from the 1,400-million-year-old Sherman granite into which it intrudes.

a hefty, 28.3-carat, gem-quality yellow diamond from the Kelsey Lake diamond pipe, the site of North America's first commercial diamond mine, just south of the Wyoming border.

Upon the discovery of Colorado's diamonds, geologists immediately began to wonder when the kimberlite pipes erupted. Luckily, a number of the xenoliths found in the kimberlite pipes are chunks of marine limestone that tumbled back down into the pipe during the eruption. Using fossils found in these rocks, paleontologists have dated the limestones as Cambrian, Ordovician, and Silurian in age. Since the limestone had to exist before it was integrated into a volcano's magma during an eruption, the kimberlite that contains Silurian limestone can be no older than Silurian in age. A handful of radiometric dates obtained from kimberlite samples pointed to a Devonian eruption age (416 to 359 million years ago).

The discovery of Silurian-age (444- to 416-million-year-old) limestone xenoliths was of particular interest because nowhere else in Colorado have rocks of Silurian age ever been found. Prior to this discovery, geologists had speculated that Colorado lay above sea level throughout the Silurian, preventing the deposition of sedimentary rocks. The xenoliths conclusively demonstrate that not only was sedimentary rock accumulating in Colorado during the Silurian, but the Front Range actually lay below sea level. Sometime in the Devonian or early Mississippian period a drop in sea level must have left the area high and dry, causing all of the previously deposited limestone to be eroded save for the few scraps that were encased in the kimberlite volcanoes.

Due to the limestone evidence and radiometric ages, it was widely assumed that all Colorado kimberlite pipes erupted during the Devonian. However, not all of the pipes contain limestone xenoliths, and researchers soon noticed that the kimberlite in some of the pipes, including the ones at Chicken Park and Boulder's Green Mountain, have compositional differences as well. Researchers at the University of Colorado set out to independently date these pipes. At Chicken Park they analyzed samples from a kimberlite dike that lies about 80 yards southwest of the pipe you've been examining. To get there, follow a very faint road to the southwest. After about 40 yards, you pass through a fence with bright orange posts. Leave the road here, cutting diagonally southwest through the pine forest. The dike forms a narrow, linear, southwest-trending meadow that you emerge into after about 40 yards of walking.

Once again, no bold kimberlite outcrop greets you. Instead, look for chunks of dark kimberlite littering the ground in the meadow. The small, sparkly crystals in the kimberlite chunks consist of the mineral phlogopite, a magnesium-rich mica that also contains radioactive potassium, making it amenable to radiometric dating. The resulting age of 616 (± 2) million years surprised researchers, as it was much older than the Devonian ages

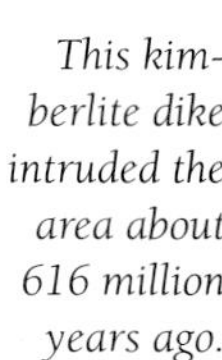

This kimberlite dike intruded the area about 616 million years ago.

obtained from the limestone-bearing kimberlites. Other researchers using a different technique later confirmed this age. It was not possible to date Boulder's Green Mountain kimberlite as precisely, but using a third technique researchers obtained an age of 572 (± 49) million years, suggesting that it intruded at about the same time as the Chicken Park kimberlites.

So, there have been at least two separate periods of kimberlite volcanism in Colorado, one in the late Proterozoic (at Chicken Park and Green Mountain), the other in the Devonian, 200 million years later. One noteworthy characteristic of kimberlite fields throughout the world is that each has hosted several separate episodes of explosive volcanism. Intriguingly, the eruption of these small but violent volcanoes seems to occur during times when the eruption area is otherwise tectonically and volcanically quiet. The Colorado kimberlites fit this pattern, as both the late Proterozoic and the Devonian were quiet geologic periods. Geologists have scratched their heads very hard trying to figure out what recipe is needed to create such a small pool of magma at the base of the continental lithosphere (the diamond-forming depth), and then bring it to the surface rapidly enough to create a diamond pipe when other geologic processes go quiet.

Clearly, one necessary ingredient is heating at the base of the lithosphere to generate magma. Geologists suspect that the necessary heating for most kimberlites is provided by a hot spot—a plume of hot material rising from the mantle that persists for tens of millions of years. It is possible that Colorado hosted such hot spots during both the late Proterozoic and the Devonian, but if so, they have left no legacy other than these kimberlite pipes. A second ingredient may be the presence of deep-seated fractures penetrating the entire lithosphere—up to 120 miles deep. These would provide a natural conduit along which the kimberlite magma could ascend, potentially explaining how the magma rose so quickly. The fact that the Colorado-Wyoming kimberlites line up in a north-south direction supports the idea that deep-seated fractures facilitated the rise of kimberlite magma.

But why would fractures pierce the lithosphere here, along the Front Range? Although Colorado was relatively quiet, globally the time of the Chicken Park diamond pipe emplacement was tectonically eventful: Pangaea's predecessor, the supercontinent Rodinia (vignette 14), split apart from about 750 to 550 million years ago. Colorado lay well east of the main rifting, which occurred along the modern I-15 corridor in Utah, so no major faulting occurred in the state at this time. However, the presence of north-south dikes in southwestern Colorado indicate that the state was subjected to east-west extensional forces during Rodinia's breakup. If similar north-south trending fractures existed on the Front Range, they would likely have facilitated the kimberlite magma's rapid ascent.

It is likely that just such a set of preexisting fractures was indeed present on the Front Range. The Pikes Peak Batholith (vignette 14) was intruded 460 million years before the Chicken Park diamond pipes along a north-south-trending fracture south of and in line with the State Line kimberlite field. Geologists deduce that the fracture the batholith intruded is a southern extension of fractures beneath the kimberlite field. Intrusion of the Pikes Peak granite was likely associated with the assembly of Rodinia. The Chicken Park and Green Mountain diamond pipes may well be telling us that those fractures that formed during that compressional tectonic episode were reactivated during Rodinia's breakup, allowing the kimberlite magma to well up. Interestingly, most kimberlite diamond pipes around the world erupted during the Mesozoic or the early Cenozoic, when the supercontinent Pangaea was breaking apart. Many geologists believe that enhanced mantle heating during supercontinent breakup is what triggers diamond pipe emplacement. If that is true, the State Line diamond pipes owe their existence to Rodinia splitting apart at the seams! It was certainly doing so during the late Proterozoic eruption of the Chicken Park diamond pipes, and the supercontinent was still actively breaking up 200 million years later, during the second, Devonian episode of kimberlite eruption.

The Front Range diamond pipes lie very close to the boundary between the Rocky Mountains and the Great Plains. It is quite possible that the very same lithospheric-scale fractures along which the kimberlite intruded were reactivated 65 million years ago, when the Laramide orogeny hoisted the Rocky Mountains skyward. The same was likely true 300 million years ago, when the Ancestral Rockies rose in nearly the same location as the modern mountains (vignette 5). It is extremely difficult for geologists to conclusively link such distinctly different and temporally separated events. But one thing is abundantly clear: the narrow strip of real estate known as the Front Range has repeatedly been the locus of a great deal of geologic activity for over 1 billion years. It is the presence of the kimberlite pipes, and especially the diamonds they contain, that provides the most concrete evidence that the fractures that resulted from the region's tectonic activity cut all the way through the crust and into the mantle.

It is clear that the Chicken Park and other Front Range diamond pipes have provided geologists with important insights into the region's geologic history. There is, in fact, one more important event to add to that list, and it pertains to the very birth of the continental crust that is now Colorado. Save one tiny outcrop in the extreme northwest, the state's oldest rocks date from the early Proterozoic eon, about 1,780 million years ago. But in Wyoming, rocks of much greater antiquity (from the Archean eon, over 2,500 million years old) are common. Geologists have been able to draw a line on a map that neatly separates Wyoming's old (Archean-age) continental crust from the relatively youthful (Proterozoic-age) crust of Colorado. Because it runs near Cheyenne, it is called the Cheyenne Line.

Abundant evidence indicates that Colorado's continental crust was forged in several chains of volcanic islands that formed above multiple subduction zones between about 1,780 and 1,700 million years ago. Soon after they formed, these islands collided with what was then the edge of the North American continent: the Cheyenne Line. That series of collisions welded the land we now call Arizona, Colorado, and Nebraska onto the edge of North America (vignette 7). It turns out that the diamond-bearing kimberlites of the State Line field lie south of the Cheyenne Line, on the younger, Proterozoic continental crust. But globally, diamonds are consistently associated with older, Archean-age crust. This fact has led many geologists to conclude that a piece of Wyoming's Archean lithosphere lay beneath northern Colorado, supplying diamonds to the kimberlite magma as it erupted. That is precisely the configuration one would expect if Archean North America (for example, Wyoming) were attached to a slab of oceanic lithosphere that was subducting to the southeast, beneath Colorado's chain of volcanic islands. When the last of the oceanic crust was subducted, the island chain was thrust northwestward, up over the edge of the continent. In this scenario, the edge of the Archean continent underlies the volcanic mountain complex in northern Colorado. The Cheyenne Line marks the place where that old continental margin emerges from underneath Colorado's younger crust.

Since diamonds were first discovered in the State Line kimberlite field in 1975, 306 diamonds have been recovered from Chicken Park. Although most of the State Line diamonds are of the poorer, industrial grade, some valuable gemstones have also been discovered. This economic bounty was sufficient to warrant the development of the Kelsey Lake Mine, North America's first commercial diamond mine, in a kimberlite pipe just south of the Wyoming border. The mine operated from 1996 to 2003, and its closure was due to legal problems, not because it ran out of ore. Colorado is likely to reap additional economic rewards from its kimberlite in the future.

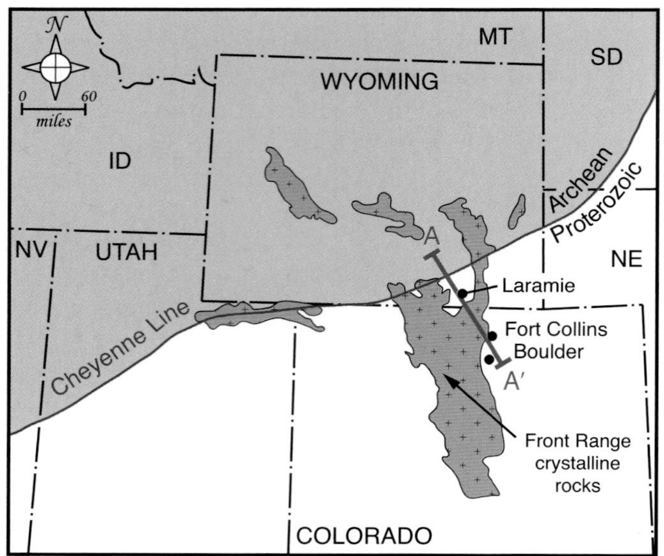

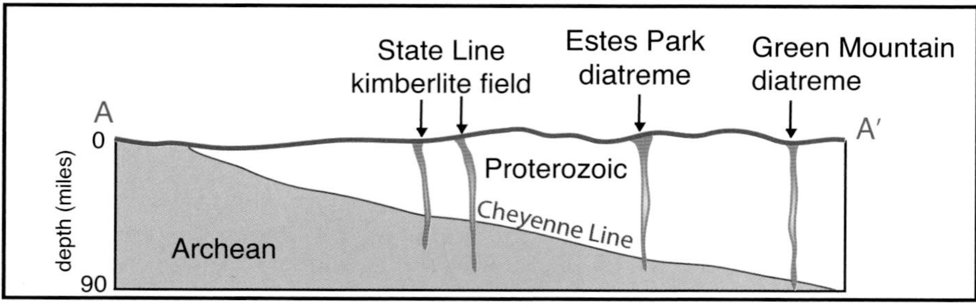

The Cheyenne Line is a suture along which the Proterozoic-age volcanic island arcs that make up Colorado were welded onto North America's Archean-age coastline, which lay in southern Wyoming. (Modified from Lester and Farmer, 1998.)

The thought of finding a sparkling diamond in the rough might be just the incentive you need to mount a prospecting expedition to Chicken Park, one of the few kimberlite diamond pipes located on public land. But before you see too many dollar signs passing before your eyes, it is worth contemplating how many diamonds kimberlite like this can actually serve up. The Chicken Park kimberlite has assayed at 6.7 carats of diamond per 100 tons (200,000 pounds) of ore. As you scour the diamond pipe and associated dike discussed in this vignette, you will likely encounter at most 100 pounds of ore. So even if you were the first person to examine these specimens (which you most certainly aren't!), the law of averages suggests that you will find about 0.003 carat of diamonds. Given that a carat is 0.2 grams, your best hope is to put any sample you find at Chicken Park on a grinding wheel. If your wheel gets scratched, you are probably the proud owner of a diamond about the size of that first one discovered in 1975. The diamonds of Chicken Park are no hoax, but the most rewarding aspects of a trip here are likely to be the chance to surround yourself with the park's natural beauty and the excitement of discovery that comes from piecing together these less-well-known events in Colorado's fascinating geologic history.

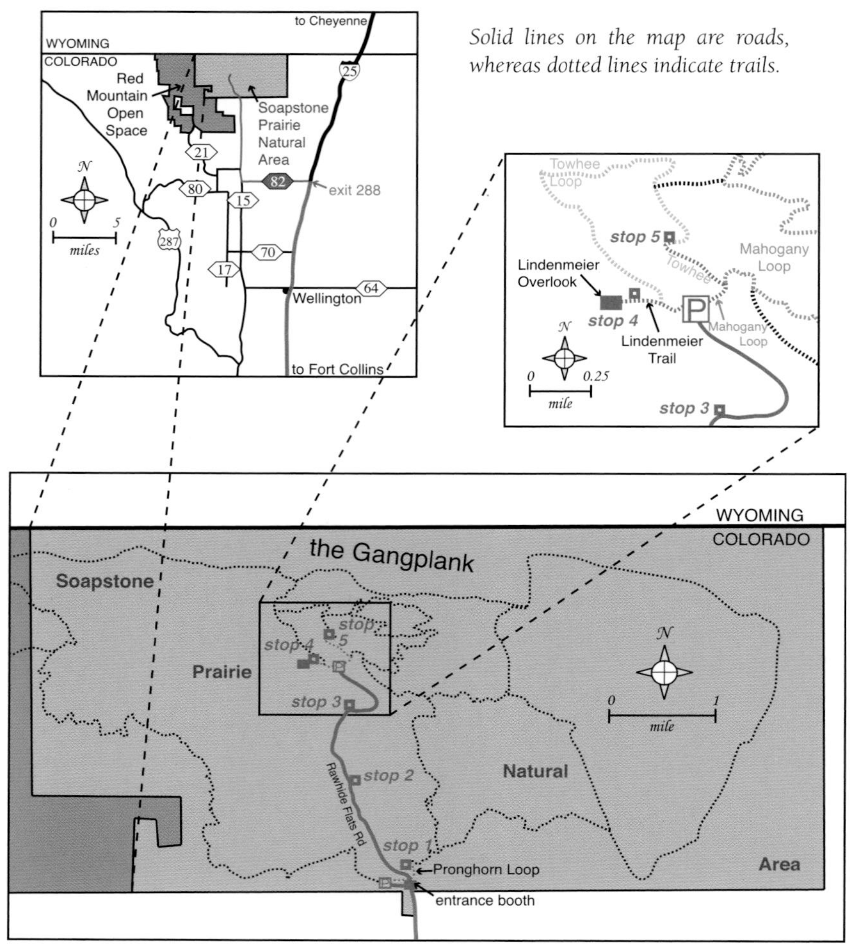

GETTING THERE: All stops are located in Fort Collins's Soapstone Prairie Natural Area, which is open from dawn to dusk March 1 through December 1 (for additional information check www.fcgov.com/naturalareas/finder/soapstone). From Denver travel north on I-25 to exit 288 (County Road 82/Buckeye Road). Turn left (west) onto County Road 82 and follow it 6.1 miles to its end. Turn right (north) onto County Road 15, a good gravel road. Follow County Road 15 for 1.2 miles. It bends to the right and becomes Rawhide Flats Road, which is signed to Soapstone Prairie. You enter the natural area at a gate after 4.2 miles; the official entrance station lies 2.2 miles farther up the road. At the entrance booth, turn left and drive 0.1 mile to a parking lot. Walk back to the entrance booth along the Pronghorn Loop, crossing the road and continuing another 300 yards to the first small wash, the east wall of which consists of Pierre shale (stop 1).

To reach stop 2, drive back to the entrance booth and turn left, heading another 0.9 mile north along Rawhide Flats Road to a small gravel pullout on the right atop a small rise on a narrow neck of land separating two small washes. Stop 3 lies 1.4 miles farther north along the same road, at the point where the road bends sharply to the right (east) and a gated service road branches off to the left. Park just before the gate. To reach stop 4, continue 1

2

WALKING THE GANGPLANK
Soapstone Prairie Natural Area

An explanation for why mountain ranges formed where they did was a major early success of plate tectonic theory; in fact, the explanation was key to the theory's widespread adoption. But during the 1960s and early 1970s, when the efficacy of the theory was still being hotly debated, skeptics pointed to Colorado and Wyoming's Rocky Mountains as prime evidence that plate tectonics could not account for some mountain ranges. The principal reason for this skepticism was that these mountains lie over 600 miles away from the nearest plate boundary. Decades of research have allayed those original objections, and plate tectonics is now a preeminent theory in geology. Scientists routinely use it to explain the existence of the Rockies. But new questions have arisen, making the southern Rockies one of the most puzzling mountain ranges on the planet. When and how the peaks we see rose to their present stature is one of the hottest unresolved issues in Colorado geology. And the question is of more than local interest; its eventual resolution will have implications of global significance by enhancing our understanding of the ways that plate tectonics creates topography.

more mile and park in the parking lot at the end of Rawhide Flats Road. Follow the concrete, handicap-accessible Lindenmeier Trail, which begins next to the toilet and reaches the obvious Lindenmeier Overlook in 0.3 mile. Stop 4 is at a patch of bare, light gray ground on the hillslope to your right (north) about 100 yards before the overlook.

To reach stop 5, return to the parking lot and follow the Mahogany Loop, which heads east from the northeast side of the lot. At 0.2 mile turn left (north) onto the Towhee Loop. Stop 5 is about 0.5 mile (a ten- to fifteen-minute walk) from the trailhead. It is the first obvious outcrop, which lies 20 feet above the trail midway along its eastward traverse above the wash. From here you can either return to your car or complete the Towhee Loop. You reach the plateau crest—the top of the Gangplank—0.6 mile beyond stop 5. Turn left (west) to complete the loop, which returns to the parking lot. The entire Towhee Loop is 3.1 miles long with 400 feet of elevation gain.

Ironically, despite Soapstone Prairie being part of the Great Plains and not the Rockies, no place in Colorado possesses a better record of what happened to the mountain belt after its initial formation. The peaks first rose during the Laramide orogeny, which in the Front Range lasted from about 67 to 53 million years ago (vignettes 8, 16). Exposed at Soapstone Prairie is a nearly complete sequence of post-uplift sedimentary rock layers. In this vignette we will examine the characteristics of this sequence and determine their relationship to the nearby Rockies, all with an eye to deducing how the mountains have evolved since their birth.

The beginning of the story can be examined at stop 1. Exposed in the east wall of Wire Draw are several outcrops of olive green, Cretaceous Pierre shale. This was the last sedimentary layer to accumulate prior to the start of the Laramide orogeny. The outcrop consists of numerous very thin mudstone layers that all tilt gently down toward the northeast. This mud accumulated on the calm, quiet floor of the last sea to ever occupy Colorado. Just a few million years after settling to the seafloor, the Pierre mud, along with all underlying rock layers, was tilted, faulted, and folded as the Rockies rose. Stop 1 is located a few miles east of the mountains' edge, so here the Pierre underwent only gentle tilting and folding.

Unlike the Pierre, the rest of Soapstone's rock layers were deposited *after* the Laramide orogeny had ended, so they are not similarly tilted. In fact, the overlying White River Group sediments, composed of a mix of

Once mud that settled onto an ancient seafloor, Pierre shale layers now tilt gently northeastward at the Soapstone Prairie entrance station. The dominant tilt of the layers is eastward, but due to gentle folding the layers locally have a component of north or south tilt as well.

volcanic ash and river mud, rest upon progressively older rock layers the farther west (closer to the mountains) you go. Here at stop 1, White River Group sediment lies directly above the 70-million-year-old Pierre shale, but just 3.5 miles to the west, at the toe of the mountains, it sits atop the 300-million-year-old Fountain Formation. This contrast is due to two events: first, the tilting of all pre-Laramide sedimentary layers to the east of the rising Laramie Mountains (the name for this northern extension of the Front Range), and second, the erosion of those tilted layers by rivers flowing off of the newly risen mountains. This erosion planed the tilted layers, forming a flat, gently eastward-inclined surface composed of progressively younger layers to the east. The erosion surface formed sometime between the Laramide uplift of the mountains, which ended in early Eocene time, and deposition of the overlying White River Group, whose oldest sediments accumulated during the latest Eocene (around 37 million years ago). We can thus deduce that the erosion surface, commonly called the Rocky Mountain Erosion Surface (or the Late Eocene Erosion Surface), formed during the late Eocene.

Stop 2 provides a panoramic view in all directions. To your west stand the Laramie Mountains, the easternmost vanguard of the Rockies. To your east the Great Plains stretch to the horizon. To the north rises a plateau capping a prominent escarpment. This plateau is the Gangplank, the primary feature we have journeyed here to see. It is so named because it forms an inclined plain leading from the Great Plains up to the crest of the Laramie

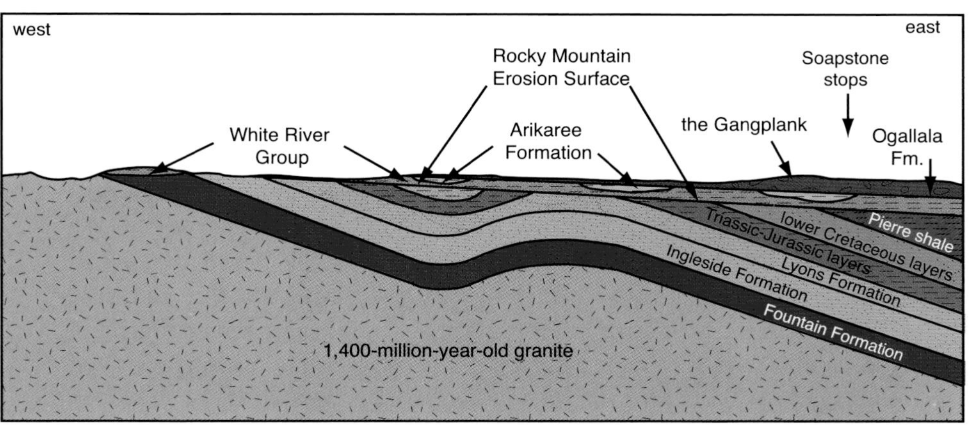

Extensive erosion between the end of the Laramide orogeny and deposition of the White River Group created the Rocky Mountain Erosion Surface, an unconformity between the White River Group sediments and underlying layers. Another episode of erosion occurred after the deposition of the White River and before the deposition of the Arikaree Formation, and yet another before the deposition of the Ogallala Formation. The smooth upper surface of the Ogallala forms the Gangplank, which stretches all the way to the crest of the Laramie Mountains.

Mountains. This attribute made it a singularly important landscape feature during America's westward expansion because it provided an ideal place for the transcontinental railroad to climb to the crest of the Rockies. Because of its importance, the Gangplank was the subject of some of the very first geologic study to take place in the American West. Interstate 80 has since joined the railroad in exploiting this ramp, so the Gangplank remains a crucial transportation link across the Rockies to this day.

The Gangplank forms the drainage divide between Colorado's South Platte River and Wyoming's North Platte River. Erosion by both rivers has removed the youngest rock layers in the sedimentary stack to both the north and south, but in between the Gangplank preserves this valuable archive. The erosion accomplished by these rivers is on display across the Colorado Piedmont, the vast, gently rolling plain that stretches south from here to Denver. The South Platte and its tributaries have stripped a 2,000-to-3,000-foot-thick stack of rock layers from this landscape. Because of this, Fort Collins lies 3,000 feet lower than the top of the Gangplank, and the Pierre shale forms the surface rock across most of the piedmont. The North Platte has done the same thing in southern Wyoming, leaving Torrington, nestled along its banks, 2,000 feet lower than Cheyenne, which is perched on the Gangplank.

Looking east, we can trace the eastward continuation of the Gangplank, which is the high land bristling with windmills north of a noticeable escarpment. The wind blows incessantly across the Gangplank, making it an ideal place to generate wind power. The escarpment that bounds the southern edge of the Gangplank is known as the Chalk Bluffs. The famous Pawnee Buttes (not easily discerned from here) consist of Gangplank remnants that were cut off from the main plateau by erosion.

To the north look for the pinkish to light gray rock forming the low, gentle land below the Gangplank escarpment. This material belongs to the Oligocene-age White River Group and, above it, the similar-looking, Miocene-age Arikaree Formation (deposited between 28 and 19 million years ago). We will examine these formations at stops 3 and 4. Capping the Gangplank are prominent brown layers of the Ogallala Formation, which was deposited about 18 to 5 million years ago, during Miocene and early Pliocene time, making it the Front Range's youngest named sedimentary formation. All these layers tilt gently down to the east, mimicking the tilt of the plateau surface. As we will see at stop 5, the Ogallala is not an exceptionally strong rock. Yet its relative resistance to erosion (compared to the softer material below) is precisely what has protected the Gangplank from the ravages of erosion. The Gangplank is the only place along the Rocky Mountain Front where the Ogallala Formation is preserved adjacent to the mountains. Everywhere else erosion has stripped it away and rivers have carted its debris downstream.

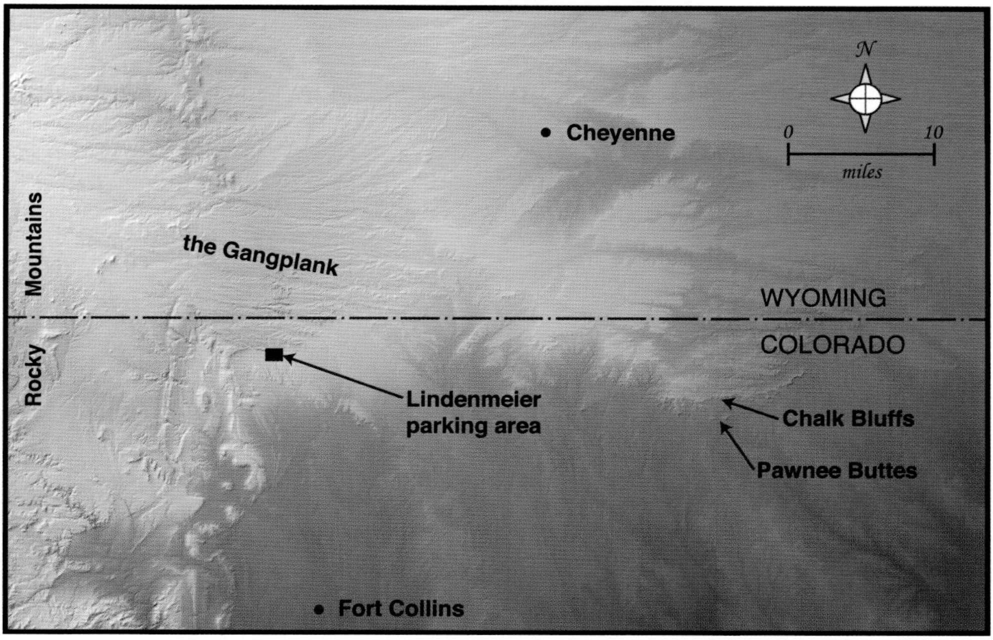

The Gangplank is the smooth, high elevation, gently tilted plateau (shown here in white and brown shades) that joins the Great Plains (green shade) on the right with the Rocky Mountains on the left. Fort Collins lies on the Colorado Piedmont, which has been lowered by river erosion. Notice the rougher topography of the mountain front here, where the Rockies have been reexposed due to erosion of the sediment blanket that still exists in the form of the Gangplank.

The Gangplank is the gently east-tilting plateau visible to the north from stop 2. The gray and pinkish slopes near the plateau's base consist of White River Group and Arikaree Formation sediments. The more erosion-resistant, brown rock forming the escarpment belongs to the Ogallala Formation.

We are fortunate that the Ogallala has survived here because it provides a unique and valuable insight into what happened to the Rocky Mountains after the Laramide orogeny ended. The inevitable fate of all mountains, once tectonic forces cease to drive them skyward, is to be reduced by erosion to mere stumps. The Gangplank shows us that as the mountains eroded, they were inexorably buried in their own debris. If you drive west on I-80 from Cheyenne to the Lincoln Monument at the crest of the Laramie Mountains, you climb 2,600 feet, but reaching the crest of the mountains comes as something of a surprise because it doesn't feel like you ever left the Great Plains. In fact, you didn't, because the Gangplank plateau, capped with the Ogallala Formation, merges seamlessly with the 1,400-million-year-old granite of the Rocky Mountains. The mountains have effectively

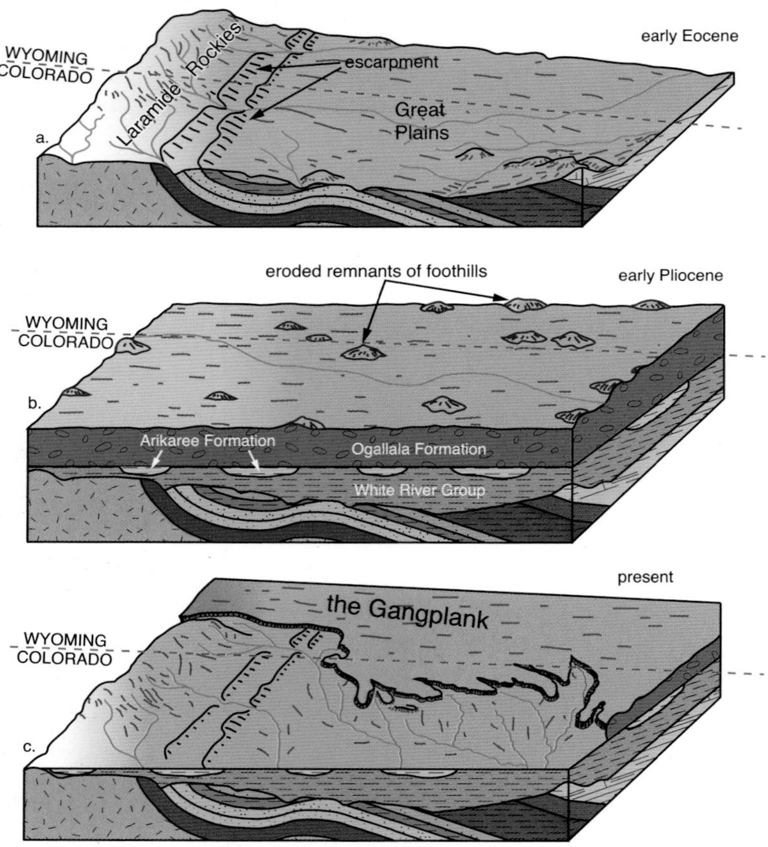

(a) The Laramide Rockies had formed by the early Eocene, but the young mountains were separated from the Great Plains by a steep escarpment. (b) By the early Pliocene the Laramide mountains had been almost completely buried by White River, Arikaree, and Ogallala sediments. (c) The modern topography south of the state line consists of the exhumed Laramide foothills. Along the Gangplank, the covering sediment has not yet been removed.

disappeared, buried by Plains sediment. From stop 2, you can see that the Gangplank climbs westward right up to the mountain crest.

Geologic evidence preserved in other areas of Colorado suggests that the burial of the Rocky Mountains wasn't just a local phenomenon; it was widespread. The Gangplank, therefore, provides us a glimpse of what the topography along the entire Front Range looked like 10 to 5 million years ago. At that time the Rockies were less a mountain range and more the apex of the long, westward-rising incline of the Great Plains.

Let's head now to stop 3. The low hills to either side of the road consist of light greenish gray, powdery material. Despite its lack of competence, this material is part of the Brule Formation, the upper formation of the Oligocene-age White River Group (the lower formation of the group being the Chadron). Notice how small and uniform the sediment is. As much as 70 percent of this material is volcanic ash that was blown into the area from volcanoes as far away as Nevada. The ash then mixed with locally derived debris shed off the Rockies. In order to deliver so much ash from such a long distance, the volcanoes had to erupt with exceptional violence, and the total amount of ash they produced had to be enormous. Eruptions of that period fit the bill on both counts, as the volcanoes were associated with the Ignimbrite Flare-up (vignettes 11, 13).

The White River Group sediment achieves its greatest fame as the rock that forms the spectacular scenery in South Dakota's Badlands National Park. Such fine-grained, ash-rich sediments are ideal for the preservation of bones thanks to the alkaline (high pH) conditions the ash establishes. White River Group rock has yielded abundant and scientifically significant mammal fossils from multiple sites across the Great Plains (although none have been found at Soapstone yet). The first White River fossils were discovered in the 1840s, making it one of the American West's first targets of paleontological research. Among the many finds are extinct members of the horse, camel, pig, and cat families.

At stop 4, the nondescript hillside composed of light gray sediment, which also composes the trail cut, is the Arikaree Formation, just a few lenses of which exist at Soapstone. It is nearly indistinguishable from the underlying Brule Formation because it accumulated under similar conditions, and the Ignimbrite Flare-up volcanoes supplied it with copious volumes of ash. The abundant Arikaree ash was every bit as effective as the underlying Brule at preserving fossil bones, and many significant mammal fossils have also been found in its layers. The most important of these fossil sites is Nebraska's Agate Fossil Beds National Monument, where hundreds of rhinoceroses and other animals that roamed the savanna here 19 million years ago died along the banks of a water hole during a severe drought. The Arikaree Formation buried the Rockies still deeper, adding to the growing blanket of sediment.

The hillside at stop 4 consists of a white, chalky material that is a mixture of river-deposited mud and windblown volcanic ash belonging to the Arikaree Formation. The red chunks of granite tumbled down from the Ogallala Formation above.

Let's hike now to stop 5, where we can examine the last rock to accumulate during this period of mountain burial. The character of the Ogallala Formation is noticeably different from the underlying formations. For one thing, it is actually cemented well enough to be recognizable as a rock. For another, the layers consist of much larger grains. Fist-sized cobbles of granite and foliated metamorphic rock fragments are embedded in a matrix of very coarse sand. The sand grains consist of clear quartz and pink feldspar, the durable remnants of the 1,400-million-year-old granite bedrock that composes the Laramie Mountains. Usually sand grains have relatively smooth, round edges thanks to the tumbling they endure during transport in rivers. These sand grains, in contrast, have sharp, angular edges, revealing that they did not travel far from their source. Also present in the Ogallala, but not visible here, are beds of algal limestone that were likely deposited in lakes that shared the alluvial plain with the rivers. Ash is still present in the Ogallala beds, but it constitutes a much smaller percentage than it does in the underlying formations. There are two reasons for this. First, the Ignimbrite Flare-up was winding down, so the volcanoes were supplying far less ash. Second, erosion of the Rockies had likely accelerated, causing rivers draining the mountains to deliver more and larger sediment particles to the plains, thereby diluting the ash.

About 5 million years ago the Ogallala Formation blanketed the Great Plains of Colorado and adjacent states. But at that time, the episode of vigorous mountain erosion that had provided the sediment for the Ogallala Formation moved onto the adjacent Great Plains. The North and South Platte and the Arkansas, among other rivers, breached the capping Ogallala Formation and began to excavate the Great Plains' stack of sedimentary

The Ogallala Formation consists of angular, very coarse sand produced from the weathering of the Laramie Mountains' granite bedrock. It also contains pebbles and cobbles of granite (top middle and right) and metamorphic rocks (top left).

From the Lindenmeier Overlook you can glimpse the famous Lindenmeier excavation site, which consists of the bare riverbank below the rolling crest of the Laramie Mountains. Lindenmeier artifacts, from the ancient Folsom culture, have literally rewritten North American history books. Twice as old as the Egyptian pyramids, these artifacts reveal that Paleo-Indians lived here and hunted giant mammoths and bison 10,000 years ago.

layers. Near the mountain front, they made short work of removing this very soft rock; the surface of the Great Plains in the river valleys is thousands of feet lower now than it was then (vignette 20).

The hard, crystalline rock of the Laramide Rockies resisted erosion far better than the soft sedimentary rocks of the Great Plains. Consequently, the Laramide Rockies reemerged from beneath their blanket of sediment. As the elevation of the Great Plains dropped relative to the ranges, the steepness of the mountain rivers increased dramatically. They gained sufficient power to carve spectacular canyons, such as the Royal Gorge (vignette 18), into the hard, crystalline rock. Thanks to this differential erosion between the present-day mountains and plains, Colorado's modern landscape emerged.

Soapstone's rocks have revealed the fascinating story of mountain creation, burial, and reemergence that swept Colorado during the last 65 million years. Geologists agree that the rock record is clear and hard to interpret any other way. But that agreement disappears when the question turns to *why* mountain erosion accelerated 18 million years ago, initiating deposition of the coarse-grained Ogallala conglomerate, and culminated in erosion of the Great Plains beginning about 5 million years ago. For decades geologists assumed, quite reasonably, that the change 18 million years ago was due to renewed uplift of the Rocky Mountains, and that the excavation of the Great Plains beginning about 5 million years ago was triggered by an acceleration of that uplift. The only problem with this hypothesis is that no tectonic compression, the usual suspect when it comes to mountain building, was occurring at this time. Tectonic compression results in reverse faults, on which one slab of crust is placed atop another, thereby raising the mean elevation. Colorado was tectonically active during the last 18 million years, but that activity manifested as the opening of the Rio Grande Rift (vignettes 13, 20), which entails extension of the crust, not compression. Extension results in normal faults, on which a slab of crust drops down relative to another, which lowers the mean elevation of a region. That said, many rifts, such as the famed East African Rift, cross high topography. It is not normal faulting, but rather the rise of anomalously warm mantle material, that is responsible for high rift topography.

Despite these troubling uncertainties, geologists universally accepted that there had been a geologically recent, post-Laramide uplift event in the Rockies because nobody could think of an alternative mechanism to explain the Ogallala Formation, which would have required a dramatic energy increase in the streams that deposited it, or the vigorous river incision of the Rockies and Great Plains that began about 5 million years ago. Then, in 1990, two geophysicists who were examining mountain belts around the world proposed an alternative: that climate change can trigger the deposition of conglomerates, such as the Ogallala, and the carving of canyons, such as the Royal Gorge, even in the absence of mountain uplift. They pointed out that, worldwide, geological studies of widely scattered, unrelated mountain ranges all concluded that a pulse of uplift occurred during the last 5 million years. Yet some of these supposedly recently uplifted ranges are clearly tectonically dead! The geophysicists concluded that climate change is a far more likely mechanism for a global increase in erosion than unrelated, simultaneous pulses of uplift. The Rockies figured prominently in their deliberations given the lack of reverse fault activity during the geologically recent past.

Geologists have long known that the balance between river erosion versus river deposition responds quickly and vigorously to changes in climate (vignette 6). So in hindsight this hypothesis should not have struck anyone as revolutionary. But nobody had previously thought to apply a principle commonly accepted at the scale of a river basin to the landscape scale of a mountain range.

The implications of this hypothesis for the evolution of mountain ranges everywhere caused a burst of research activity, including in the Rockies. The question that scientists now posed was, when did the Rockies attain their present elevation? Despite the question's simplicity, answering it is extremely difficult. Earth scientists have at their disposal a number of tools that measure when and how fast rocks approach Earth's surface when erosion removes the material above them. They also possess an array of tools that can measure the rate at which individual points on a landscape, such as mountain peaks, are rising relative to sea level. But because one point is being eroded, and hence lowered, while another is being raised, such individual height determinations don't tell you if a mountain range as a whole has been raised during a given period of time.

One of the best tools we possess to determine past elevation comes, surprisingly, from the shapes of fossil leaves. Suitable fossil leaf assemblages for such analysis are not abundant, but fortunately Florissant Fossil Beds National Monument (vignette 12), located high in the Rockies west of Colorado Springs, has plenty of suitable leaves. This relatively new technique indicates that 34 million years ago Florissant stood at the same elevation as it does today, if not higher. The leaf data thus support the hypothesis that the Rockies did not rise during the last 5 million years but that some other process, such as global climate change—specifically a dramatic cooling of the planet that began 14 million years ago and accelerated about 3.5 million years ago—is what led to the excavation of the buried Laramide Rockies. The evidence for this cooling is found in records worldwide.

It appeared that, after a radical readjustment of their thinking, geologists were converging on a new consensus regarding the Rockies' post-Laramide history. But during the last few years several earth scientists have marshaled new evidence in support of the idea that the Rockies have indeed risen relative to sea level within the last few million years.

Seismic studies have revealed that the Colorado Rockies lack the deep crustal roots that normally underlie mountains. These roots form via the stacking of crust during tectonic compression. Such mountain roots provide the buoyant support necessary for the high topography of most ranges. So what's holding the Colorado Rockies up? These seismic studies have further revealed that the mantle underlying Colorado is anomalously hot, and it is hottest under the mountains. Hot material is buoyant, providing a viable explanation for the support necessary for Colorado's high topography.

Though the seismic studies tell us the mantle is hot beneath Colorado today, they tell us nothing about *when* that heat arrived. The coarse grains characteristic of the Ogallala Formation and the shift from deposition to erosion on the Great Plains could be neatly explained if the hot mantle began to well up between 18 to 5 million years ago, as many geologists suspect, thereby initiating a post-Laramide phase of uplift and subsequent accelerated erosion. In contrast, other geologists deduce that rising hot mantle was the source for the immense volcanic eruptions of the Ignimbrite Flare-up that began 37 million years ago. It is hard to envision how such an extraordinary volume of magma could be generated without a blister of hot mantle, and if that blister was already in place 37 million years ago (an idea the Florissant data support), it couldn't be the source for renewed uplift of the Rocky Mountains 18 to 5 million years ago.

But the hypothesis that Colorado and Wyoming were raised and tilted by such a mantle blister after the Ogallala Formation was deposited has gained support from analyses done here on the Gangplank. We know from its sedimentary characteristics that the Ogallala Formation was deposited in a series of rivers. Geologists have developed a technique by which we can reconstruct the slope down which those Ogallala rivers flowed. We can then compare that depositional slope to the slope of today's Gangplank to see if the Ogallala Formation slopes eastward because that is the direction the rivers flowed, or because it was tilted eastward by an episode of uplift in the Rockies after the conclusion of Ogallala deposition. Scientists have concluded that the Gangplank was indeed tilted up to the west sometime after the Ogallala was deposited. The most plausible explanation for that tilt is that the Rocky Mountains rose relative to the Great Plains during the last 5 million years. The gentle tilt the scientists documented would not be produced along discrete faults, but rather by the gentle, regional doming that would accompany the rise of hot mantle material.

So, we geologists face a bit of a conundrum when it comes to the history of the Rockies. We have learned that the Rockies were initially formed by tectonic compression during the Laramide orogeny. But we don't know whether or not those mountains were as high as the ones that exist today.

Regardless, they were buried in debris derived from their own erosion and from ash delivered eastward from volcanoes of the Ignimbrite Flare-up. Streams draining the gentle, eastward-sloping plain that was the Rockies were apparently reinvigorated about 18 million years ago, causing them to deposit the Ogallala conglomerate. By 5 million years ago those streams were vigorous enough to begin excavating sediment from the Great Plains, and the old Laramide Rockies reemerged, resulting in the Front Range's present abrupt escarpment. We don't yet know if this renewed erosion was triggered by a fresh pulse of mountain uplift, by global climate change, or both.

It can be frustrating when science doesn't provide unambiguous answers to our questions. But in reality, the most intellectually stimulating questions are those for which the current state of science can do no more than frame the debate, illustrating how dynamic the practice of science really is. Here at stop 5 you are halfway up to the plateau top. Consider completing the short hike to the top of the escarpment so you can walk the Gangplank, contemplating both the impressive history of the Rocky Mountains that scientists have been able to reconstruct so far and the creative scientific thinking that will be necessary before we can tell the rest of the story.

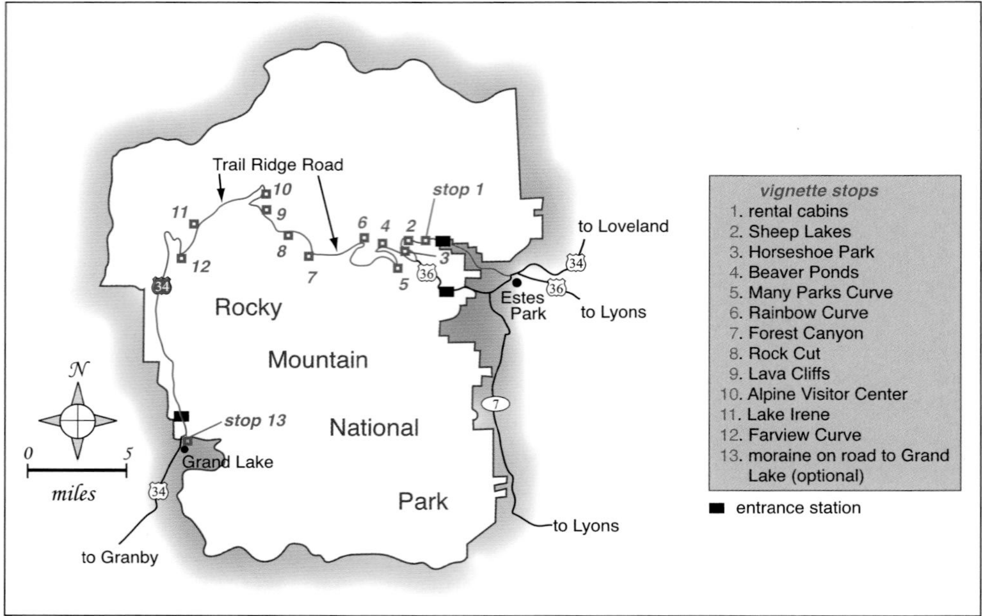

GETTING THERE: This vignette discusses the glacially carved landscape visible from twelve scenic pullouts along US 34 (Trail Ridge Road), the famous serpentine byway that snakes over the Continental Divide in Rocky Mountain National Park. From downtown Estes Park, follow US 34 west for 4.5 miles to the Fall River entrance station. Reset your odometer here. Stop 1 is an unmarked pullout to the left just beyond the rental cabins at 0.9 mile. Stop 2 is at the Sheep Lakes scenic pullout 1.7 miles from the entrance. Stop 3 is at Horseshoe Park, located on the left, at mile 3.1.

At mile 4 you reach the junction of US 34 and US 36. Turn right and continue on US 34, up Trail Ridge Road. Stop 4 is the Beaver Ponds, on the right at mile 5.9. Stop 5 is Many Parks Curve. Park in the marked lot on the right side of the road at 8.2 miles and use the crosswalk to access the viewpoint. Stop 6 is Rainbow Curve, on your right at mile 12.3. Stop 7 is at Forest Canyon, on the left at mile 15.3. Stop 8, the Rock Cut pullout, is 2.2 miles farther along at mile 17.5. Stop 9, the Lava Cliffs pullout, lies on the right at mile 19.7. The Alpine Visitor Center is stop 10, at mile 21.9. Stop 11 is the Lake Irene parking lot, on the right at mile 26.7. Stop 12 is Farview Curve, on your left at mile 28.5.

From here you can either return to Estes Park by reversing the route, or you can exit the park on its western side. If you continue west, at mile 44.4 turn left onto the major road to downtown Grand Lake. Follow this 0.4 mile and pull off into the dirt parking area immediately before the road cuts through a small hill, which is a glacial moraine (stop 13).

Trail Ridge Road tops out at over 12,000 feet in elevation; be prepared for cold and storms even in the height of summer. Because of snow, the highway is usually closed west of Many Parks Curve (stop 5) from mid-October to late May. Altitude sickness is a danger at such high elevations, and even mild exertion will likely leave you short of breath.

3

NATURE'S MASTER SCULPTOR
Trail Ridge Road

For most of the last 2.6 million years, Earth's high-latitude regions have been buried under vast ice sheets up to 2 miles thick. Colorado lay too far south to be completely locked in that icy grip, but its high peaks were cold enough to birth massive glaciers, the tongues of which slithered down adjacent valleys. These glaciers quarried out huge blocks of rock from the mountainsides, transforming a once gently rolling upland into a truly rugged landscape. Ice is Earth's master sculptor, and in Colorado, Rocky Mountain National Park is its magnum opus.

While the last 2.6 million years of Earth's history are collectively referred to as the Pleistocene ice ages, the environment was anything but static. During that time the climate fluctuated repeatedly, causing glaciers to alternately grow in the surrounding mountains, then melt away. Each time the glaciers advanced, they flowed down the national park's valleys to about the location of Estes Park (elevation 7,600 feet). During each such glacial episode, Earth's mean annual temperature dropped in response to changes in the amount of energy the planet received from the sun. This drop in solar energy was triggered by slight changes in the tilt and wobble of Earth's spin axis, combined with equally slight changes in the maximum distance Earth wandered from the sun during its annual circuit.

These changes in Earth's orbit are cyclic, so no sooner had they conspired to cool the planet than they reversed direction and warmed Earth up again, creating a so-called interglacial episode, during which glaciers retreated. These regular changes in Earth's orbit as they relate to climate are known as Milankovitch cycles in honor of Milútin Milankovic, the Serbian scientist who, in the first half of the twentieth century, connected them to the geologic record of ice advance and retreat.

In this vignette we will see evidence of these climatic fluctuations as we journey into the mountains and across the Continental Divide to examine the variety of landforms glaciers create, both through their ability to carve out solid rock and by their penchant to dump large quantities of that

Trail Ridge Road (the ribbon winding through the forest) meanders through glacial grandeur, offering stunning views of Rocky Mountain National Park's alpine beauty and first-hand knowledge of the erosional processes that created this magnificent landscape.

quarried debris into the valleys they dissected. Our trip begins in the town of Estes Park, which sprawls across a broad depression at the foot of the high peaks.

As you ascend toward the park entrance along US 34, the bedrock that surrounds you in the valley of the Fall River is granite. This igneous rock was emplaced during a major intrusive episode about 1,400 million years ago. Huge pods of granite were injected into older metamorphic and igneous rocks along a line ranging from Arizona to Labrador, Canada, including several areas in Colorado (vignette 7). The resulting rock, known throughout Colorado as the Silver Plume granite, forms the bedrock for about half of Rocky Mountain National Park, including much of the rock exposed along Trail Ridge Road.

At the Fall River entrance station (elevation 8,240 feet), a veneer of rubble called glacial till covers the granite bedrock. *Till* is the term for rock debris a glacier quarried and carried down a valley, frozen within or lying atop its river of ice. Till is defined by its huge range in particle sizes, from blocks the size of houses to fluffy glacial flour—chunks of rock ground to a powder as glaciers dragged them across hard bedrock. When a glacier melts, this debris is indiscriminately dumped together, forming till. The till at the entrance was deposited during the second-to-last glacial episode, known throughout the Rockies as the Bull Lake glacial episode, which occurred about 130,000 years ago.

At 0.5 mile from the entrance station the road cuts through a prominent ridge of till. There is no pullout here from which to safely examine it, but passengers can see the big rock chunks embedded in glacial flour that identifies this material as till. Stop 1 is a pullout 0.4 mile beyond the road cut. Here the low ridge immediately north of the road and the arc of low, pine-clad hills running across the valley to the southeast are a continuation of the till pile in the road cut you passed through. They were deposited during the last glacial episode, which reached its zenith about 20,000 years ago and is known across the Rockies as the Pinedale glacial episode.

Till accumulates along the toe (terminus) and sides of a glacier, where melting ice releases its imprisoned debris. If the climate is stable for a time, the location of the ice margins remains fixed, allowing a substantial pile of till to build up—the reason being that the glacial ice is constantly flowing downhill, transporting ever more till to its stationary terminus. At the toe of the glacier, till forms a low ridge running perpendicularly across the valley but parallel to the glacier's toe. These low ridges are known as terminal moraines and represent the farthest reach of a glacier. The till pile here is

Stop 1 illustrates the hodgepodge of big blocks and finer-grained rock flour that characterize glacial till. Absent road cuts such as this, till is best recognized by large rock chunks protruding from the soil that rapidly forms atop till in today's warm, interglacial climate.

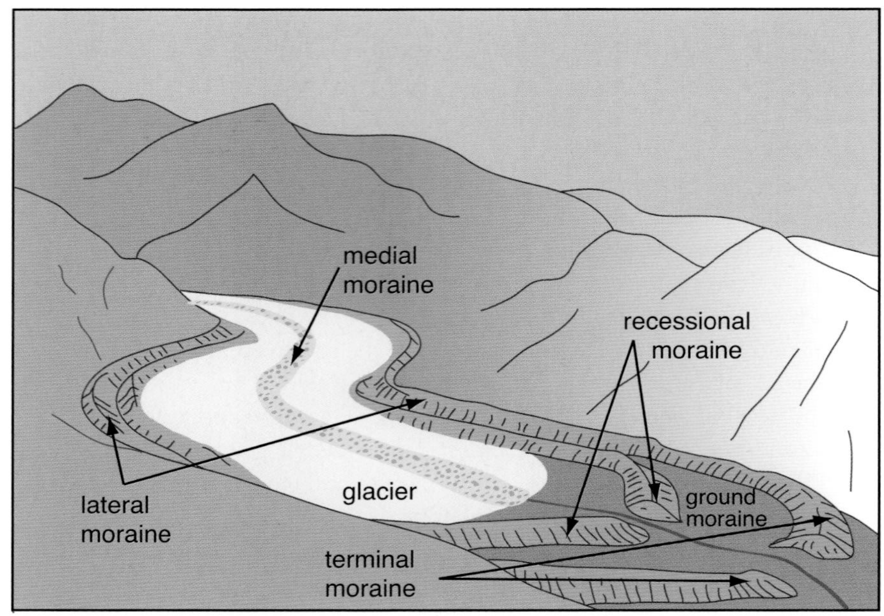

Ridges of till known as moraines can form at the toe (terminal moraine) or side (lateral moraine) of a glacier, where ice melts and dumps its embedded debris. If the climate warms, the glacier melts back, placing the toe higher up the valley. The debris piled in this manner is called a recessional moraine. Medial moraines form below the point where two glaciers merge. When rapid climate warming causes especially fast melting, till is spread evenly along the ground rather than forming a distinct ridge. Such low piles of till are called ground moraines.

part of the terminal moraine that formed at the toe of the Fall River glacier, which filled the Fall River valley cyclically during the Pleistocene.

West of this terminal moraine lies the grass-covered flat of Horseshoe Park. Horseshoe Park's lovely meadow consists of fine-grained sediments deposited in a lake that formed as the most recent glacier melted, the water ponding behind the terminal moraine. Pine trees grow on the poorly sorted material that composes the moraines, whereas the fine-grained lake sediments support grass but few trees. The concentration of trees on moraines is common, and the sharp contrast you see here between meadow and trees will allow you to easily spot this terminal moraine from stop 6.

The Milankovitch orbital fluctuations take Earth through a single glacial-interglacial cycle approximately once every 100,000 years. Typically, the planet slowly cools for the cycle's first 80,000 to 90,000 years (the glacial episode), then abruptly heats up, remaining warm for the cycle's last 10,000 to 20,000 years (the interglacial episode). Earth's last glacial episode (the Pinedale) began about 115,000 years ago. We entered the most recent interglacial episode (called the Holocene) just 10,000 years ago.

Milankovitch theory implies that more than twenty glacial-interglacial cycles transpired during the Pleistocene, but in the Rockies only three sets of moraines exist. The question is, why?

The answer lies in the relative size of each glacial episode. The youngest moraine is always found closest to the source of ice. Successively older moraines lie down valley, farther from the source. This is precisely what you've observed on this drive, with the Pinedale-age (20,000-year-old) terminal moraine of stop 1 found closer to the mountain source than the older, Bull Lake–age (130,000-year-old) moraine, which lies around the entrance booth. This is to be expected because glacial episodes vary in strength. If a younger, colder episode creates glaciers larger than those of an earlier episode, the new glaciers will obliterate all traces of their smaller predecessors. Because of this, only the moraines belonging to the biggest of the earlier glacial episodes will be preserved in the landscape. Here in Colorado, the relative size to age of the glaciers was such that only three sets of moraines are preserved. Elsewhere, four moraines survive.

Ironically, the strongest geologic evidence in support of the Milankovitch cycles does not come from moraines, but rather from marine sediments. The slow, steady accumulation of sediment on the deep seafloor provides a much more continuous record of climate change than do episodically deposited glacial sediments. The predicted 100,000-year Milankovitch rhythms of global warming and cooling (and the accompanying waxing and waning glaciers) are clearly revealed in the relative abundance of warm- versus cold-loving plankton fossil shells found in marine strata and in the relative proportions of two isotopes of oxygen contained in those shells.

Proceed to stop 2 (Sheep Lakes pullout), which lies a short distance up the road and has a view of two small lakes adorning Horseshoe Park. These lakes are a favorite watering hole for bighorn sheep and elk, making this a particularly good place to spot some of the park's majestic wildlife. Sheep Lakes represent another type of glacial landform. They are both kettles—potholes that form when ice blocks are stranded by a melting glacier. As they melt, glaciers dump prodigious volumes of till (called a ground moraine), littering the landscape with a low, uniform blanket just as it emerges from thousands of years of captivity beneath ice. Till builds up around stranded ice blocks, thus creating a depression within the ground moraine once the blocks have melted. Lakes then form in these depressions. Vast sections of the Great Plains are pockmarked by thousands of these kettles, colloquially called "prairie potholes."

Stop 2 is also an ideal place to observe the shape of a landscape sculpted by powerful glaciers. From Sheep Lakes, look west up the deep, graceful, U-shaped Fall River valley. Prior to the Pleistocene ice ages, the Fall River and others draining the Front Range carved narrow, V-shaped defiles into the mountain flanks. This is because rivers concentrate their erosive power

The U-shaped Fall River valley, seen here from stop 2, is characteristic of glacial erosion. From this vantage point, the U shape is most obvious in the tree-covered portion of the valley that lies below and between the two most prominent snowfields. The undulating meadow is part of Horseshoe Park, which is mantled by mud deposited in a lake dammed during the last glacial retreat by the terminal moraine you visited at stop 1. The small kettle in the foreground is one of the Sheep Lakes.

at their beds, carving narrow channels ever deeper to form V-shaped valleys. In contrast, when glaciers creep downhill, they drag abrasive blocks along both the valley floor and its walls, expanding valleys both downward and outward. The resulting valleys have wide, flat floors and extremely steep sides, the classic U-shaped profile that is so apparent here.

The overlook at stop 3 provides a different vantage point to examine the U-shaped profile, as well as an interpretive sign to help you locate interesting geographic features. Note the extremely steep northern and southern valley walls, carved into the granite by generations of Fall River glaciers.

The low, rubble-covered ridge that parallels the Fall River valley below Bighorn Mountain (the interpretive sign lists this mountain) is a lateral moraine deposited 20,000 years ago by the most recent Fall River glacier. Lateral moraines form the same way as their terminal cousins, only along the glacier's sides instead of at the terminus. As glaciologists have observed firsthand at modern glaciers, moraines protrude just a short distance above the glacial surface, so the top of this moraine gives you an accurate sense of just how thick the Fall River glacier was.

Stop 3 offers the first good opportunity to examine yet more landforms carved uniquely by glaciers. Locate Ypsilon Mountain, the handsome mountain to the northwest. Composed of alternating bands of dark gneiss intruded by lighter Silver Plume granite, 13,500-foot Ypsilon sports a snow gully descending straight down from its summit. The rock at your feet is the same intermingled gneiss and granite. Ypsilon, like Switzerland's famous Matterhorn, is a glacial horn—a pyramid-shaped peak formed by the intersecting walls of three or more glacial valleys, which developed as divergent glaciers whittled away at the peak. Ypsilon is the only remaining high spot between the surrounding valley floors.

Between Ypsilon Mountain and the more subdued peak to the north lies the Roaring River valley, whose telltale U shape indicates it once hosted a glacier—a smaller one that ultimately fed the much larger Fall River glacier. Where a tributary stream flows into a larger river, they meet at the same elevation, but the same is not true for ice. The master glacier is thicker and carries a much larger load of abrasive debris, so it can scour out a deeper valley. Therefore, where two glaciers meet, their surfaces lie at the same elevation, but their bases do not. Once the glaciers melt, the tributary valley floor lies high above the master's, just like you see here. Because of this mismatch, geologists call the tributary a hanging valley. The steep, bare slope below Ypsilon that separates the floor of the tributary valley from the lower Fall River valley is littered with the telltale rubble that reveals it to be a continuation of the same lateral moraine visible beneath Bighorn Mountain. A worthwhile detour if you have time is the nearby Endovalley picnic area, where you can see Thousand Falls tumbling down the steep terrain separating another such hanging valley from the lower Fall River valley.

Ypsilon's flanks also sport two additional glacial features. The first is a cirque, which is the bowl-shaped bite carved out of the mountain's steep eastern side (the one below the vertical snow gully). Cirques form at the very top of a glacier in a process akin to plunging a scoop into a new carton of ice cream and making a divot. The cirque's extremely steep back wall, called the headwall, marks the uppermost limit of glacial ice. High winds blew much snow off the ridge above, preventing it from supporting a thick glacier. Since the cirque below did host one, with each passing year the glacier carved more material from its bed, continuously steepening the cirque's walls and lowering its base elevation, while the region above barely changed.

Both the left and right flanks of the Ypsilon cirque consist of sharp ridges known as arêtes. The knife-edged crest of the left (south) arête makes it particularly striking from this vantage point. Arêtes form at the divide between two glaciers. As each glacier widens its valley, the intervening ridge becomes ever narrower and steeper, leaving behind the knife-edged spine that inhabitants of the Alps first christened an arête.

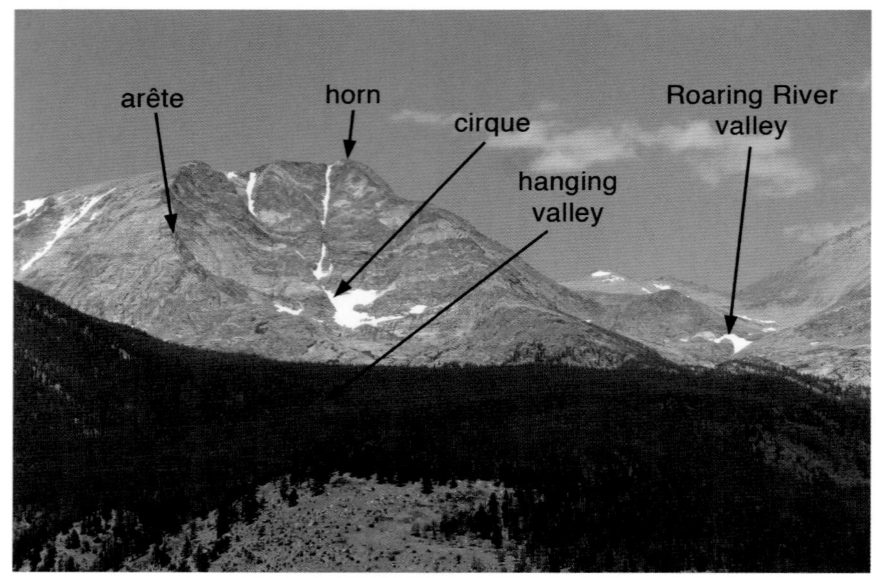

Ypsilon Mountain viewed from stop 3.

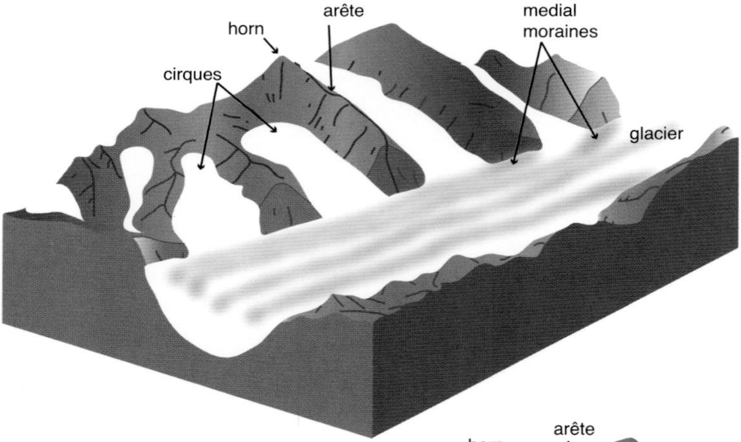

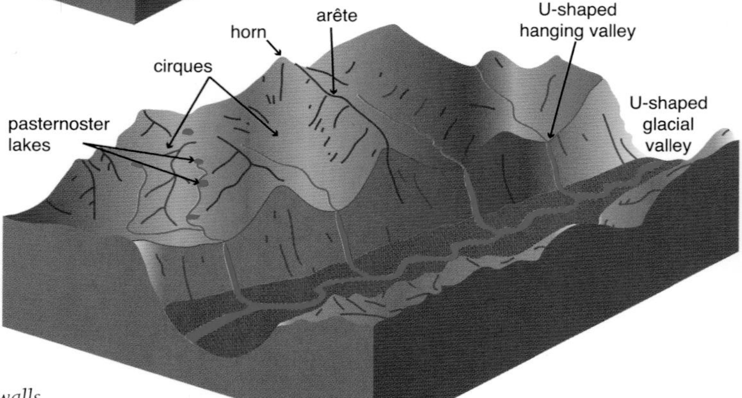

Glacial erosion produces unique and especially rugged mountain topography, which is on display throughout Rocky Mountain National Park. Besides features already described, paternoster lakes fill bedrock depressions in U-shaped valleys when glaciers melt, and creeks tumble over the steep headwalls of hanging valleys.

After drinking in stop 3's views, proceed to stop 4, where you can stroll down a short boardwalk to observe a series of beaver ponds along Hidden Valley creek. Directly behind the ponds lies a long, low east-west ridge. Its rubbly composition indicates that this, too, is a moraine. The fact that it parallels Fall River reveals it to be a lateral moraine.

Here, along the banks of Hidden Valley creek, we are standing high above Horseshoe Park, which forms the floor of a master glacial valley. Hidden Valley's name stems from the fact that the lateral moraine above the ponds conceals this valley from viewers in Horseshoe Park. Lateral moraines form, as mentioned earlier, along the edges of glaciers. If the glacier fills the entire width of the valley, then the lateral moraine is piled up against the valley's steep bedrock walls. But recall from our terminal moraine observations at stop 1 that the glacier that carved the Fall River valley during the Bull Lake glacial episode was bigger than the one that occupied the valley during the more recent Pinedale glacial episode (the one that deposited the lateral moraine here). Not only did the Bull Lake–age glacier extend farther down the valley, it was also wider. Because of that fact, the Pinedale-age glacier wasn't wide enough for its edges to butt up against the valley's steep

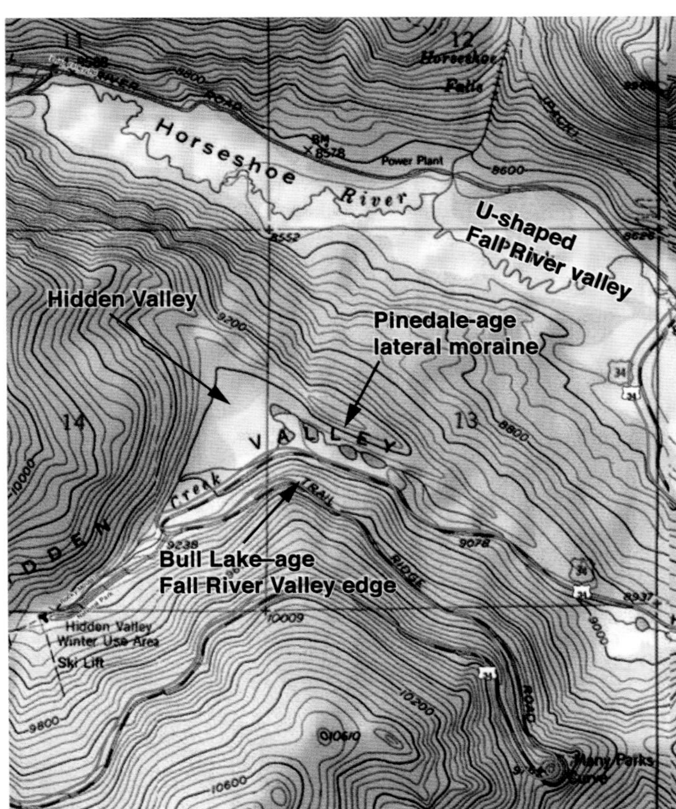

Hidden Valley lies between the steep, Bull Lake–age south wall of the Fall River valley and the Fall River glacier's Pinedale-age lateral moraine.

sidewall, which lies immediately to your south (and which you will climb up as you traverse the next section of Trail Ridge Road). The road and the ponds lie in the narrow gap between the Bull Lake–age and Pinedale-age lateral moraines, thus hiding them from viewers in Horseshoe Park.

West of the beaver ponds, Trail Ridge Road sweeps through a hairpin switchback. Just beyond the switchback the road climbs steeply up the south sidewall of the Fall River valley to Many Parks Curve (stop 5). From the lookout point a panoramic view unfolds over the valley of the Big Thompson River, the valley immediately to the south. The 14,259-foot glacial horn of Longs Peak, the highest point in the park, towers above a flat, treeless meadow that is strikingly reminiscent of Horseshoe Park. The similarity is more than casual. Like Horseshoe Park, the appropriately named Moraine Park was home to a moraine-dammed lake as the Pinedale-age glacier that filled the Big Thompson River valley melted 10,000 years ago. The meadow is flanked on both sides by low, forest-covered, east-trending ridges, which are lateral moraines.

The park's most famous horn (albeit with a flat top rather than the more typical pointed shape) is Longs Peak, seen here from the east. Its 2,000-foot cirque headwall, one of the tallest in North America, is a favorite playground of rock climbers. Note the U-shaped valley that descends from the lake nestled in the cirque.

Beyond Many Parks Curve, the road continues to climb steeply, winding its way around the upper reaches of Hidden Valley. As the road switches back at the next ridge crest, you are treated to one of the most spectacular vantage points in the entire park. From Rainbow Curve (stop 6), high above Horseshoe Park, the views east and north provide a bird's-eye perspective on the many glacial features you've seen from ground level. Horseshoe Park's flat, treeless floor flanked by steep granite sidewalls illustrates the U-shaped profile of a glacial valley. Directly below you, Trail Ridge Road runs past the beaver ponds just to the right of the Pinedale-age lateral moraine. It is easier from this perspective to see that the Pinedale-age glacier didn't quite fill the older glacial valley, the flank of which the road climbs just south of the ponds. To the north, directly across the Fall River valley, rises the Ypsilon Mountain horn. Its distinctive, vertical snow gully drops down the steep headwall of the mountain's east-side, crescent-shaped cirque, which is cradled by sharp arêtes. The hanging valley of the Roaring River lies between Ypsilon and Bighorn Mountain. It plunges down Horseshoe Park's steep northern flank at a prominent, treeless scar that was created on the morning of July 15, 1982, when the manmade Lawn Lake dam collapsed, sending 129 million gallons of water rushing down Roaring River, toppling every tree in its path. When the wall of water reached the flat floor of Horseshoe Park it slowed, causing it to drop the boulders it was carrying. The resulting cone of debris is called an alluvial fan. You can

Looking east, the view from Rainbow Curve beautifully illustrates many glacial features in Rocky Mountain National Park.

examine this geologic feature in detail from the Alluvial Fan parking area on the Endovalley Road. From there the floodwater barreled toward Estes Park, which it inundated to a depth of 6 feet, before the dam at Lake Estes finally corralled it.

About 2 miles beyond stop 6, the road climbs above timberline, the elevation above which trees cannot grow. Here in Colorado timberline averages about 11,500 feet—about the same elevation, coincidentally, that the upper extent of the glaciers reached in the park during the Pleistocene. Here the road completes its steep ascent up former glacial valleys and emerges onto a gently rolling upland. Timberline thus provides an easy-to-visualize reference showing, crudely, which areas of the park hosted thick valley glaciers 20,000 years ago and which lay above the glaciers, collecting snow that lacked sufficient thickness to form the glacial ice that flows vigorously downhill. It is flow that enables a glacier to chisel the landscape so effectively. Because the uplands avoided robust glacial chiseling, their topography has changed little since preglacial times.

Stop 7 offers a striking example of how radically glaciers altered the landscape of the country's ninth national park. From the Forest Canyon vista point you gaze a long way down into the densely treed Forest Canyon. The Big Thompson glacier occupied this canyon during the Pinedale and previous Pleistocene glacial episodes. The prominent peak beyond Forest Canyon is Terra Tomah Mountain. The gently rounded dome is a

The gently rolling terrain above timberline. The prominent peak on the right is Longs Peak. Glaciers descended from its summit on all sides, making it a horn.

Prior to the Pleistocene ice ages, Terra Tomah Mountain's summit was connected to the same rolling, preglacial upland that is visible in the foreground, and the deep gorge of Forest Canyon, in which the trees nestle, was a gentle stream valley. The cirque on Terra Tomah's flank exposes dark metamorphic rocks.

continuation of the rolling upland through which you have been driving, which is characteristic of the park's preglacial topography. In stark contrast, gouged out of the near side of Terra Tomah is a textbook-perfect, steep-walled cirque. Prior to the Pleistocene, from where you stand the terrain rose gradually to the summit of Terra Tomah, interrupted only by a comparatively small valley. It was the chiseling of the landscape by ice that transformed that gentle, pre-Pleistocene valley into today's deep chasm. So, too, ice carved the cirques, horns, sheer cliffs, and breathtaking vistas that make the park so extraordinary. Prior to the Pleistocene the park was undoubtedly scenic, but it lacked the grandeur that today draws millions of annual visitors.

Stop 8 lies at Rock Cut, where spires of the Proterozoic, metamorphic schist and dark-and-light-banded gneiss protrude above the rolling upland. The view to the south, across Forest Canyon and up the U-shaped Gorge Lakes valley, is spectacular. Terra Tomah's gently sloping top is clearly visible. To its right (west) stands the triangular horn of Mt. Julian. Several cirques form the heads of small tributary valleys whose glaciers coalesced to form the Gorge Lakes glacier. You can see two alpine lakes in the chain of six that stair-step their way down the valley. Such chains of lakes are common in the alpine portions of glacial valleys. They form in areas where the rock is a bit weaker due to its composition or a higher density of fractures. Glacial abrasion attacks these weaker areas with particular zeal, scouring them a bit deeper than is possible to either side, thus carving out a hollow where a lake can later nestle.

Such chains of lakes reminded early geologists of the strings of rosary beads carried by Catholic priests, so they called them paternoster lakes (lakes of our father). Downstream of each one you can see a knob of harder rock that the glacier had to slide up and over. Composed of very hard Silver Plume granite, these knobs go by the tongue-twisting French name of *roches moutonnées* (sheepback rocks). Gently sloping on one side and very steep on the other, their characteristic shape is the direct result of the flowing ice.

When a glacier meets such resistant rock, it piles up against it on the up-glacier side, increasing the pressure in the ice. In a process identical to the one that helps an ice skate glide on ice, this pressure increase causes a thin film of ice to melt, lubricating the glacier enough so that it glides smoothly up and over the obstacle. But once the meltwater trickles over the knob to the down-glacier side, the resulting drop in pressure causes it to refreeze, usually once it has percolated into cracks. As water freezes, it expands, helping pry blocks from the bedrock, which the ice then picks up. This

The cirques hold late summer snow in this view up the Gorge Lakes valley, which hosts a chain of beautiful alpine lakes. Mt. Julian is the triangular horn on the left.

plucking process is one of the major ways glaciers acquire the debris they use to scour the bases and sides of their valleys, in the process forming the steep down-glacier faces of the roches moutonnées.

From stop 8, Trail Ridge Road continues its gradual ascent across the rolling upland to the Lava Cliffs viewpoint (stop 9). The semicircular chasm below Lava Cliffs is a classic cirque, complete with a nearly vertical headwall. The most interesting thing about these cliffs is that they consist of welded volcanic tuff, a rock type that we have not yet encountered in the park. In contrast to the Precambrian-age crystalline rocks we've been looking at, these igneous rocks are mere infants. Between 29 and 24 million years ago, a series of volcanoes erupted in the Never Summer Mountains, which lie along the park's western boundary. An ash flow belched from one of these volcanoes moved eastward across the formerly rolling upland and came to rest here still hot, where it welded to form this dense tuff. This sudden, intense volcanic activity was part of a massive volcanic episode called the Ignimbrite Flare-up (vignettes 11, 13), which swept across much of Colorado, including the San Juan Mountains, the West Elk Mountains, and the South Park area.

Just beyond Lava Cliffs the road reaches its highest point: 12,183 feet above sea level. From here it descends to Fall River Pass, where you can tour exhibits at the Alpine Visitor Center (stop 10). The center is perched at the lip of the cirque that fed the Fall River glacier. From the center you get an expansive view eastward down the entire length of the Fall River valley, with the glacial horn of Ypsilon Mountain rising to its left. At stop 3, you saw Ypsilon's east side, complete with two glacially carved valleys flanking it. From here you can see the third glacial valley necessary to carve such a horn, this one trending northwest in front of the peak.

Just beyond the visitor center Trail Ridge Road bends around a switchback at Medicine Bow Curve, and the arrow-straight, classically U-shaped valley of the Cache la Poudre River comes into view. The bulky, rounded mountain directly above the valley (northwest) is Specimen Mountain. Like Lava Cliffs, this is another remnant of a volcanic flow that issued from a volcano in the Never Summer Mountains. The Never Summers themselves are visible behind and left of Specimen Mountain.

From Medicine Bow Curve the road does a rather unusual thing; it *descends* to the Continental Divide at Milner Pass, a "mere" 10,758 feet—just over 2 miles—above sea level. Note that the pass lies below timberline. This fact will assist you as you reconstruct the glacial events that produced the feature you examine at the next stop. The Continental Divide separates the land that drains westward to the Pacific Ocean from the land that drains eastward to the Atlantic. Because the slopes on either side must point in opposite directions, it is natural to expect that the divide comprises the highest ground around. In fact, if a large valley separates two high ridges, the divide doesn't necessarily lie precisely on the highest spot. That is exactly the situation here, where Forest Canyon's uppermost section captures water that falls on the *west* side of Trail Ridge and diverts it *eastward* to the Atlantic Ocean.

At 0.5 mile after beginning the descent down the west side of Milner Pass, the Lake Irene parking area (stop 11) provides an excellent view of Sheep Rock, located east of the road. From its shape, you can verify that it is a roche moutonnée. However, when you consider that Sheep Rock stands on the west side of the Continental Divide, you unearth a puzzle. The steep side of the roches moutonnées you saw in the Gorge Lakes valley pointed downhill, just as you would expect. But here, Sheep Rock's steep side is on the northeast—its *uphill* side! So the ice here must have flowed up and over Milner Pass. Since gravity drives the flow of glaciers, this claim seems outlandish. It turns out, though, that the crucial number that determines what is downhill for a glacier is the height of its surface, rather than the height at its base. If a glacier is thick enough and if its surface is high enough, it can actually flow uphill—at its base. Recall that timberline provides a good estimate for the height of the Pleistocene glacier tops in the park. Note that Sheep Rock lies entirely below timberline. Because the top of the ice lay above the height of Milner Pass, the glacier to the west was

Sheep Rock's gentle, up-glacier side is on the right, which is downhill, and its cliffy, down-glacier side is on the left, which is uphill. This reversal of the expected gentle and steep sides of a roche moutonnée provides evidence that, given the right circumstances, ice can actually flow uphill. Milner Pass lies just off the picture on the left.

able to flow up and over Sheep Rock before heading down the Cache la Poudre valley to the east.

What glacier was big and powerful enough to flow up and over the Continental Divide? The answer lies at stop 12, the Farview Curve overlook. The deep, U-shaped valley you see below belongs to the Colorado River. Beyond the valley rise the rugged peaks of the Never Summer Mountains. The Colorado River valley hosted the largest glacier in the entire park. It was 20 miles long and over 2,200 feet thick. Using timberline as your reference, try to visualize the dimensions of this vast river of ice. At this overlook, the glacier surface would have towered above you. This visual reconstruction may make is seem more plausible that a glacier could flow over the Continental Divide, especially at relatively low Milner Pass.

From here, Trail Ridge Road descends steeply into the Colorado River valley and follows it to the park exit at Grand Lake. If your itinerary takes you this way, try to identify examples of the same glacial features you saw on your journey here. Particularly worthwhile is a stop at an outstanding terminal moraine in the town of Grand Lake (stop 13). If, instead, your destination lies along the Front Range, you can return the way you came, affording you another opportunity to view the masterpiece wrought by nature's master sculptor.

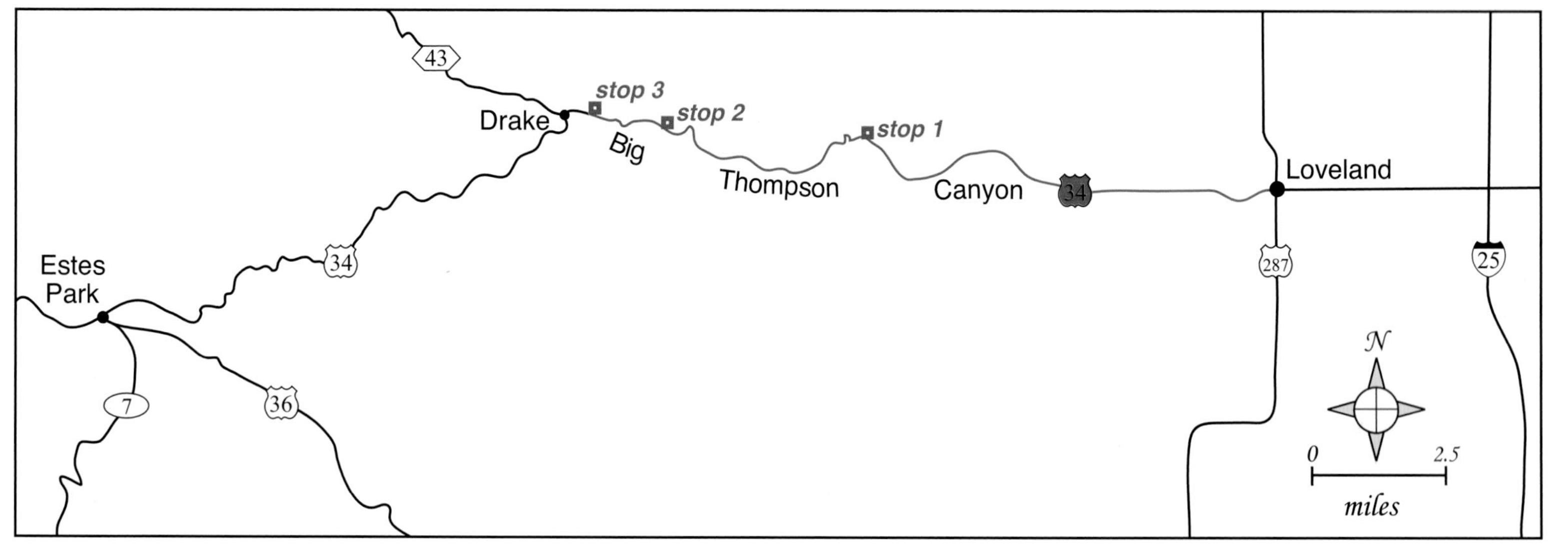

GETTING THERE: From Loveland proceed to the junction of US 34 and US 287. Reset your odometer and turn west on US 34. Stop 1, a wide, paved pullout on the right near the mouth of the Big Thompson Canyon (milepost 83), is 9.3 miles from the junction. At 14.7 miles you reach stop 2, a wide gravel pullout on the left about 150 yards upstream of milepost 78. The road cut across the highway contains deposits left behind by the flood. At 15.5 miles you reach stop 3, the memorial at a wide pullout on the right near milepost 77, 100 yards beyond a sign for a rest area.

4

CATASTROPHE IN THE CANYON
The Devastating Big Thompson Flood

Geology profoundly influences the daily life of every human being. Geological processes have provided the raw materials from which we have shaped our civilizations. They have created the soil in which we grow our food, and they influence the climate that dictates everything from how we dress to what we do after work. We typically take these geologic processes for granted; most function at such a leisurely pace that they are essentially invisible to us. But every once in a while a geologic process shakes off its lethargy and proceeds at a pace impossible to ignore, often with disastrous consequences. Such was the case on the evening of July 31, 1976, when the most deadly flood in Colorado's history roared down the Big Thompson Canyon. Within a few hours of the first raindrops, 144 people were dead, 418 homes and 438 cars were buried or flattened, and a major U.S. highway had been erased from the map.

Stop 1 is an appropriate place to contemplate the events of that fateful day. This portion of the Big Thompson Canyon is appropriately called the Narrows. Though spectacular, this deep slit is clearly not a good place to be standing during a flash flood. That truth was graphically illustrated that July evening in 1976 when a wall of water 20 feet high rampaged through this defile, obliterating everything and everyone in its path.

The small building in the pullout is the river gauging station that, every day since 1887, has measured the flow of the Big Thompson River. Prior to the 1976 flood, the greatest flow ever measured at this spot was 8,000 cubic feet (60,000 gallons) of water passing this point each second. During the flood, 31,200 cubic feet per second (233,000 gallons per second) flowed where you stand—almost four times the previous record! For comparison, a typical July flow is just 50 to 250 cubic feet (375 to 1,875 gallons) per second, depending on whether or not it has been raining.

How could this modest-looking river unleash such a monumental torrent? The answer lies in several factors: the mountainous geography of the Colorado Front Range, the area's typical summer meteorology, and an

The Narrows, which the river carved from 1,700-million-year-old quartzite. During the devastating Big Thompson flood, water here reached a height of 20 feet and a speed of 17 miles per hour.

atmospheric anomaly that occurred that July night. All of Colorado was in a celebratory mood that Saturday evening as the state prepared to mark its one-hundredth birthday the next day. Thousands of people—more than on a typical summer weekend—had flocked to the mountains to recreate. The weather was unexceptional: hot during the day, with thunderstorms building toward late afternoon. There was no hint that anything was meteorologically amiss.

One of the most reliable and welcome summer Front Range visitors is the weather pattern known as the North American monsoon, which brings regular afternoon thunderstorms during July and August. These patchy, brief, yet often intense storms bring much-needed rain and an invigorating cool down during the hottest part of the year. *Monsoon* is a term that means a seasonal shift in wind patterns. The differential heating between land and sea that occurs during the summer causes an almost complete reversal of dominant wind patterns near Earth's surface. This reversal draws moisture from the ocean over the continent. Centered in northwestern Mexico and the American Southwest, the North American monsoon causes the predominant westerly winds to change direction, bringing southern, subtropical moisture from both the Gulf of California and the Gulf of Mexico.

Colorado's monsoon storms typically form in late afternoon, after the day's intense solar heating has caused surface air to rise high enough for its moisture to condense into a thunderhead. Once formed, the towering thunderhead typically dumps up to an inch or so of rain on a localized area in less than an hour before it is hustled along to the east by strong, high-elevation winds, which maintain their normal westerly flow even during the monsoon. Because the storm cells are small, one spot can be subjected to a 1-inch downpour while a mere mile away no rain may fall. This fact was graphically illustrated during the Big Thompson flood; although a 20-foot-tall wall of water roared through the Narrows due to heavy rains higher up the canyon, it didn't rain a drop here that night.

Along the Front Range, the wettest, most intense monsoon storms occur when the airflow comes from the southeast, bringing abundant moisture from the Gulf of Mexico. When the monsoon winds push this soggy air up into the foothills of the Rockies, the elevation gain causes the air to cool. Because cool air can't hold as much water as warm air, the process is akin to wringing water from a sponge. The land beneath is deluged, receiving as much as 2 to 3 inches of rain in just an hour or two. That much rain coming down that fast on steep topography, which causes the rain to rapidly run off the land rather than percolate into the ground, is a time-tested recipe for flash flooding. During the monsoon season, flash floods are an ever-present risk in the Front Range foothills. But because the storms are small and spotty, it's anybody's guess which canyon is most at risk on any given day.

On that ill-fated July evening, just such a strong southeasterly flow of very moist air was streaming into Colorado from the Gulf of Mexico. The winds shoved a patch of this air up against the foothills above the Big Thompson and Cache la Poudre river canyons, causing big thunderstorms to build. It looked like the area was in for a gully washer of a storm and perhaps localized flooding. While all of this meteorology was normal for the season, one crucial thing was not: the usually reliable high-elevation winds—those above 10,000 feet that could be counted on to push the thunderstorms eastward once they formed—were not blowing with their usual force.

About 6:30 p.m. the thunderheads began to dump the expected torrents on a narrow (5-mile-wide) swath of the Big Thompson Canyon. People took shelter from the downpour, expecting the rain to soon ease. But the storm didn't budge. It rained and rained and rained. In places, 7.5 inches of rain fell in the first hour, and 12 inches fell that night—more than half a year's worth of moisture and far more than forecasters' highest predictions.

Photographer and geologist James Balog took this photo of the devastation in Big Thompson Canyon the day after the flood. Even a day later the river was flowing extremely fast and deep.

The land was incapable of absorbing that much water falling that fast. Water flowed across every hillside in sheets, pouring into the nearest gully or creek. The tributaries dutifully delivered their flows to the Big Thompson, rapidly building a wall of water that roared downstream. The flood stripped soil, rocks, trees, houses, and bridges from the landscape and carried them along.

The wall of water rose even higher when it was forced through the Narrows. The following day geologists could tell from the stripped vegetation that the water had reached a height of 20 feet and speeds of 13 to 17 miles per hour. Time has healed the scars left by the flood, but the water rose to about the base of the cliffs across the river. The road was submerged. Many of the people who died that night were trapped in their cars as they tried to outdrive the flood. It is apparent that at those flood speeds one car racing down the narrow, twisting road here would just barely be able to outrun the flood. Once the highway became clogged with evacuating cars, as it was that night, the victims never stood a chance.

Though the devastation in the canyon was total, few signs of it remain today. The road, a major artery providing access to Rocky Mountain National

Park, was soon repaired, and the vanished houses, businesses, and summer cabins were abandoned or rebuilt. It is therefore difficult today to appreciate what this place looked like in the flood's immediate aftermath. But the road cut at stop 2, across the highway and to the north (right), vividly illustrates the water's immense power. It consists of debris with boulders the size of dining room tables that waning floodwaters deposited that night as much as 10 feet above the road. During ordinary flows you would never see boulders this size rolling down the riverbed because the river's power is woefully inadequate to move them. But when water is moving as quickly as it was during the flood, Herculean feats like this do occur. The biggest boulder that geologists could document as moved by the flood measured a whopping 12 by 12 by 23 feet and weighed 275 tons. That is about the weight of nine fully loaded dump trucks!

In terms of both loss of life and property damage, the Big Thompson flood was the worst natural disaster in Colorado's history. As horrific as the loss of life was, the situation would have been far worse were it not for the heroic efforts of two police officers. Both lost their lives in the flood, but through their sacrifice they saved hundreds of others. It is appropriate to reflect on their heroism at stop 3, the monument erected in their honor, and contemplate the threat posed by future flash floods.

The flood deposited these boulders, which lie above the modern road and normal river level at stop 2.

Sergeant Willis Purdy of the Colorado State Patrol had finished his shift earlier that night when a call came over his radio that severe weather was causing significant problems in the Big Thompson Canyon. He decided to lend a hand, and as he drove from Loveland he ordered the evacuation of hundreds of people in the vulnerable lowlands between the city and the canyon. Even as floodwaters swept his car away, he radioed his situation and implored fellow officers to evacuate more people downstream. Estes Park patrol officer Michael Conley had traveled to Loveland on his day off. As he returned home the seriousness of the situation was immediately apparent to him, and he pitched in to help his fellow citizens during their moment of need. Officer Conley rescued sixty people before floodwaters swept him away.

While the officers' quick actions saved many lives that night, in the flood's aftermath the job of protecting Coloradans from a repeat shifted to meteorologists, hydrologists, and public officials. Scientists needed to assess what had happened and determine how they could provide more warning. Public officials needed to examine and refine zoning laws and evacuation plans in order to minimize future risk.

Scientists already knew that the combination of summer weather patterns and steep terrain made all of the Front Range foothills vulnerable to

The monument honoring officers Willis Purdy and Michael Conley, whose heroic efforts to warn people of the Big Thompson flood saved hundreds of lives.

flash floods. Several damaging events had occurred on other foothills rivers in the one hundred or more years since records had been kept, though none had been as devastating as the 1976 Big Thompson flood. Scientists realized a key question they needed to answer was how frequently a flood of that magnitude could be expected. The answer would provide public safety officers with crucial information they needed to plan appropriately.

Scientists assess the likelihood of a certain size flood the same way that meteorologists predict the probability of rain: they assign a percent chance. Since floods have a much lower probability of occurring than rain, geologists report the chance for a given year, not day. They therefore talk about the 10-year flood or, most commonly, the 100-year flood. These numbers are purely statistical: A 10-year flood has a 10 percent chance of occurring in any given year, so on average a flood this size will occur once each decade. The same logic holds for the 100-year flood, which, on average, occurs once every century. It is important to realize that this recurrence interval is mathematical, so it is entirely possible—though unlikely—for two 100-year floods to strike the same river in back-to-back years. The 100-year flood is the most famous because, as the biggest flood with a reasonable chance of occurring in a human lifetime, it is the one most commonly used to determine zoning laws.

How do hydrologists determine the volume of a 10-year or 100-year flood? Ideally, they calculate it using data from gauging stations like the one you saw at stop 1. If a gauge has a long history, like the one on the Big Thompson, scientists can accurately determine the size of a 10-year or other fairly high-frequency flood. They can then map the land area that will be inundated by water to develop maps of the flood zone. One response to the Big Thompson flood was to deploy many more monitoring gauges on vulnerable rivers throughout the Front Range foothills so that these flood recurrence intervals could be better characterized. These gauges also provide early warning of a rapidly rising river so emergency notice can be sent out.

After the Big Thompson flood, public policy officials wanted desperately to know: Was this the 100-year flood? The 500-year flood? How likely was it that they would have to deal with such a tremendous event again? The answer would significantly influence their decisions. The difficulty in answering such questions is that even our longest-running gauges likely record at most one such event—and, more typically, none at all. Scientists are therefore forced to extrapolate the meager gauge data they do have to try to determine how much land will be covered by a given flood. Given the overriding importance of public safety, such extrapolation is necessary and valuable, but no scientist feels comfortable extrapolating data, and none would vouch for the robust reliability of these estimates.

Geologists surveying the flood's effects quickly realized that they might be able to extend the record from the one hundred years the gauges provide to thousands of years by studying flood deposits like the one you examined at stop 2. Such deposits reveal the portions of the landscape that were covered by a past flood, and the size of the largest sediment particles testify to the power—and hence the velocity—of the water. When combined with dating techniques, geologists thought these measurements could reveal the recurrence interval of a flood of a given size.

This promising line of inquiry was vigorously pursued in the Big Thompson flood's aftermath. Unfortunately, geologists learned that many factors influence the height of a flood wave and the size of the sediment particles that wave can move, greatly complicating such analyses. A bevy of post-flood scientific papers attempted to determine how frequently an event of this magnitude will recur, but estimates varied widely. Some investigators believe that an event the size of the 1976 Big Thompson flood can be expected much more frequently than once every five hundred years, while others believe that prior to 1976, the Big Thompson had not experienced a flood of this size for several thousand years.

Regardless of the exact recurrence interval, the substantial work done on prehistoric floods provided sobering insights into how many people would be vulnerable if a comparable flood struck another Front Range drainage. When public safety officials rank the risk of damage and loss of life, thanks to the sheer number of people and amount of infrastructure in harm's way, the cities that sit along riverbanks at the foot of the mountains from Colorado Springs to Fort Collins are most at risk.

The city of Boulder provides an example of the preparation that scientists and planners have undertaken in hopes of minimizing this risk. A 100-year flood (with a water flow of 11,000 cubic feet per second) last struck Boulder in 1894, making the city statistically overdue for another big event. A national hazards assessment published in 2004 by the University of Colorado listed a flash flood on Boulder Creek as one of six disasters waiting to happen, along with a devastating hurricane striking New Orleans, which occurred just a year later. Boulder is ranked as the number one flash flood risk in the state. The magnitude of possible devastation was revealed when workers excavating the foundation for the Boulder County Justice Center unearthed debris deposited by a flood that roared down Boulder Canyon several thousand years ago. Based on the presence of 6-foot boulders, geologists estimated the water was traveling 10 to 11 miles per hour even after it exited the canyon and washed over the valley where the modern city of one hundred thousand sits. They believe the flood had a volume between 30,000 and 53,000 cubic feet per second, comparable in size to the Big Thompson event and three to five times bigger than Boulder Creek's largest historical flood.

Boulder is not the only city in danger. Every Front Range city sitting at the mouth of a canyon (including Fort Collins, Golden, Colorado Springs, and many more) is vulnerable. Public safety officials must balance the costs of protecting people from such huge disasters with the relative likelihood of their occurrence. In the absence of robust data, that is a challenging task. Nevertheless, city, county, state, and federal officials have responded to the threat in tangible ways. They have improved Front Range weather monitoring and streamflow gauging equipment, passed new zoning laws for the portions of cities that lie within the 100-year floodplain, and purchased and destroyed some buildings that stood within that floodplain. They've also required that new buildings built on a floodplain be engineered to resist flood damage, and that new bridges be designed to shift, not rip out and become floating battering rams, in the event of a flood. Officials have installed flood sirens to warn residents of the need to evacuate, and they have mounted a vigorous education campaign that includes brochures, signs, billboards, public meetings, and websites. As you drive through the Big Thompson or another Front Range river canyon, you'll see one part of this education campaign in the many signs imploring people to climb to safety in case of a flash flood. It is important to make people aware of the need to climb instead of flee, because many of the Big Thompson victims died as they tried to outrace the flood in their cars.

If anything positive has come out of the Big Thompson flood, it is that both officials and the state's populace have gained an awareness that they live in an area terribly vulnerable to flash floods. This enhanced appreciation that the normally ponderous pace of geologic processes does occasionally speed up will hopefully protect the lives of many Front Range residents and visitors when the next flash flood inevitably comes.

If you are in a canyon, especially during monsoon season, and see the water turn muddy and begin to rise, you should climb to safety.

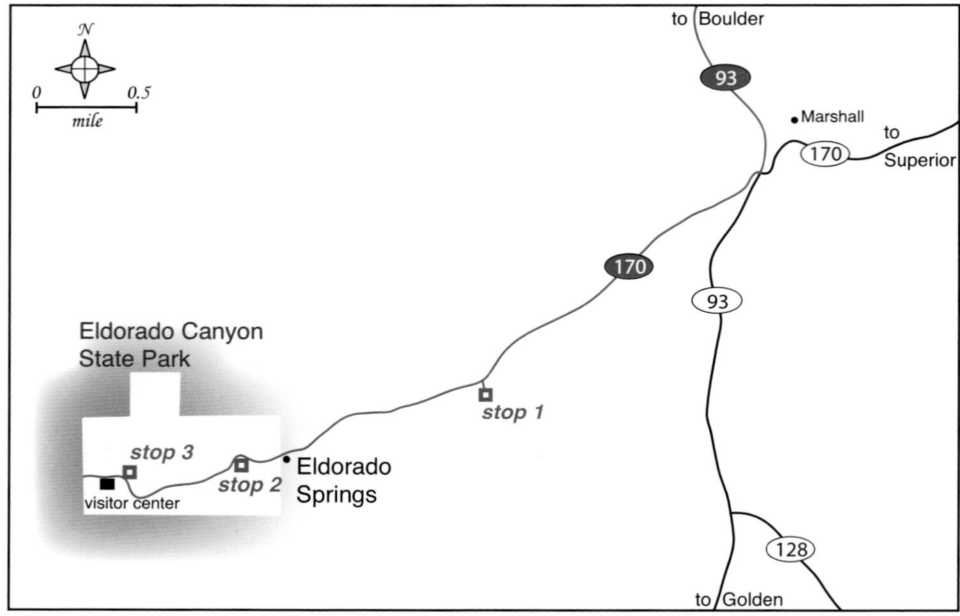

GETTING THERE: From downtown Boulder follow CO 93 south and turn right (west) onto CO 170. After 1.8 miles turn left into the Doudy Draw parking loop, stop 1, and examine the boulders lying along the inner edge of the parking loop. To reach stop 2, continue west on CO 170, through the town of Eldorado Springs, to Eldorado Canyon State Park, which is 3.2 miles from the CO 93 junction. Park just beyond the entrance booth and head to the rock outcrop immediately south of the booth. To reach stop 3, walk or drive 0.7 mile farther up the park's gravel road to the car bridge across the river. Park in the gravel lot just beyond the bridge and walk back (east) across the bridge to the pyramid of smooth, hard, bluish gray rock on the south side.

5

DÉJÀ VU ALL OVER AGAIN

Mountains Come, Mountains Go at Eldorado Canyon State Park

For humans, mountains are a metaphor for permanence, as embodied in common phrases like *old as the hills*. But when we, who live a mere one-hundred-year life span, can expand our outlook to include the millions or billions of years that Earth's rocks have witnessed, mountain ranges seem much more ephemeral. Like seas, deserts, and vast floodplains, mountains come, and mountains go. Thus like all ranges, the majestic peaks of today's Rockies—as enduring as they seem—are destined to be leveled by the inexorable forces of weathering and erosion.

Geologists have the thrilling but painstaking job of trying to reconstruct what a landscape like the Front Range has looked like over the sweep of geologic time. To unravel billions of years of Earth's history, geologists hang their hats on one fundamental principle: uniformitarianism. This maxim is often summarized as "the present is the key to the past." This means that when geologists examine a rock, they assume that the processes that formed it were not radically different from the processes that occur today—in other words, they are uniform. Therefore, if you find a match between the properties of an ancient sedimentary rock and a modern environment where similar sediments are accumulating, it's a good bet that the ancient area resembled the modern environment when the rock was deposited. With this principle in mind, let's take a look at the rocks of Eldorado Canyon State Park.

Stop 1 lies on the High Plains just east of the state park and the modern Rocky Mountains. Looking south from the parking area, a series of terraced mesas dominate the vista. The highest and most extensive of these, Rocky Flats (vignette 6), rises about 600 feet above your current elevation in the valley of South Boulder Creek. Each of these mesas is veneered by debris shed off the Rockies within the last 2 million years. Even more recent incision by South Boulder Creek carved the valley in which you are standing,

Eldorado Canyon's soaring walls reveal that mountain ranges occupied the area long before the modern Rockies.

leaving behind these elevated remnants of the earlier and higher Great Plains. Boulders that once veneered Rocky Flats have toppled down into the parking area due to the creek's incision; you can easily examine them.

Most of the boulders fall into three groups. The first consists of reddish pink, pebbly sandstone derived from the 300-million-year-old Fountain Formation, the rock that forms Boulder's majestic Flatirons and Denver's world-famous Red Rocks Amphitheatre (vignette 9). The second group is made of tan, pebble-free sandstone belonging to the Lyons Formation, of which the spectacular Garden of the Gods towers (vignette 16) are constructed. The final group of boulders consists of exceptionally hard, white to bluish gray chunks of metamorphic rock. Some of them are smooth, while others have a lumpy texture. The smooth rock is quartzite, which is metamorphosed sandstone. The lumpy rock is metamorphosed conglomerate, and the lumps are pebbles embedded within it. The sandstone and conglomerate were deposited together about 1,700 million years ago, then later metamorphosed. The presence of ancient, metamorphosed conglomerate is of special significance for us, as we will discuss at stop 3.

The boulders that litter the area, some of which measure up to 6 feet across, were all shed from the modern Rockies, whose ramparts rise a mile west of here. Not surprisingly, it takes a swift, strong current to transport

Eldorado Canyon

Rocky Flats mesa

stop 1

Stop 1 lies on the Great Plains at the foot of the current Rocky Mountains and adjacent to the Rocky Flats mesa.

This boulder in the stop 1 parking lot is metamorphosed conglomerate that was deposited about 1,700 million years ago.

rocks this large. Energetic mountain streams can transport larger particles; they gain their energy from both water volume and the steepness of the terrain. Because South Boulder Creek loses much of the gravitational urgency imparted by the steep mountain slopes just a short distance after entering the Great Plains, it begins to meander a bit more lazily across the plains. If you travel just a couple miles downstream, this decrease in energy is evident in the sediments, with the riverbanks lined with sand instead of the boulders and cobbles you see here. Were you to travel down South Boulder Creek to the South Platte River and on to its confluence with the Missouri and ultimately the mighty Mississippi, you would see a progressive decrease in the size of the sediment lining the banks. The Mississippi ain't called the Big Muddy for nothing!

Uniformitarianism dictates that, as we see in this modern setting, an ancient sedimentary rock that contains bigger particles was deposited closer to its mountain sediment source. Let's put this idea to the test in Eldorado Canyon.

We'll begin by looking at the tan rock south of the park entrance booth (stop 2). This is the Lyons sandstone, deposited about 280 million years ago. In places like Loveland and the rock's namesake town of Lyons, 24 miles to the north, this clean-breaking rock is quarried to produce flagstone used in buildings, rock walls, and patios throughout the region, including the distinctive buildings of Boulder's University of Colorado campus. The Lyons sediment consists exclusively of fine-grained sand. Whatever the formation's depositional environment, the lack of big sediment particles shows that it didn't accumulate at the foot of a towering mountain range like the one that exists here today. The Lyons's characteristics therefore tell us that the topography of Colorado's Front Range has changed over time. The Lyons possesses sweeping crossbeds, layers of sediment that were deposited at an angle to one another. The crossbeds are not easy to spot here, although they are apparent on the first big wall that rises north of the river. Elsewhere, the crossbeds are readily apparent (vignette 16), and it is along them that the rock breaks perfectly smoothly. The character of the crossbeds is identical to those formed in modern sand dunes, thus revealing to geologists that the Front Range was covered by desert sand dunes 280 million years ago.

If we could look beneath the nearby town of Eldorado Springs, the point that the Front Range landscape has changed dramatically over geologic time would be driven home even more forcefully. The town is built upon 250-million-year-old red mudstone belonging to the Lykins Formation. Using our uniformitarian logic, the tiny particle size tells us that the currents that deposited the Lykins were sluggish. Indeed, the formation was deposited on a broad, gentle coastal plain that sweltered under a desert sun (vignette 9).

The fine-grained, uniform Lyons sandstone possesses crossbeds, like these (defined by the dashed lines) in an outcrop in Lefthand Canyon, north of Boulder. The crossbeds reveal that the Lyons accumulated in an ancient desert.

Walk west 150 yards along the gravel road and cross the turbulent South Boulder Creek on a footbridge. Note the creek's powerful roar and the huge boulders it has managed to move downstream in this mountainous area. As you step off the bridge on the creek's north side, the trail forks around the toe of a rock outcrop—our next objective. All the rock around you consists of the Fountain Formation. This is the source formation for the red boulders you encountered at stop 1.

The Fountain Formation is a sedimentary unit that was deposited about 300 million years ago, during the Pennsylvanian period. The outcrop here consists of two distinct types of layers, each containing different particle sizes. The thinner, maroon layers consist of fine-grained sand, whereas the thicker, light pink to tan layers contain pebbles and cobbles embedded in coarser sand. The biggest cobbles are fist sized, attesting to the fact that a vigorous current, albeit one far less powerful than the modern creek underneath the footbridge, transported them here 300 million years ago. Notice also that the contact between these two sediment types undulates wildly.

When geologists combine all of the information available from this and the park's many other Fountain Formation outcrops, a clear picture emerges of what Eldorado Canyon looked like 300 million years ago. What is today a narrow canyon carved into the flank of the Rocky Mountains was back then an alluvial fan accumulating at the toe of an earlier mountain range known as the Ancestral Front Range, which was one of several ranges that composed the Ancestral Rockies. Those mountains were heaved up by tectonic activity that created folds and faults similar to those present in the modern Rockies. An alluvial fan is a massive cone of sediment that accrues where a river exits mountains, loses much of its energy, and consequently drops the bigger, heavier sediment particles it is transporting. On average days this river carried nothing larger than the fine-grained maroon sand. But when occasional floods (vignette 4) roared out of the mountains, the raging floodwaters scoured channels into the maroon sand that lay on the fan's surface, creating the undulating contacts you see. As the flood waned, the thicker layers of cobble-bearing conglomerate were deposited. Throughout the park you will see this alternation between sandstone and conglomerate layers repeated again and again. We know that this ancient range could not possibly be the same range as the modern Rockies because of the much smaller particle sizes in rocks of younger age, such as the Lyons sandstone and the Lykins Formation, which clearly indicate that no mountains occupied this area when they were deposited.

Both types of sedimentary layers in the Fountain Formation at stop 2 were deposited on an ancient alluvial fan at the toe of the Ancestral Front Range. The thinner, finer-grained maroon layer was deposited during normal conditions of water flow. Periodic floods deposited the thicker, light pink to tan layers. The wavy contact between them resulted from scour of the underlying maroon layer during a flood. Cobbles (inset) transported by the powerful flood currents consist of the same blue quartzite you examined at stop 1 (dashed box shows location of inset photo).

About 300 million years ago the Eldorado Canyon area was part of a massive apron of coalescing alluvial fans, cones of sediment deposited at the toe of a mountain range, like this one in Death Valley.

The biggest cobbles embedded in the Fountain Formation at stop 2 consist of the same hard, bluish gray quartzite you examined at stop 1. This means that the quartzite that is today exposed in the modern Front Range was also exposed 300 million years ago in the Ancestral Front Range. Not only did these ancestral mountains lie in nearly the same location as the current Rockies, they were composed of the same rocks.

Geologists have conducted similar analyses of sediment particle size and composition for Pennsylvanian-age rocks throughout Colorado. By collating the results across the entire region, we can reconstruct the positions and compositions of the Ancestral Rockies ranges. For example, the Fountain Formation that lines the road up Boulder's scenic Flagstaff Mountain contains cobbles the same size as those here in Eldorado, but they are made of granite instead of quartzite. Flagstaff, too, was part of an alluvial fan that lay at the base of the Ancestral Front Range, and like the mountains today, the Pennsylvanian-age mountains in the Boulder area consisted of granite. Denver's Red Rocks Amphitheatre (vignette 9) is also made of Fountain Formation, and it, too, hosts cobbles of similar size. Most of the ampitheatre's cobbles consist of gneiss, again mirroring the composition of the modern mountains just to the west.

Southern Colorado's spectacular Crestone peaks consist of rocks the same age as the Fountain Formation that contain boulders twice the size of a basketball. The bigger size tells us that the Crestone area was closer to the ancestral mountains than was Eldorado Canyon. Conversely, Fort Collins's Horsetooth Reservoir is surrounded by exposures of Fountain Formation containing far more pebbles than cobbles, indicating that Fort Collins lay farther from them than did Eldorado. Particularly important exposures of the Fountain Formation lie in Colorado Springs (vignette 16), where coarse conglomerates such as those here at Eldorado Canyon are interfingered with limestone beds that possess marine fossils. East of Denver, oil and water wells intersect buried Pennsylvanian-age marine mudstone. By piecing all these clues together, geologists have deduced that the Ancestral Front Range was a coastal mountain range that lay just west of Eldorado Canyon, with the Denver area straddling the shoreline.

Geologists have performed the same exercise in other directions as well, with surprising results. Heading west from Eldorado Canyon into the modern Rockies, there are no Pennsylvanian-age rocks whatsoever. Can this absence be attributed to modern erosion having stripped off the entire stack of sediments? The presence of younger sedimentary rocks in a few key locations, including the Dillon-Keystone area, indicate that this can't be the sole explanation—modern erosion would have removed those sediments as well.

Instead, this absence of Pennsylvanian-age rocks between older and younger rocks—a sandwich missing its filling—marks what geologists call an unconformity. An unconformity is a time gap in the rock record, and it forms if rocks of the missing age either were never deposited or were removed by erosion before the existing, younger sediments were laid down. The best explanation for the unconformity in the Dillon-Keystone area is that no sedimentary rocks were deposited there during the Pennsylvanian period. The reason? The region was part of the Ancestral Front Range, not adjacent to it, so 300 million years ago Dillon was an area of active erosion, not deposition.

The application of uniformitarianism across the region has allowed geologists to reconstruct the geography of the Ancestral Rockies, despite the fact that erosion had obliterated the range by about 250 million years ago. Vail Pass on I-70, west of Dillon, has many outcrops of pink rocks nearly identical to those in Eldorado Canyon. Vail's Pennsylvanian-age conglomerates were deposited on an alluvial fan that lay on the *western* side of the Ancestral Front Range, whereas those in Eldorado Canyon formed on the range's *eastern* flank. As you head even farther west on I-70, you encounter Pennsylvanian-age sedimentary rocks consisting of progressively smaller particles, the predictable result of streams that were moving away from the Ancestral Front Range. By the time you reach the Eagle River valley, near the town of Gypsum, the Pennsylvanian-age rocks consist of ocean-deposited limestone and evaporites, showing that the Ancestral Rockies were not just coastal mountains—they comprised an island range. Continuing farther west in Colorado and eastern Utah you encounter a repeat of the sequence of Pennsylvanian rock units just described as you cross the Ancestral Uncompahgre Range, another range within the Ancestral Rockies.

We can use the principle of uniformitarianism to push our inquiry further back in time. Proceed to stop 3 to examine an outcrop of the Coal Creek quartzite, which is found only in a narrow band of foothills between Eldorado Canyon and Coal Creek Canyon, 3.5 miles south of here. Like all of Eldorado Canyon's rock layers, these once-horizontal units were tilted down to the east during the Laramide orogeny.

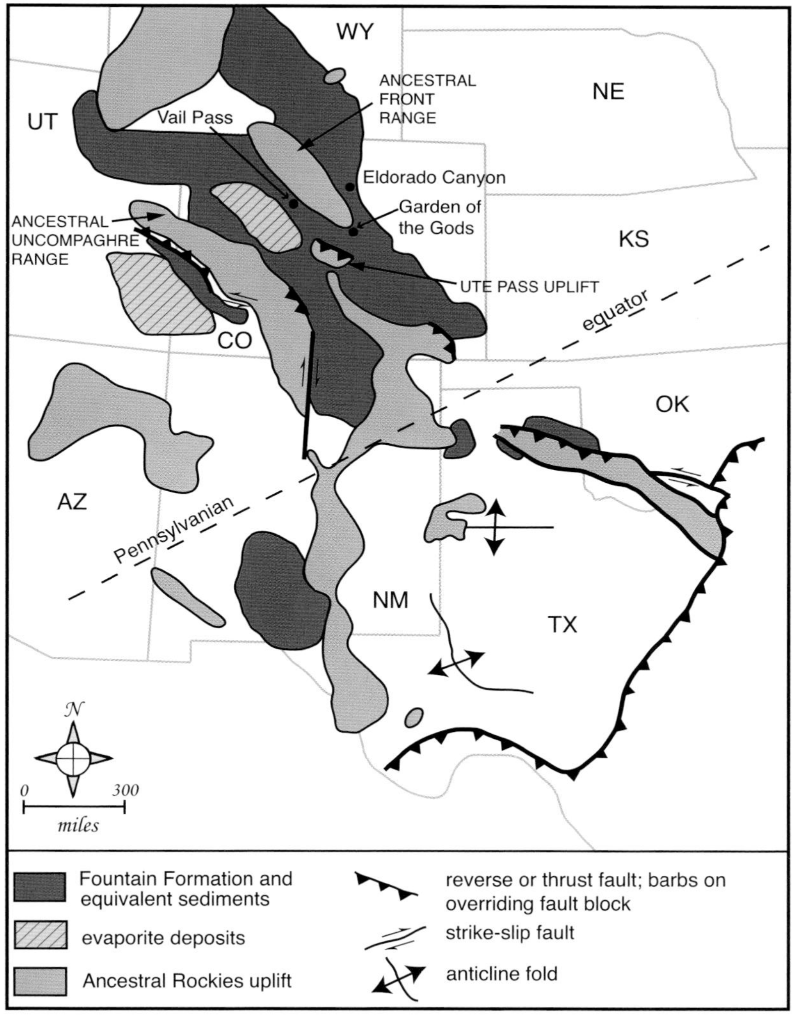

The Ancestral Rockies lay very close to today's mountains. Today's Eldorado Canyon formed in an alluvial fan lying at the east toe of the Ancestral Front Range, while the Vail Pass area was another alluvial fan shed west off the range. The Fountain Formation at Garden of the Gods (vignette 16) accumulated on an alluvial fan shed off the Ute Pass uplift.

The bedding layers of the Coal Creek quartzite, a metamorphosed sandstone, tilt down to the left (northeast).

This quartzite is one of the older rocks in Colorado, checking in at a whopping 1,700 million years old. The fact that this formation exists in just one compact locality allows us to add some startling details to our story. We know that 1,700 million years ago the sediment that became the quartzite's parent sandstone was accumulating in the area destined to become Colorado (vignette 7). That sandstone was then buried deep in the Earth, where intense heat and pressure metamorphosed it, fusing its sand grains together. The original sedimentary layers are still evident in this slick, bullet-hard outcrop. Since we found chunks of the quartzite embedded in the Fountain Formation at stop 2, we know that by 300 million years ago the deeply buried rocks had been hoisted back to the surface in the mountain building episode that created the Ancestral Front Range. Some of the quartzite was quarried by energetic rivers and came to rest on a huge alluvial fan at the range's eastern toe, which lithified as the Fountain Formation. What quartzite was not eroded away was once again buried beneath more sediment as the Ancestral Front Range was eroded away.

But then, 64 million years ago, the state was wracked by yet another mountain building episode, the Laramide orogeny. This orogeny heaved the quartzite remnants skyward once more in the Laramide Rockies. Exceedingly powerful floods that poured out of those mountains 36 million years ago deposited numerous boulders and cobbles of Coal Creek quartzite in the Castle Rock conglomerate near the city of Castle Rock (vignette 11). The Laramide Rockies were, in turn, eroded and buried (vignette 2). The quartzite outcrop you see here marks the third mountain range in which this rock has been exposed, this time in the modern Rockies. It was during this most recent exposure event that the quartzite blocks you examined at stop 1 were eroded from the range and deposited with the Rocky Flats sediment.

Recall that at stop 1 you saw two kinds of bluish gray boulders. The smooth ones consisted of quartzite, just like the outcrop here. The lumpier type was metamorphosed conglomerate, the pebbles of which give it the lumpy texture. This metamorphosed conglomerate is also part of the Coal Creek Formation. Unfortunately, its only outcrops lie in the rugged, difficult-to-access hills between here and Coal Creek Canyon. However, with a bit of inference we can once again apply our uniformitarianist thinking to the interpretation of these rocks and go back farther in time.

Much as South Boulder Creek does today, 1,700 million years ago a river coursed through Eldorado Canyon State Park. Sand and pebbles accumulated on its banks, forming layers of sandstone and conglomerate that were later metamorphosed into the bluish gray quartzite and metamorphosed conglomerate. Because pebbles accumulated on the riverbanks, we can infer that the region lay reasonably close to the mountain range that was their source. The park wasn't in the mountains, otherwise the metamorphosed conglomerate would contain boulders like those we found at stop 1, nor at the mountains' toe in an alluvial fan, in which case it would contain cobbles like those we found in the Fountain Formation at stop 2. It's likely that the ancient mountain range lay a few tens of miles from where we are standing. It probably was raised at Colorado's very birth, when a plate collision appended the state's rocks onto the North American continent (vignette 7).

Our careful scrutiny of the rocks exposed in the modern Rockies has revealed that these mountains are at least the fourth range that has stood on or near this spot over the immensity of geologic time. The Laramide Rockies were here 64 million years ago. Before that, the Ancestral Rockies stood a stone's throw west of this spot 300 million years ago. And 1,700 million years ago another range stood just miles away. The inexorable forces of weathering and erosion, which repeatedly transformed the state into a nearly featureless plain, leveled one range after another. But each time the patient forces of plate tectonics built yet another range near where the old one once stood. The modern Rockies will also be erased one day, but given enough time, another range will likely rise to grace the state—in the immortal words of baseball legend Yogi Berra, like "déjà vu all over again."

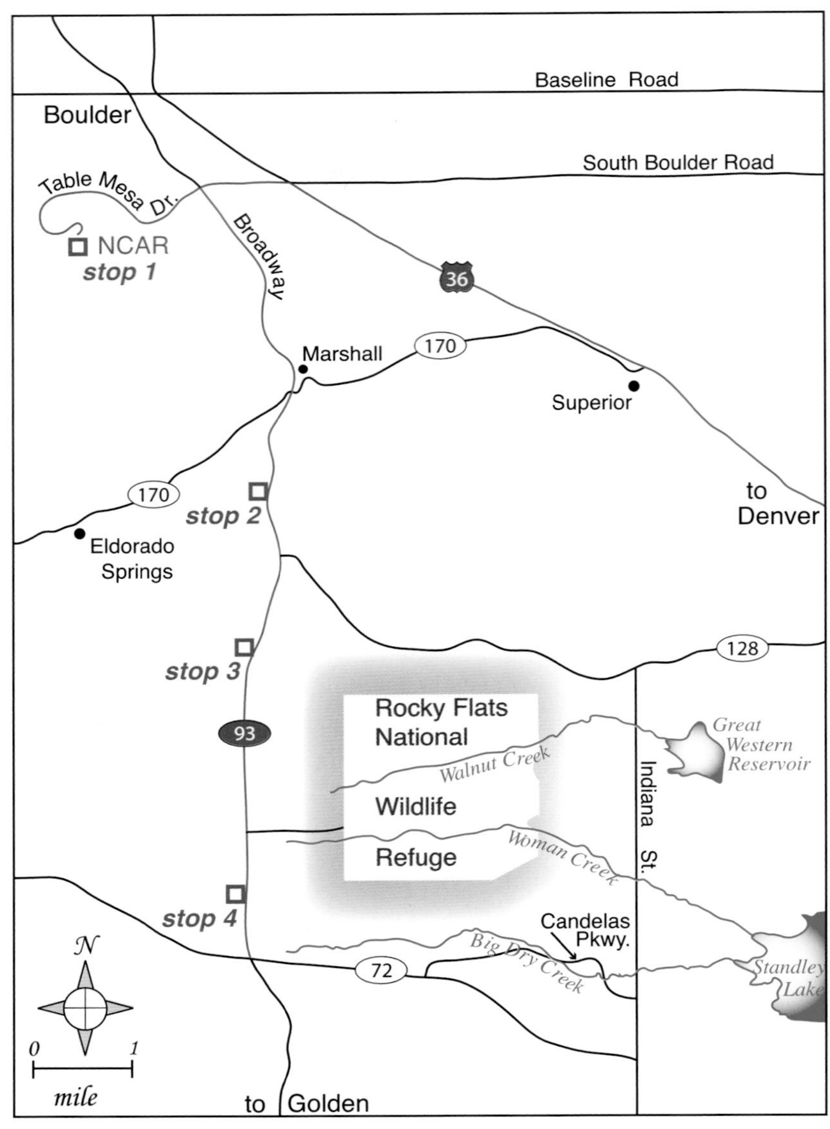

GETTING THERE: Stop 1 is on top of the mesa holding the National Center for Atmospheric Research (NCAR) in Boulder. From Denver, head west on US 36 and take the first Boulder exit (South Boulder Road/Table Mesa Drive). Turn left at the traffic light, heading west on Table Mesa Drive. After 1.1 miles you reach the intersection of Table Mesa Drive and Broadway. Table Mesa Drive continues to climb for 2.4 miles to the NCAR facility. Park at the lowest point in the parking lot, on its southeast side, where it is farthest from the building. Follow any of several 20-yard-long trails that lead to the mesa's southern edge, where you are treated to a panoramic view to the south.

6

FROM PEDIMENTS TO PLUTONIUM
The History of Rocky Flats

If we could visit the Front Range of 2.5 million years ago, it would be easily recognizable. The Rocky Mountains stood where they do today and topped out at about the same elevation. From their feet, the Great Plains' grassy carpet rolled eastward. Yet two major changes still lay in store for the region: the great Pleistocene ice ages, and the arrival of human beings.

In the mountains the ice ages were marked by the repeated comings and goings of huge rivers of ice that transformed a gently rolling upland into the majestic, craggy Front Range we know today (vignette 3). When humans first moved into Colorado 12,000 years ago, they used the land to satisfy their needs but did not transform it. But with the arrival of the twentieth century and the startling technological advances that enabled humans to literally move mountains, we began to alter our landscape in geologically noticeable ways. In this vignette we will trace the geological and human history of Rocky Flats, a grassy mesa and former nuclear weapons facility, now converted into the Rocky Flats National Wildlife Refuge, that stands between Boulder and Golden. Initially shaped by ice age forces, Rocky Flats's lasting legacy is now the result of Cold War–era human activities, which still determine how we use this landscape today.

As you leave the Boulder city limits en route to stop 1, you climb a grassy slope to the top of Table Mountain, on which stands the futuristic-looking

To reach stop 2, backtrack to Table Mesa and Broadway. Reset your odometer here. Turn right (south) on Broadway, which becomes CO 93, and head south for 3.8 miles to a wide, gravel pullout on the right during the road's ascent of a long hill. Stop 3 lies 1.7 miles farther south at a small dirt pullout on the right, immediately in front of the sign that marks the Jefferson County line. To reach stop 4, proceed another 2.3 miles south on CO 93. Park in a gravel pullout on the right at a traffic light that marks the junction between CO 93 and the access road to the old Rocky Flats nuclear weapons facility.

building housing the National Center for Atmospheric Research (NCAR), a leading climate research center. To your right (north) a second grassy mesa, which slopes noticeably down to the east away from the mountains, is clearly visible across the intervening valley. This is Enchanted Mesa. The nest of small towers on top of it belong to the National Institute of Standards and Technology, a national laboratory best known as the home of the atomic clock, which synchronizes time for the entire world. Enchanted Mesa sits at a lower elevation than Table Mountain, a fact that will be important for our later discussion. Both mesas are constructed of bedrock that was planed off by erosion and then topped by a thin veneer of loose sediment. This makes them both remnants of what geologists call pediments. A pediment is a gently inclined erosion surface, veneered with gravel, that develops at the foot of a mountain range.

At stop 1 follow the short dirt path to a panoramic vista looking southeast. The most prominent landscape feature is a large, eastward-sloping mesa (another pediment remnant) that hosts a cluster of giant windmills

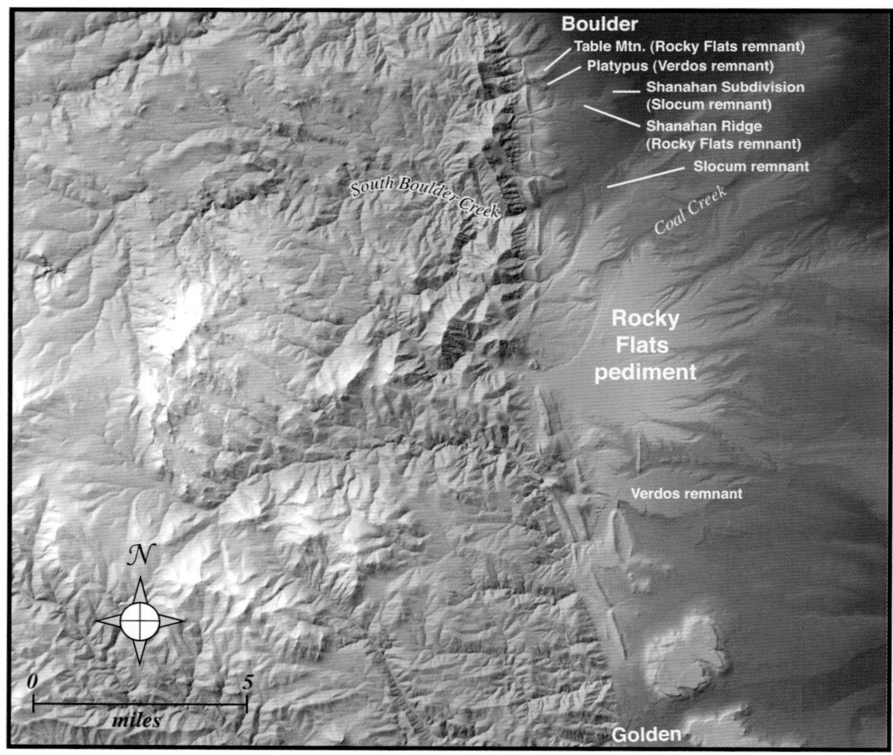

This color relief map of the Front Range illustrates the various remnants of the Rocky Flats, Verdos, and Slocum pediments between Boulder and Golden.

The NCAR research lab (stop 1) is built upon Table Mountain, which is a remnant of the Rocky Flats pediment. The pyramid-shaped hill to its left and below it is Mt. Platypus, a tiny remnant of the Verdos pediment. This photo was taken from Fairview High School, which stands on the lower Slocum pediment.

belonging to Golden's National Renewable Energy Lab. Clearly, one important human use of Front Range pediments is for scientific laboratories! The pediment upon which the windmills stand is Rocky Flats. From this vantage point you can see that Rocky Flats is at approximately the same elevation as Table Mountain, where you stand. These two mesas were once connected in a continuous, flat-topped, eastward-sloping plane called the Rocky Flats pediment (or surface). Numerous creeks, including Bear Canyon Creek, whose valley lies directly below you, later dissected this once-continuous pediment.

In addition to the Rocky Flats pediment, remnants of two lower, younger pediments are also visible from here. Look first for an isolated knob crowned by large boulders rising just in front (north) of Bear Canyon Creek. Its summit lies about 260 feet vertically below you. Though this knob has no official name, our kids have dubbed it Mt. Platypus, so we shall call it the same. Behind Platypus, on the south side of Bear Canyon Creek, is a small, pine-clad mesa standing at the same elevation as the Platypus summit. Platypus, the mesa at the same elevation, and Enchanted Mesa are all remnants of the Verdos pediment. Behind the Verdos mesa is a higher, eastward-sloping, forested mesa that stands at the same elevation as NCAR. Known as Shanahan Ridge, this higher mesa is yet another remnant of the once continuous Rocky Flats pediment.

From this perch you can also discern, southeast of Mt. Platypus, another mesa, even lower, dotted with homes. Useful landmarks are the small, kidney-shaped Viele Lake sitting in front of the mesa and the gray concrete high school that stands on the mesa immediately above the lake. This

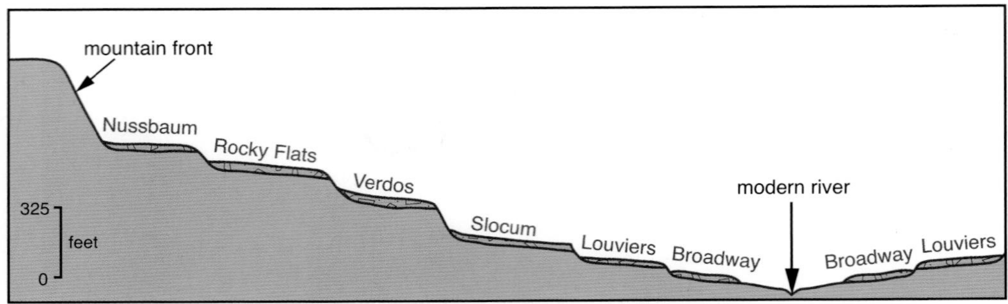

A flight of six pediments exists across the Front Range. The highest (Nussbaum) pediment is the oldest, with each lower pediment correspondingly younger. (Modified from Madole, 1991.)

suburban mesa is a remnant of the Slocum pediment. The three pediments visible from here are part of a flight of six pediments that form a kind of giant's staircase throughout the Front Range. Rarely do all six appear together at the same place, but almost everywhere in the urban corridor you will see at least one or two of them. Many residents of cities such as Colorado Springs, Pueblo, and numerous Denver suburbs live on one or another of these pediments.

What geological events formed this series of pediments and then carved them into the flight of stairs we see today? The fact that the tops of Table Mountain and Mt. Platypus are littered with cobbles and boulders provides an important clue. Erosion during the Pleistocene beveled off the Great Plains' bedrock, forming the smooth, continuous, eastward-sloping Rocky Flats pediment. Floods periodically washed cobbles and boulders out of the mountains and onto the pediment surface. Landslides and rockfalls scattered even bigger boulders over those portions of the pediment adjacent to the steep mountain front, including here at NCAR. This rock debris is called alluvium. Though variable, this alluvial veneer is a few feet to a few tens of feet thick. It overlies a tilted stack of bedrock layers several thousand feet thick that underlies the Great Plains, which begin right here at NCAR. At stop 3 we will get a roadside glimpse of just how thin this veneer is.

Head now to stop 2. As CO 93 leaves Boulder (at 1 mile on your odometer), it descends off the Slocum pediment and into the valley of South Boulder Creek. It then climbs back up onto the Slocum at the traffic light south of town (the junction with CO 170, at 3.1 miles on your odometer) before ascending the north flank of the Rocky Flats pediment. After you park, take a moment to reorient yourself. To the west lies a gash in the mountain front carved by South Boulder Creek. The magnificent slot through which the creek exits the mountains is Eldorado Canyon (vignette 5). In

At stop 2 you can see South Boulder Creek exit the mountains at Eldorado Canyon. Flanking it are remnants of the Slocum, Verdos, and Rocky Flats pediments.

the foreground stretches the gentle South Boulder Creek valley, framed to both north and south by low remnants of the Slocum pediment. In the distance to your right looms NCAR atop Table Mountain, a remnant of the Rocky Flats pediment. The pimple of Mt. Platypus rises just in front of it. You are currently at about the same elevation as Mt. Platypus, on part of the Verdos pediment. At the same elevation to the east across the highway lies a narrow topographic shelf littered with rounded cobbles. This sediment marks the Verdos pediment's alluvial veneer. To your left, the edge of the Rocky Flats mesa is prominent. Here above South Boulder Creek, like at stop 1, the series of pediments at different elevations forms a landscape resembling a flight of stairs.

Recall from stop 1 that the Rocky Flats pediment was once a nearly continuous surface. Incision by South Boulder Creek, Bear Canyon Creek, and others dissected the once-continuous pediment into today's discrete mesas. Why, though, does a flight of six different pediments exist instead of just one? The answer lies in the fact that rivers naturally undergo periods in which they deposit alluvium (known as aggradation), followed by periods of erosion (called incision). The veneer of cobbles and boulders you observed at NCAR was deposited during a period of aggradation along the Front Range. Later, when the rivers entered a period of incision, they excavated the very alluvium they had recently deposited. The alluvial cobbles are composed of extremely erosion-resistant rocks. Only in the river channels, where erosional power is concentrated, were the rivers able to breach the Rocky Flats pediment's alluvial armor. When they finally succeeded, they immediately attacked the much softer sedimentary shale beneath, quickly carving deeper valleys. The situation was similar to carving into a loaf of French bread. As you saw away at the hard crust you make slow progress, but as soon as you breach it, the knife slices easily through the spongy bread beneath.

Once the rivers reached the softer shale bedrock beneath the alluvial cap, they meandered back and forth across their valley floors. At each bend the rivers undercut their banks, causing repeated landslides that inexorably widened the valleys. In this manner, the combined erosional activities of the area's numerous small rivers and creeks formed a new, lower pediment (the Verdos) with small remnants of the higher Rocky Flats pediment preserved as mesas in the few places the rivers didn't manage to scour.

Eventually, the rivers switched back to a period of aggradation, causing them to deposit a second alluvial veneer across the newly formed Verdos pediment. When the rivers entered their next incisional phase, they carved and planed off another, even lower, pediment, creating yet another step in the giant's staircase. Each subsequent pediment formed in similar fashion.

The highest pediment remnant at a given location is thus the oldest, and each lower pediment is correspondingly younger. In the Denver area the Rocky Flats pediment, which stands 200 to 400 feet above its neighboring river valley, is the highest. Near Pueblo and Colorado Springs an even higher pediment, known as the Nussbaum, rises 500 to 700 feet above the area's rivers. The lowest pediment visible at stop 2, the Slocum, stands about 100 feet above the modern creek, and the three youngest pediments are lower still.

Geologists would like to know when the Rocky Flats pediment formed. If we knew that age, we would know when the Great Plains stood, on average, 200 to 400 feet higher than they do today and could also calculate the average rate at which the Plains are being eroded. However, the pediment surfaces are exceptionally difficult to date and, until recently, few reliable ages existed for any of them.

The maturation of cosmogenic radionuclide dating (a form of radiometric dating) has recently begun to improve that situation. Such dating relies on the fact that Earth is continuously bathed in a rain of high-energy cosmic rays. Many rays penetrate the atmosphere, but their downward progress is arrested when they smash into rocks at the surface. These collisions release so much energy that some of the rocks' atoms are transformed into new, radioactive particles, providing geologists with a built-in radiometric clock to calculate when that rock was first exposed to cosmic rays.

Scientists had previously hypothesized that the age of any Front Range pediment would be roughly the same across its entire surface. However, a

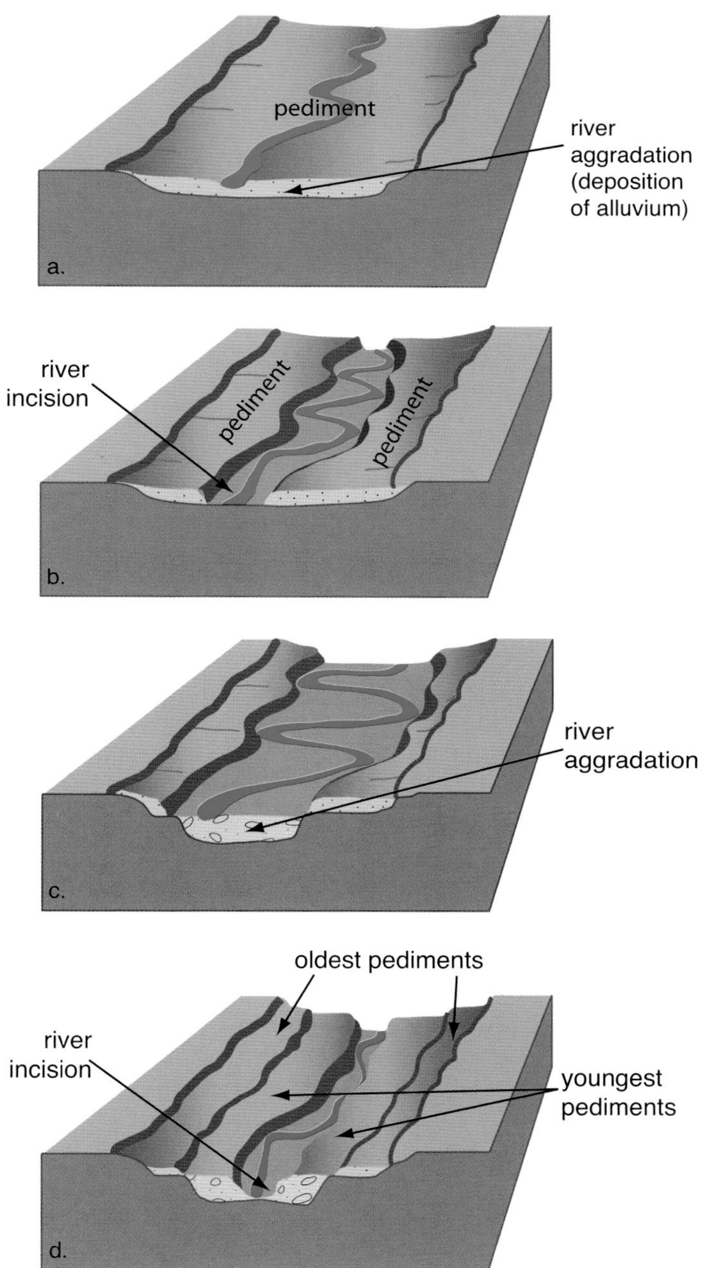

How to form a flight of pediments by alternating river incision and aggradation: (a) During a period of aggradation, rivers deposit alluvium across an eroded bedrock surface, forming a pediment. (b) During a period of incision, the rivers carve narrow canyons that breach the pediment's alluvial veneer, breaking the pediment into separate sections. (c) As incision slows, the rivers meander back and forth, planing off a new, lower bedrock surface and veneering it with alluvium. This creates a new, lower pediment. The meandering rivers also whittle away at the flanking sections of the higher pediment, leaving just isolated remnants preserved as mesas. (d) During the next episode of incision, the rivers carve new canyons through the lower alluvial veneer, carving the second pediment into remnant mesas. Additional, lower pediments are formed in a similar manner.

recent flurry of cosmogenic dates obtained on the alluvium that veneers the various pediments has revealed a far more complicated situation. Rocky Flats alluvium in the vicinity of stops 1 and 2 began accumulating about 2.4 million years ago. Incision of the pediment's eastern reaches, about 5 miles east of here, began almost immediately, cutting off the sediment supply there. However, here in the vicinity of stops 2 and 3, new alluvium was still accumulating on the pediment as recently as 1 million years ago and, closer to the mountain front, the pediment wasn't abandoned until about 400,000 years ago.

This perplexing situation becomes explicable when you closely examine a river's behavior. Every river has a beginning, called its headwaters, and an end, its mouth. Scientists can graph a river's change in elevation from its headwaters to its mouth. Geologists call such a plot the river's longitudinal (long) profile. The elevation of the river mouth is called its base level. The base level of a river that reaches the sea is, of course, sea level. For rivers that don't empty directly into the sea, like those along the Front Range, the base level is the elevation at its confluence with a bigger river.

A river is a natural system and, like all natural systems, it seeks a state of equilibrium. The long profile of a river in equilibrium traces out a concave curve, steeper at the headwaters and very gentle near its mouth. If there is any change that knocks the system out of equilibrium, the river will respond by trying to reestablish this perfect long profile. So what would happen if the river's base level were to rise, for instance with a rise in sea level? The river responds by dropping its sediment load at its new mouth, thereby lowering its slope there. This section of lower slope would, in turn, lead to deposition farther upstream, and so on. A rise in base level would therefore trigger an episode of aggradation, which would eventually restore equilibrium along the river's entire long profile.

What if the river's base level dropped, for instance if sea level fell? Once again, equilibrium is disturbed. The river's long profile is no longer concave due to an anomalously steep section at its mouth. Steeper rivers erode their beds more efficiently than gentle ones, so incision would be concentrated at this steep section, which geologists call a knick point—an especially steep gradient where erosion is concentrated. As erosion at a knick point restores equilibrium to the lower portion of the long profile, the section above becomes anomalously steep, triggering enhanced incision there. An episode of river incision thus migrates upstream over time.

Here in the Denver-Boulder area, all rivers and streams flow into the South Platte, so the confluence with this master river sets the local base level. If a period of incision begins on the South Platte, the local rivers' base levels will drop, sending a knick point up every stream in the basin. As the knick point passes a given spot on the pediment, that portion of the pediment becomes stranded above the modern river valley, cutting it

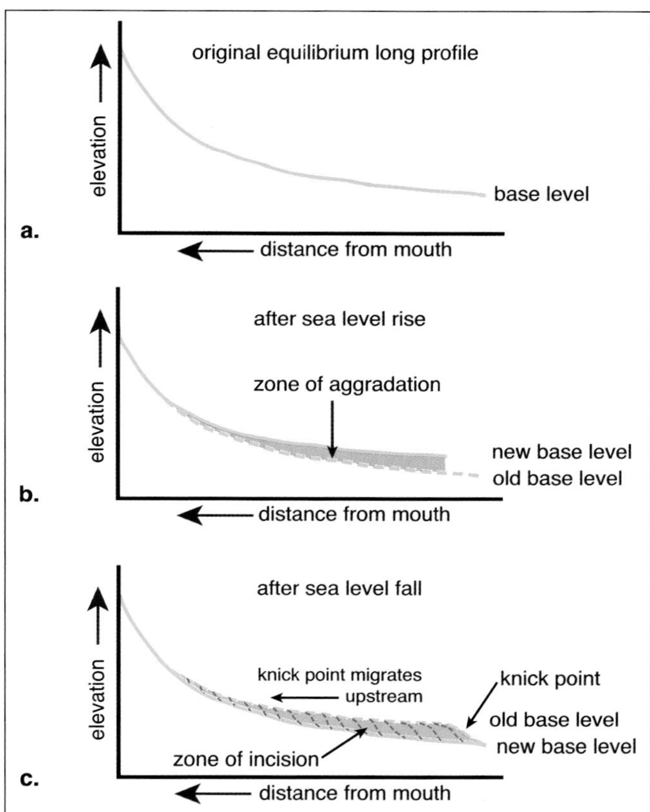

The blue line depicts the long profile of a stream in equilibrium (a). If its base level rises, the river adjusts its profile to the new, solid blue line (b) by depositing sediment. If its base level drops (c), the river's long profile develops a knick point (a zone of rapid erosion) where the river mouth used to be. The knick point (dashed line) migrates upstream, and the river's long profile reaches a new equilibrium at a lower elevation.

off from the accumulation of fresh alluvium. Upstream of the knick point, however, the pediment continues to receive sediment, explaining why the Rocky Flats pediment yields progressively younger ages the closer it gets to the mountains.

The rate at which the knick point migrates upstream depends on how powerful the stream is and on how erosion resistant the rocks are. On a big river like South Boulder Creek, the knick point migrates rapidly, carving out a valley and leaving pediment remnants in its wake, like those you see here at stop 2. On a smaller creek, the knick point doesn't migrate nearly as quickly, so we have a chance of catching it in the act, as we will do at stops 3 and 4.

En route to stop 3 the road crests the Rocky Flats mesa before dropping slightly to cross the valley of Coal Creek. It then climbs to stop 3, which sits just below the mesa crest. The road cut to your east presents a slice through the Rocky Flats pediment. The pediment is veneered with alluvium consisting mostly of round, bluish gray quartzite cobbles. Outcrops of this distinctive rock are found only between Coal Creek and Eldorado

The crumbly, olive gray rock at stop 3 is the Cretaceous-age Pierre shale, which is overlain by round quartzite cobbles, the alluvium that veneers the Rocky Flats pediment.

Canyon (vignette 5). This veneer overlies thin, steeply tilted beds of olive gray Pierre shale (vignette 9), which is so soft you can excavate it with your bare hands. These Pierre beds were tilted during uplift of the Rocky Mountains and then beveled by Coal Creek to form a pediment. During the Rocky Flats episode of aggradation, Coal Creek deposited alluvium on the pediment. Later, the creek breached this alluvial cap when it entered a phase of incision, slicing through the crumbly Pierre shale like a hot knife through butter.

To your west lies the valley of Coal Creek. At stop 2 the top of the Rocky Flats mesa stood about 500 feet above the valley of South Boulder Creek. Here, the mesa top is only about 160 feet above the Coal Creek valley. Coal Creek is much smaller than South Boulder Creek, so it has accomplished considerably less incision.

Head now to stop 4 at the entrance to the former Rocky Flats nuclear weapons facility, built atop the Rocky Flats pediment. To your west, Coal Creek Canyon forms the gap in the mountain front. In the foreground the flat, grass-covered Rocky Flats pediment slopes gently up to the canyon mouth. A line of pine trees dotting the grassy surface between you and the mountains marks the path of Coal Creek. You can see the entire height of the creek-side trees, including their lower trunks, making it clear that here Coal Creek hasn't carved a 160-foot-deep valley like the one we saw at stop 3. Stop 3 was downstream of the Coal Creek knick point, but this portion lies upstream of the knick point. It is because Coal Creek has not yet incised the Rocky Flats pediment that this is the largest remnant of that pediment found anywhere along the Front Range.

Once geologists understood how the Front Range's staircase of pediments formed, they began to search for the geologic trigger that caused the alternating periods of aggradation and incision on the South Platte. One important observation leads geologists to conclude that sea level changes were not responsible for the Front Range pediment staircase. The reason? The rivers eroded the bedrock several hundred feet below the highest pediments here where the Great Plains meets the mountains, but that incision depth gradually dies out to the east. By the time you get to the Kansas border, the rivers have not incised at all. Recall that the knick point created by a drop in sea level migrates upstream from the river mouth. If the culprit was sea level change, one would expect a pediment staircase to exist all the way from Denver to New Orleans, not for it to die out in eastern Colorado. What other mechanisms are possible?

Much research remains to be done before scientists fully understand all the details, but here is how we currently envision the process: During the Pleistocene, Colorado glaciers repeatedly grew and melted (vignette 3). During glacial periods, the glaciers quarried vast quantities of rock from

The portion of Coal Creek visible from stop 4 has not yet incised the Rocky Flats pediment.

the alpine valleys down which they flowed. Rivers were so choked with debris that they aggraded along virtually their entire lengths. When the climate warmed back up and the glaciers melted, less rock debris was generated upstream, so river sediment loads decreased. Thick forests replaced the tundra that flanked the earlier, glacial rivers. Such forests stabilize riverbanks, further reducing gravel delivery. Together, these changes switched off the rivers' aggradation cycle. Simultaneously, the glacial meltwater increased the rivers' flows, increasing their capacity to incise. Ultimately this combination of factors switched the mode of Front Range rivers from aggradation during glacial episodes to incision during interglacial episodes. Geologists have also documented that movement occurred on some Front Range faults during the Quaternary period. Any such fault slip could also trigger a temporary period of river incision, thereby potentially providing an additional control on the rivers' cycles.

We have observed how geologically turbulent the boundary between the mountains and the plains has been. Stop 4 is also a great place to contemplate the turbulent human history of the Rocky Flats pediment, a history that dictates how humans will use its land well into the future. The former Rocky Flats nuclear weapons facility, which opened in 1952, at the height of the Cold War, lies at the end of the road that intersects CO 93 at the traffic light here. Rocky Flats was selected as the site at which plutonium triggers for atomic bombs were fashioned.

As is typical with any industrial facility, a few accidents occurred during its years of operation. Among other incidents, radioactive waste leaking from barrels contaminated soil. In the Front Range's semiarid climate the soils desiccated, and the area's famously strong winds blew this radioactive dust east across the Denver metro area. In 1973 the Colorado Department of Health discovered elevated radiation levels in Walnut Creek, one of the small creeks that drains east off the Rocky Flats mesa, as well as in Great Western Reservoir, a storage facility for the city of Broomfield's drinking water.

Despite safety upgrades and the remediation of existing damage, public opposition to the plant grew through the 1970s and 1980s. Local landowners filed suit in 1975, claiming that Rocky Flats activities had contaminated their properties, and protests by environmental and peace activists became regular occurrences. With the fall of the Soviet Union and the resulting end of the Cold War, the need for Rocky Flats's plutonium triggers dwindled, and with it the incentive to maintain the facility. The plant was shuttered in 1989, but that was not the end of the story.

The U.S. Department of Energy (DOE) began an extensive site cleanup after the plant's closure, spending $7 billion demolishing and decontaminating eight hundred buildings and removing over 500,000 cubic meters of radioactive waste. The agency declared the cleanup complete in 2005. Whether that cleanup was sufficient to remove all public health hazard remains controversial. In 2001, Congress passed legislation that turned 6,400 acres of government-owned land in the less-contaminated buffer zone around the facility into a wildlife refuge, and in 2007 the DOE transferred title to 4,000 acres out of the 6,400 to the U.S. Fish and Wildlife Service, creating the Rocky Flats National Wildlife Refuge. As of this writing in 2012, public access to the refuge is still prohibited, but Fish and Wildlife was preparing to open it in the near future. Controversy surrounds the government's designation of the site as a wildlife refuge. Some argue that public access should be permanently barred due to the lingering hazard of plutonium contamination, while others are eager to recreate in the refuge's open spaces and catch a glimpse of its abundant wildlife.

Although development is blocked within the refuge, its presence enhances the value of the surrounding land, increasing development pressure. The land south and east of the refuge borders is being rapidly transformed into housing developments and commercial parks. Given the area's past plutonium contamination, a nagging question is whether new residents will face the hazards of soil and water contamination.

As part of its cleanup effort, the DOE installed stations to monitor water quality where two creeks exit the Rocky Flats site along Indiana Street (the site of the proposed Jefferson Parkway). In 2010 the DOE proposed moving both monitoring stations away from the refuge boundary onto land they still control at the heart of the Rocky Flats site, where contamination is so profound that public access is not even being contemplated. Nearby cities protested this as a step in the wrong direction when it comes to protecting public safety. No final decision had been made as we went to press.

Soil contamination in the area is another big concern. In 1970, U.S. Atomic Energy Commission scientists conducted soil contamination tests throughout the area. They found substantial plutonium contamination in soils at the heart of the site, where the plutonium triggers were manufactured, and even contaminated soil several miles downwind of the former plant near US 36 in the city of Westminster. Scientists have concluded that inhalation of even one grain of plutonium can initiate cancer. Therefore, windblown plutonium dust particles are viewed as an extreme hazard. No cleanup, however thorough, can remove all plutonium from the soil, so the question scientists wrangle over is how easily the plutonium buried in Rocky Flats soils can be blown eastward by the area's strong winds. This soil contamination is the focus of a class action lawsuit that was filed in 1990 and was decided in favor of the plaintiffs in 2006. An appeals court vacated the ruling in 2010, and most observers believe eventually the U.S. Supreme Court will decide the matter.

Despite its location on Denver's doorstep, Rocky Flats is a place apart, seemingly changeless, an island in the urban hurly-burly that surrounds it. Its tranquility is partially a product of its physical isolation following

2 million years of alternating river incision and aggradation, and partially the result of human Cold War activities. From pediments to plutonium, the modern geological history of Rocky Flats has been lively indeed.

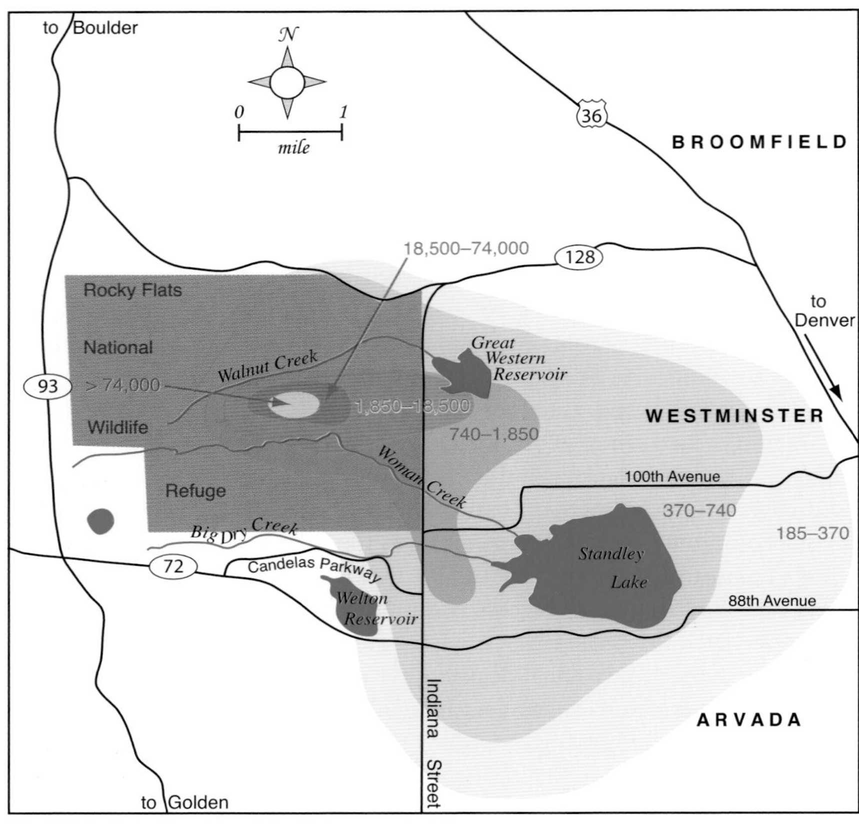

In the 1970s the Atomic Energy Commission's Health and Safety Laboratory mapped the plutonium contamination in soils at and around Rocky Flats. The numbers are in becquerels per square meter of soil (a becquerel is one radioactive decay per second). The hazard this contamination poses to the public remains controversial. (Modified from Krey and Hardy, 1970.)

WHERE COLORADO BEGAN

The Colorado Mineral Belt at Idaho Springs

Colorado in the 1850s was a sleepy outpost on the far western fringes of the Kansas and Nebraska territories. Few Euro-Americans had found reasons to settle here, so Native Americans dominated its small population. But at the dawn of 1859 things were about to change. On January 7, prospector George Jackson discovered placer gold (nuggets transported by a stream) in the bed of Clear Creek at the site of future downtown Idaho Springs. One week later lode gold—gold located in the bedrock, the ultimate source of placer gold—was discovered at Gold Hill in the foothills above Boulder. The Pikes Peak Gold Rush was on. Infected with gold fever, Euro-Americans flooded into the state by the tens of thousands, crying "Pikes Peak or Bust!"—never mind that the gold was actually found a long way away from Pikes Peak.

By 1861 so many settlers had arrived that Colorado was designated a separate territory. Gold and silver deposits were discovered in quick succession at one location after another along a southwest-trending belt stretching from Boulder in the northeast to Durango in the southwest. Boomtowns sprang up along it: Central City, Black Hawk, Georgetown, Silver Plume, Breckenridge, Leadville, Fairplay, Aspen, Gunnison, Ouray, Telluride, and many more. This metal-rich zone came to be known as the Colorado Mineral Belt. The mineral belt was formed by the intrusion of a series of magma chambers loaded with hot, mineral-rich water during and after the Laramide orogeny, the event that built the Rocky Mountains. As the magma and water passed through older rocks, they deposited valuable metals, including gold, silver, lead, zinc, copper, and molybdenum. In contrast to the "youthful" Cenozoic-age magma, the southwest-trending crustal weaknesses it exploited are of far greater antiquity. They date back to the Proterozoic eon, when Colorado first emerged from the ocean as newly minted continental crust.

By 1867 the Pikes Peak Gold Rush was over. Miners had extracted a prodigious 1.25 million ounces of gold from the state's mountains, and

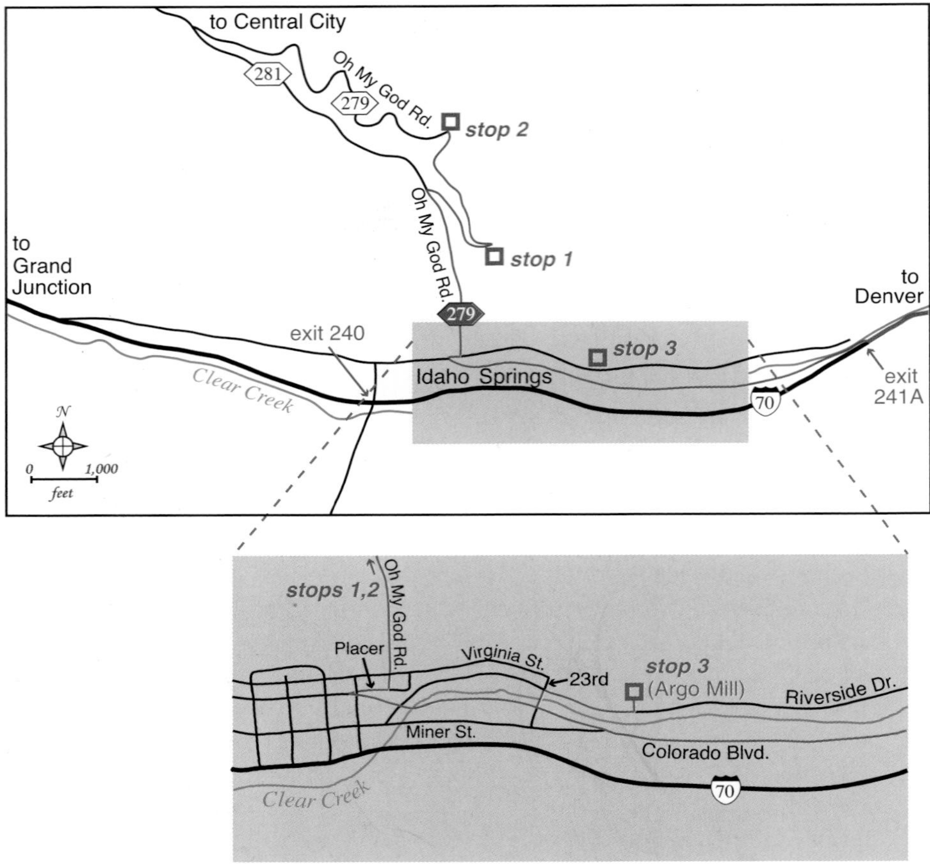

GETTING THERE: Idaho Springs lies 25 miles west of the outskirts of Denver along I-70. To reach stop 1, take exit 241A, which places you on Colorado Boulevard. Follow this 1.2 miles. Turn right onto Placer Street and then immediately left onto Virginia Canyon Road (popularly known as Oh My God Road). Reset your odometer here. The road soon turns to gravel. At 0.5 mile turn right at a sign marking "Central City" (County Road 279). After another 0.3 mile pull into a wide pullout on the right, at the beginning of a switchback to the left. The outcrop at stop 1 is the road cut immediately downhill from the switchback. Stop 2 lies 1.3 miles farther up Virginia Canyon Road (2.1 miles on the odometer). Pull off to the right at a wide spot in the road next to a vintage mine ruin. Stop 3 is at the historic Argo Mill and the modern water treatment plant. Retrace your route back to the junction of Placer and Colorado Bouldevard. Turn left (east) onto Colorado Boulevard and proceed 0.4 mile to the Idaho Springs Visitor Information Center (which has good displays about the town's mining history). Turn left onto 23rd Avenue. Cross Clear Creek, then turn right (east) onto the unmarked road that runs along its north bank. The Argo Mill's parking lot lies 0.2 mile from the turn onto 23rd Ave. Mill tours are offered daily, weather permitting. For fees and other information check www.historicargotours.com. The treatment plant is the gray building with the red roof immediately west of the mill. Displays on the water treatment process are located in the small room at the top of the stairs.

Prospectors heading for the Colorado Mineral Belt. —Courtesy of Denver Public Library, Western History Collection, X-21803

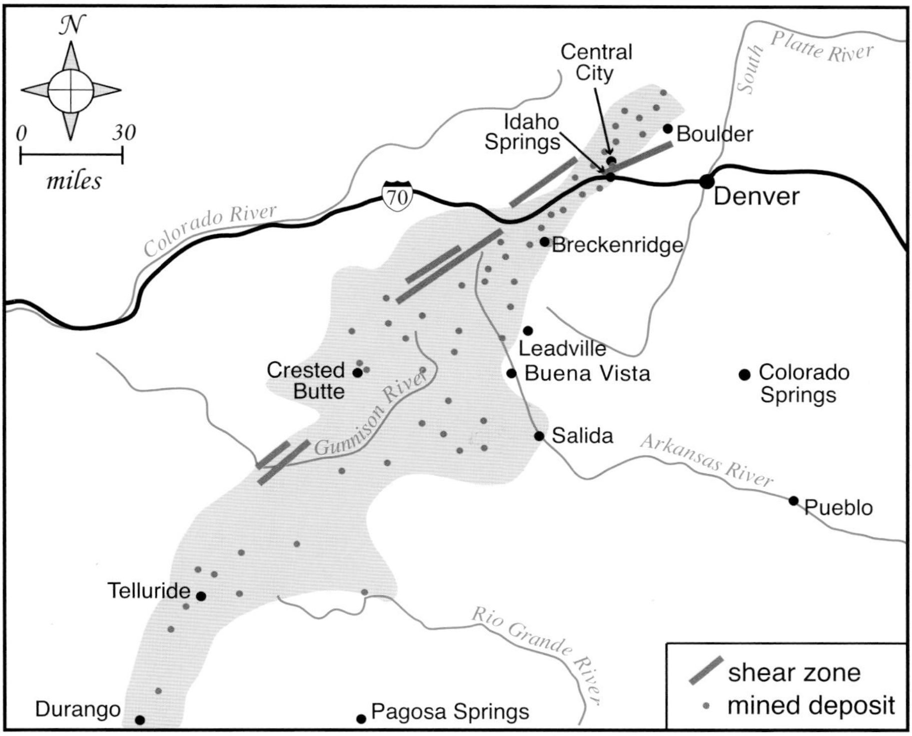

The Colorado Mineral Belt stretches southwest across the heart of Colorado from Boulder to Durango. Hot, mineral-rich fluids that welled up, at least locally, along a series of shear zones during the Laramide orogeny caused minerals to form in the belt. The Idaho Springs–Ralston shear zone runs through Idaho Springs. (Modified from Tweto and Sims, 1963.)

for many of them it was time to move on to the next big strike. But much mineral wealth remained buried beneath the hills, and a large cadre of people settled in for a lifetime of work either extracting these resources or supplying the folks who did, in the process laying the foundations for the modern state. In this vignette we travel to Idaho Springs, in the heart of the Colorado Mineral Belt, where we can visit the Front Range's oldest rocks, immerse ourselves in tales of Colorado's freewheeling mining days, and ponder the environmental legacy left by this mining activity.

During the short drive up the scenic "Oh My God" Road, built in the 1800s to connect two of the biggest gold camps, Idaho Springs and Central City, you will see many nineteenth-century mines clinging to the hillsides. Most of the rocks along this road were heavily altered by hot water passing through them (hydrothermal metamorphism), creating a stained appearance. The rocks at stop 1, however, were not altered, allowing us to examine their characteristics, which tell an absorbing tale of how the land we know as Colorado formed.

The rock in the road cut below the switchback is gneiss, a metamorphic rock that possesses dark and light bands. Abundant mica crystals lined up parallel to one another are the dominant minerals in the dark layers. The light layers consist mainly of quartz and feldspar. These layers were later folded, giving the rock a wavy texture.

The parallel alignment of mica crystals is called foliation, which formed when the rock was metamorphosed under conditions of high temperature and unequal pressure—pressure that was greater in one direction than in others. Such conditions are most common where two tectonic plates converge; the greatest pressure is in the direction of convergence. Finding a wide band of foliated metamorphic rock is strong evidence that the area lay along a convergent plate boundary when the rocks were metamorphosed. This area is no exception. Foliated metamorphic rocks between 1,780 and 1,700 million years old form a broad, northeast-trending belt that begins in northern Sonora, Mexico, continues through northern Arizona to central and northern Colorado, and on through Nebraska to Lake Superior. The rocks at stop 1, which are part of this belt, are known as the Idaho Springs Formation.

Today Colorado lies far from the nearest plate boundary, so how could this gneiss have formed at one? To answer this question we need to examine the basics of plate tectonic theory. Plate tectonics asserts that Earth's surface is not as static as everyday experience would have us suppose. Rather, the surface consists of twelve major and many smaller rigid tectonic plates, composed of material of the lithosphere, that move across the face of the globe, wafted by currents of heat in the asthenosphere below. The lithosphere consists of all the crust and the uppermost, rigid portion of the mantle. The asthenosphere, whose top lies approximately 50 miles

The rock at stop 1 is 1,730-million-year-old gneiss that was metamorphosed when Colorado was a volcanic island arc stretching along a convergent tectonic plate boundary.

beneath the surface, begins where the mantle temperature is hot enough that its rocks flow slowly, like warm taffy—only much, much more slowly.

Tectonic plates can move toward and away from each other or slide laterally past each other. A plate's crucial properties depend on which of the two types of crust—oceanic or continental—forms its upper layer. As their names imply, oceanic crust, which is dense, forms the deep ocean basins, and continental crust, which is more buoyant, makes up the world's continents. Oceanic crust is produced where two plates pull apart. Plumes of molten lava rise from below to fill the void and cool to form black basalt. Basalt's dark color stems from its rich content of iron and magnesium, two dense minerals. It is that high density that causes oceanic crust to hunker down at low elevation, where it can be covered by seawater.

Where two oceanic plates converge—at a boundary known as a subduction zone—the older, colder, and thus denser of the two dives hundreds of miles beneath the other, deep into the bowels of the Earth. As it descends it heats up, driving all the water it carried into the overlying wedge of asthenosphere. The introduction of this water reduces the melting temperature of the asthenosphere and causes it to partially melt. Only the minerals richest in silica (a chemical compound of silicon and oxygen) melt, producing what is known as andesitic magma. The buoyant magma rises to the surface, where it erupts from a chain of towering island volcanoes that, due to the geometry of spheres, on a map trace an arc following the plate boundary. Geologists, therefore, refer to such island chains as volcanic arcs. The cooled lava forms the igneous rock andesite. Because andesite has more silica than does basalt and silica has a comparatively low density, it is more buoyant than oceanic crust. This more-buoyant material is continental crust. Whereas new oceanic crust is manufactured at divergent plate boundaries, new continental crust is manufactured at subduction zones.

Many tectonic plates, for instance the North American Plate, possess oceanic crust in one portion (for the North American Plate this is the segment from the Mid-Atlantic Ridge to the East Coast of North America) and continental in another (the continent of North America is the continental portion of the plate). If, as frequently happens, the oceanic portion of such a hybrid plate is subducting beneath an oceanic plate, the oceanic lithosphere of the hybrid plate is gradually consumed in the bowels of the Earth, thereby dragging the continent ever closer to the volcanic arc seated above the subduction zone. Eventually, the continental lithosphere enters the subduction zone. Due to its high buoyancy, continental lithosphere

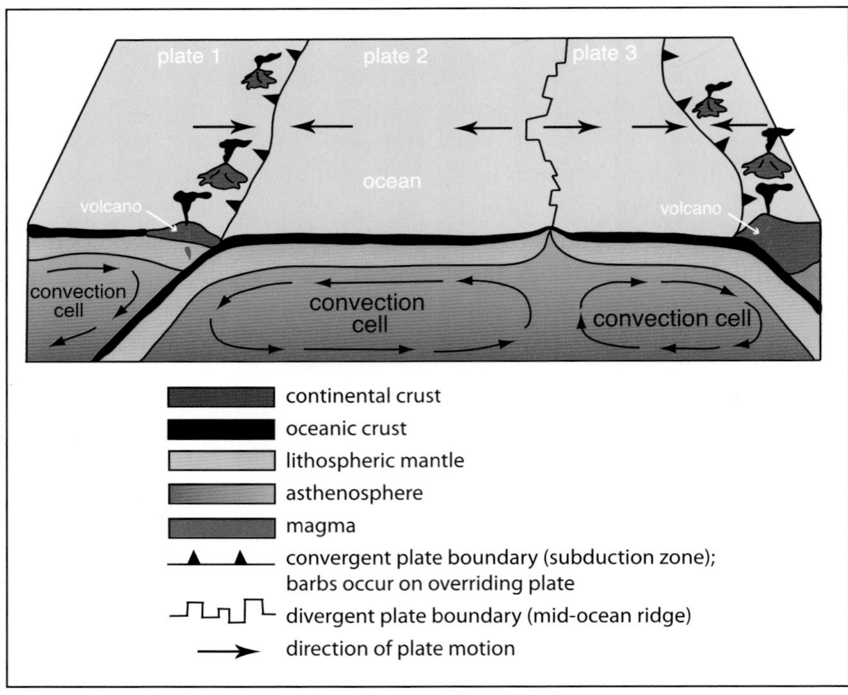

Tectonic plates composed of crust and uppermost mantle are moved by slow convection in the hotter, more-plastic asthenosphere below. Oceanic crust forms through volcanic activity where two plates diverge. Continental crust, which is more buoyant, forms at subduction zones, where two plates converge.

can't subduct. Instead, the volcanic island arc, which also consists of continental crust, is shoved up and over the edge of the continent, squeezing the rocks of both the arc and the continent like the metal of two car hoods in a head-on collision. The result is the formation of a belt of foliated metamorphic rocks along the collision boundary and the thrusting up of a mighty mountain range.

North America, like all other continents, was assembled piece by piece as it collided with one volcanic arc after another. Each collision added a strip of land to the continental margin. North America's assembly began 4,000 million years ago in the Hudson Bay area. By 1,800 million years ago the young continent consisted of eastern and central Canada, the Great Lakes area, and a long, westward appendage stretching through what is now Montana, Wyoming, and northern Utah. North America's southeastern continental margin lay in southern Wyoming at the time, almost coincident with the Wyoming-Colorado border. The scene was set to plaster the next chunk of material onto the continent, which today is a northeast-trending swath that includes most of Colorado.

As the curtain rose on this remarkable story 1,800 million years ago, the rocks that today comprise northern and central Colorado were part of a sprawling tangle of mountainous volcanic island chains. Modern Southeast Asia provides the best example of what Colorado's geography was probably like. The region hosts a tangle of small plates wedged between the much larger Australian, Pacific, and Eurasian plates. Subduction zones are producing island arcs whose volcanoes are busily manufacturing continental crust. Small seas whose floors consist of oceanic crust separate the various island arcs. Australia is sweeping northward, impinging on this chaos. Some of the arcs are colliding directly with Australia, such as the islands of Timor and New Guinea. Other arcs are on a collision course with each other.

Stop 1's Idaho Springs Formation, and all of Colorado's Proterozoic-age metamorphic rocks, bear the signature of an origin in a similar tectonic jumble. Before it was metamorphosed, the rock at stop 1 consisted of a stack of mud and sand layers interspersed with ash beds. The mud and sand were derived from the erosion of an arc's volcanoes, and the ash from their eruptions. As the millennia passed, the stack of eroded debris grew thousands of feet thick at the foot of the volcanoes, burying the layers deeply enough to first turn them into rock (mudstone and sandstone) and then metamorphose them to gneiss.

Colorado's first continental crust formed about 1,800 million years ago, forged in the fires of several volcanic arcs. The first of these arcs collided with the southeast coast of North America (then in southern Wyoming) about 1,780 million years ago. The suture zone marking this first collision is called the Cheyenne Line (see the Cheyenne Line figure on page 22).

Like bugs smashed on a truck's windshield, the remaining volcanic arcs collided one after the other with the continent as intervening ocean basins were subducted. Each collision accreted new land that would become Colorado, pushing the continental margin ever farther southeastward. After a brief pause, the whole story reprised itself beginning about 1,650 million years ago when another series of volcanic arcs was appended to the continent in a virtually identical manner. When the dust settled, Colorado lay far from the plate boundary, just as it does today.

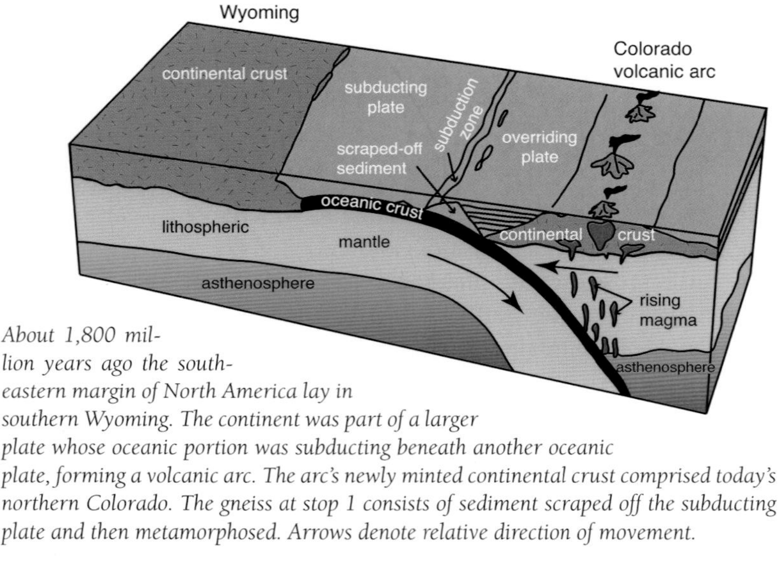

About 1,800 million years ago the southeastern margin of North America lay in southern Wyoming. The continent was part of a larger plate whose oceanic portion was subducting beneath another oceanic plate, forming a volcanic arc. The arc's newly minted continental crust comprised today's northern Colorado. The gneiss at stop 1 consists of sediment scraped off the subducting plate and then metamorphosed. Arrows denote relative direction of movement.

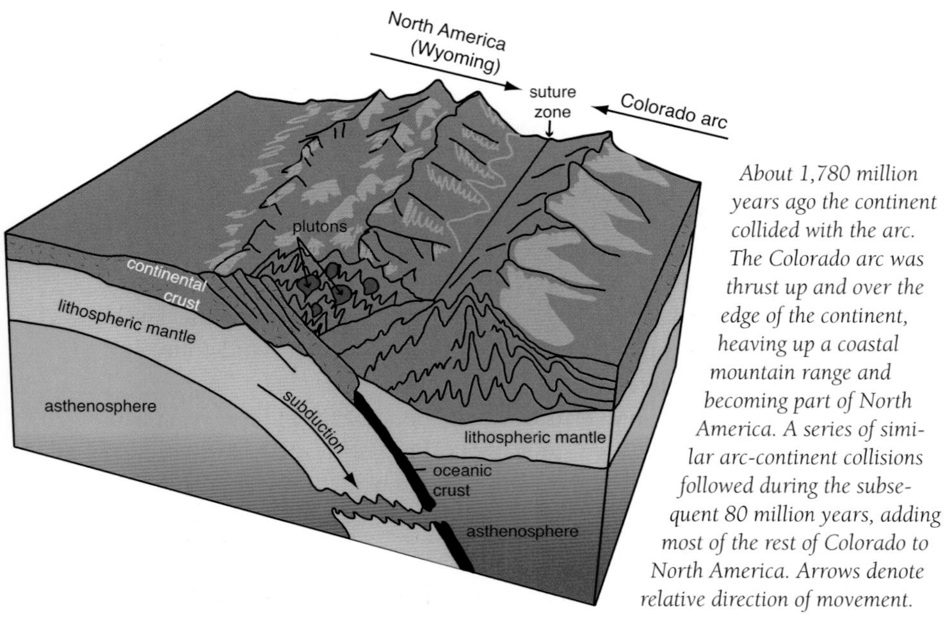

About 1,780 million years ago the continent collided with the arc. The Colorado arc was thrust up and over the edge of the continent, heaving up a coastal mountain range and becoming part of North America. A series of similar arc-continent collisions followed during the subsequent 80 million years, adding most of the rest of Colorado to North America. Arrows denote relative direction of movement.

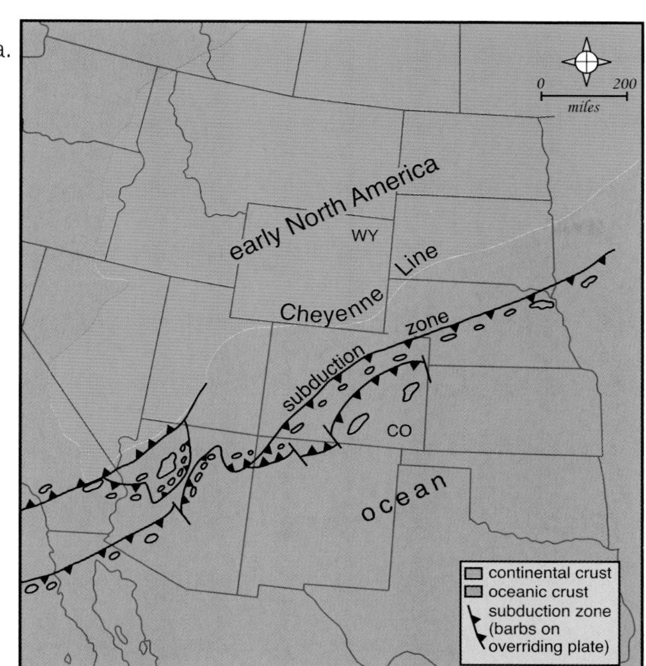

(a) Around 1,800 million years ago, what is now northern and central Colorado was a complex series of volcanic arcs separated by small seas that stood offshore of the early North American continent. (b) Colorado at that time was likely as geographically complex as modern Southeast Asia, where the Australian continent is bearing down on a tangle of volcanic arcs and intervening small seas.

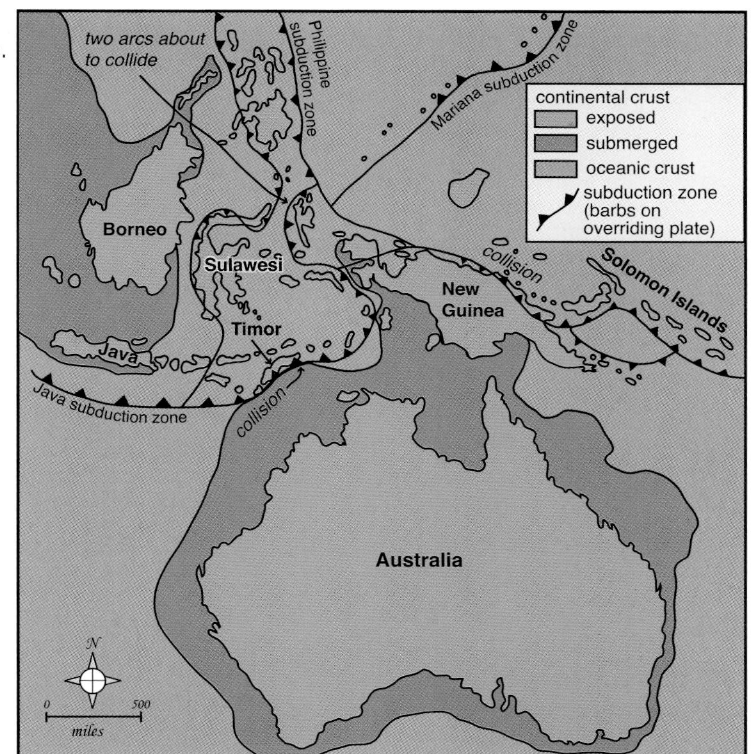

The intervening seas allow us to distinguish one volcanic arc from another in Southeast Asia. Here in central Colorado, however, those seas were subducted long ago as the rocks of one arc were squashed against the rocks of another. Geologists are currently engaged in the painstaking detective work necessary to distinguish the various arcs, but the job is far from complete. Although the details of which Colorado arc collided where are still being worked out, the telltale scars such tectonic battles leave are indelibly preserved in rocks like those at stop 1.

Each collision left behind a seam, which geologists call a suture zone. Like a cut on your knuckle, a continental suture heals very slowly, and the seam along which each volcanic arc was attached to the continent has remained a persistent zone of weakness. As you will see at stop 2, long after the collisions that formed Colorado were finished, magma exploited several of these weaknesses, helping to form the Colorado Mineral Belt in the process.

The yellow rock debris surrounding the wooden mine ruin at stop 2 consists of tailings. This crushed rock is residual material left over from the pulverizing of ore, the first step in the long process needed to extract metal from it. The yellow color in this tailings pile, as well as the many other piles visible farther up the hillside, comes from sulfur. The hot water that percolated through these rocks during the Laramide orogeny deposited numerous sulfide minerals (a process called hydrothermal metamorphism), metals chemically bonded with sulfur. Many of the most valuable ores consist of sulfide minerals, such as sphalerite, chalcopyrite, galena, and tennantite. Pyrite, another sulfide mineral, will be a principal player in our later tale of the environmental problems left behind by mining.

If you walk down the road to the right of the mine ruin, you will see that not only are the tailings yellow, so too are the outcrops. Most of the rock here is the same Idaho Springs Formation gneiss you examined at stop 1. Look for the foliation, which is nearly vertical, and the thinner, erosion-resistant beds composed of quartz and feldspar. Like the tailings, the gneiss was stained a dingy yellow by hot, mineral-laden water associated with magma intrusions of the Laramide orogeny.

The magma intrusions and their associated hot water began to well up in the Idaho Springs area about 65 million years ago. Locally, they did so mainly along the northeast-trending Idaho Springs–Ralston shear zone. A shear zone is a large, crustal-scale fault zone that can range from a few hundred feet to a few miles across. The rock in a shear zone has been much more intensively deformed than the rocks to either side of it, so it is especially susceptible to reactivation during each new tectonic episode that sweeps through the area. The rocks at stop 2 owe their deformation and their mineral-rich alteration to their location in the heart of the shear zone. The Idaho Springs–Ralston shear zone formed around 1,750 to 1,700

The gneiss at stop 2 was infused with sulfur by hot, mineral-laden water during the Laramide orogeny, which stained it yellow.

million years ago, during the initial wave of arc-continent collisions that formed northern and central Colorado.

About 70 feet downhill from the mine you can see several dikes of light-colored granite that intrude the darker, surrounding gneiss. They are related to the 1,442-million-year-old batholith of which nearby Mt. Evans is composed. These granitic intrusions also took advantage of the weak rock of the shear zone long before the hydrothermal metamorphism related to the Laramide orogeny. Both the granite and gneiss were altered by this more recent hydrothermal metamorphism. The early miners quickly learned that in the Colorado Mineral Belt, it was the passage of those hot fluids through rocks that was the key to mineralization, not the identity of the host rocks themselves. Consequently, every rock type within the Idaho Springs–Ralston shear zone through which hot fluids migrated hosts valuable ore.

Proceed now to stop 3, the Argo Mill, which is listed on the National Register of Historic Places. After it was built in 1913, this mill was the main location where gold ore extracted from the area's many mines was processed. The informative Argo tour allows you to follow the gold-extraction process. And when the tour is over, you can enjoy panning for gold using the equipment provided.

The tour starts at the small Double Eagle mine, located behind the mill. You can walk along the drift, the main tunnel by which miners entered the

The dark metamorphic rocks of the Idaho Springs Formation contrast with the vertical dike of lighter granite that is linked to the nearby Mt. Evans Batholith.

The historic Argo Mill still houses much of the original milling equipment, allowing visitors to see how gold was extracted from the ore hauled down from the surrounding hills.

mine and ore was extracted. You pass several labeled ore veins en route. Where the drift encountered a vein, miners would work upward along it, letting gravity assist in ore removal. The shaft hollowed out along a vein is known as a stope. Long veins were usually worked from drifts at several different elevations.

When the gold rush began, drifts were excavated by brute force using pick and shovel. Later, pneumatic drills made the work much easier, though the early ones were known as "widow makers" because the men who operated them often died within six months. The sharp-edged dust particles that filled the air shredded the miners' lungs. The drills became much less deadly when designers added a slot to feed water into the drill, drastically reducing the amount of dust kicked up.

From the Double Eagle the tour continues to the upper mill entrance. Before entering the mill, be sure to take the short walk to the Argo Tunnel, which miners bored 4.16 miles through the mountain from Central City down to the Argo Mill. Its purpose was twofold. First, it acted like a very low-elevation drift, into which the many rich mines that lined its path could discharge ore into 4-ton carts for direct and speedy delivery to the mill. Second, and even more importantly, the tunnel provided drainage. As the mines followed rich veins deeper into the bowels of the mountain, pooling groundwater became a big problem. If the mines were not drained they would become inoperable. Boring the Argo Tunnel underneath the mines provided this necessary function.

The authors' daughter, Kailas, explores the main drift in the Double Eagle mine.

The year 1893 is painted on the Argo Tunnel entrance. That was the year the tunnel was begun, but it was not completed until 1910. The tunnel starts 1,300 vertical feet below Central City, where it is a spacious 12 feet wide. It slopes down to Idaho Springs at a 0.3 percent grade and narrows to 6 feet wide at the 2.5-mile mark. In 1943 an underground explosion permanently closed the tunnel. Starved of the feedstock the tunnel provided, the mill closed a short time later. Although no ore has passed through the tunnel for decades, water still does—at an average rate of about 300 gallons every minute. Because this water is toxic, the tunnel was added to the federal Superfund list in 1983. The gray metal building with the red roof just below the tunnel entrance is the plant built to clean the water before it flows into nearby Clear Creek.

The Argo was known as a custom mill because it was designed to process the diverse ores produced from the many mines along the tunnel's route. Because each ore type required a slightly different processing technique, the mill was exceptionally large and contained an unusual diversity of equipment. The mill was built on a slope to let gravity do much of

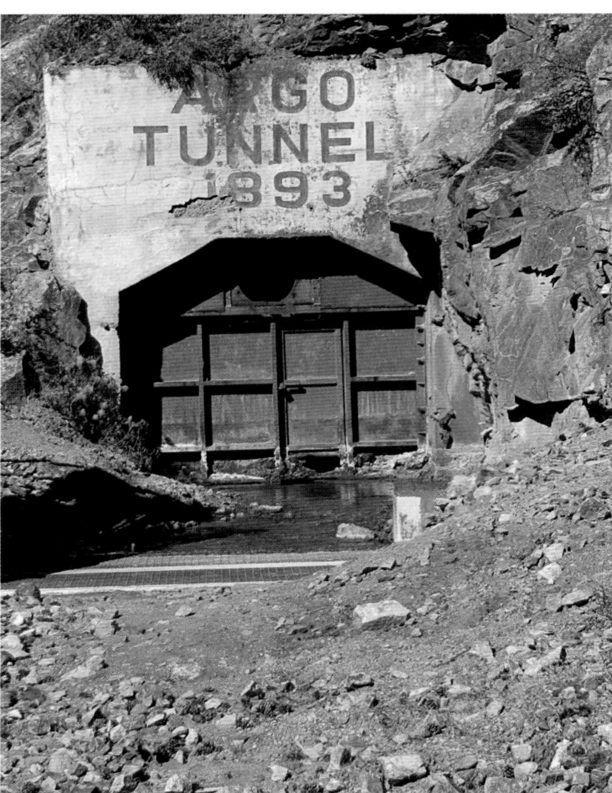

The water flowing from the Argo Tunnel is red due to metal contamination. The water flows through the drain visible in front of the tunnel entrance to the Argo Water Treatment Plant.

the work of ore transport through the concentration process. Both yesterday and today, the first step in the process is to crush the ore. Through crushing, the metal is more easily extracted by both physical and chemical processes.

As the ore carts, each carrying 3 to 4 tons of rock, exited the tunnel, they dumped their loads into the bins visible at the top of the mill. Depending on the ore type, one or several different crushing processes were used. The stamp room housed twenty machines that crushed the ore using 1,000-pound stamps that were raised and then dropped onto the ore. Nearby stands the remains of an arrastra, a grinding tool that consisted of a rotating heavy stone or metal ingot. The Spanish introduced this technology, one of the first rock-crushing mechanisms devised, to America. The Argo also possessed a ball mill, a giant cylindrical tumbler in which ore and heavy iron balls resembling shot puts were rotated. Ball mills remain a popular crushing technique today.

Once crushed, the gold ore was separated from waste materials and then amalgamated by adding mercury to it. Gold adsorbs onto mercury, forming a gold-mercury amalgam, similar to the silver-mercury amalgam used in tooth fillings. The amalgam was then heated, causing the mercury to vaporize, thus separating it from the now concentrated gold. Another method for concentrating gold was the flotation process. A variety of chemicals, including pine tar, were mixed with water and agitated to form bubbles. The gold concentrated in the bubbles, which were skimmed off the top. Such flotation techniques are still commonly used in today's mines. One important concentration technique used in the Argo Mill and still popular today is cyanide leaching (vignette 13). Whichever concentration step(s) was used on a particular ore, the final refinement was typically the same: a smelter. Smelting, which entails heating the concentrated ore to its melting temperature, was never done at the Argo; instead, the ore was shipped to places like Denver for this final step.

Next to the Argo Mill, another industrial process is occurring today in the Argo Water Treatment Plant. Due to the historic mining, the water flowing through the Argo Tunnel is highly acidic and loaded with metals such as iron, zinc, cadmium, copper, manganese, and aluminum. High concentrations of these metals are toxic to fish and people. Clear Creek, which supplies water to over 250,000 people in the Denver area, has severely degraded water quality due to the metals it contains.

Why is the tunnel water so toxic? Pyrite and other sulfide minerals react chemically with water and oxygen. The chemical reaction splits the metal from the sulfur, which goes on to form sulfuric acid, a strong acid that dangerously alters the water to form so-called acid mine drainage. Heavy metals are much more easily leached from rock by acidic water, so acid mine drainage is almost always accompanied by a toxic load of heavy metals.

The water issuing from the Argo Tunnel carries with it, on average, 50,000 parts per billion zinc, 6,000 parts per billion copper, and 175 parts per billion cadmium. Trout are poisoned by metal toxicity at average values of 500 parts per billion or less of zinc, 22 parts per billion or less of copper, and 2 parts per billion of cadmium, although these figures vary slightly by species.

The water treatment plant runs around the clock, removing the metals and buffering the pH of the water pouring from the tunnel. The result of the multistep chemical and physical filtering process is a reddish brown, nontoxic solid waste called filter cake, which is eventually dumped in a landfill, and clean water, which is released into Clear Creek.

Prior to construction of the water treatment plant, Clear Creek carried an average of 1 ton of metal downstream each day. The Argo Tunnel water accounted for as much as half of that load. The water treatment plant now removes the metals with 99.89 percent efficiency, thus cutting Clear Creek's metal load dramatically.

Red filter cake, consisting of the metals removed from the Argo Tunnel water, is loaded into a dumpster for transport to a landfill.

To spend a day in Idaho Springs, surrounded by some of the state's oldest rocks, is to experience the history of Colorado: the tectonic history, when massive Earth forces assembled a ragtag collection of island chains into the state's bedrock; the economic and environmental history, when miners extracted mineral wealth, creating the need for ongoing environmental cleanup; and the human and political history, when George Jackson dipped his pan into Clear Creek one January day and set in motion a chain of events that resulted in the modern state of Colorado.

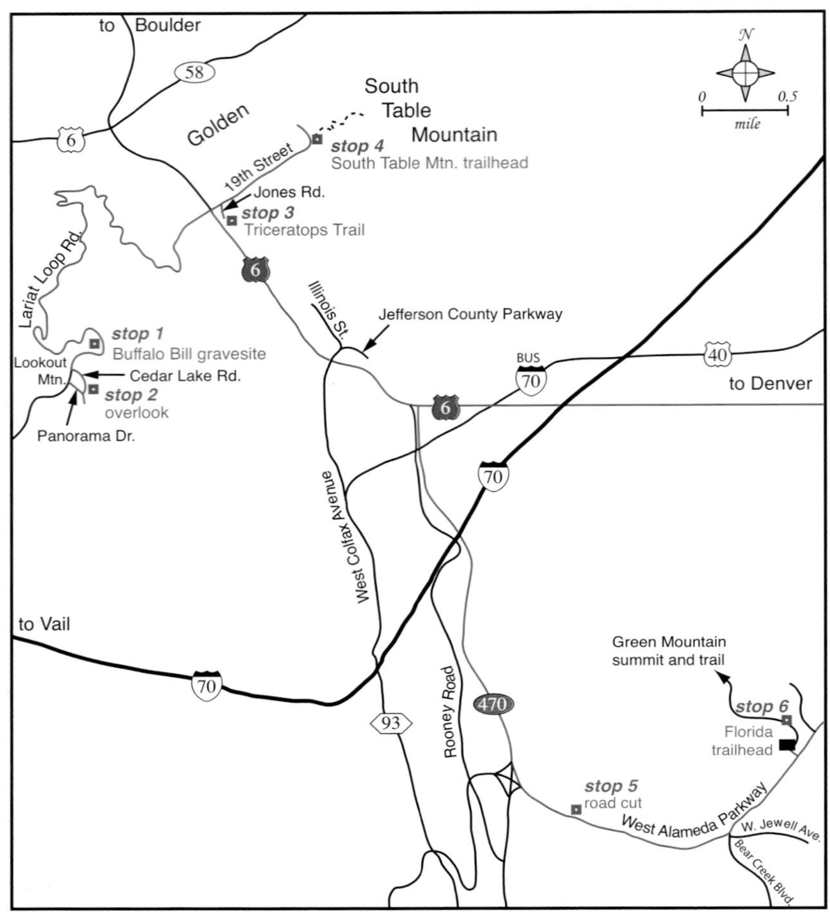

GETTING THERE: This excursion begins at the top of Lookout Mountain. From downtown Denver follow 6th Avenue (US 6) west toward Golden. About 2 miles beyond the junction with CO 470 you reach a traffic light at 19th Street. Turn left (southwest) onto 19th Street, which becomes Lariat Loop Road and climbs Lookout Mountain. About 5 miles from US 6, turn right into the Buffalo Bill gravesite.

To reach stop 2, turn right onto Lariat Loop Road and follow it 0.2 mile, then turn left onto Panorama Drive. Follow it 0.1 mile and turn left on the unmarked road just 20 yards beyond Cedar Lake Drive. Follow it 0.2 mile to a dirt pullout on the right, where you have a sweeping view of the plains. To reach stop 3, retrace your route down Lookout Mountain to the 19th Street/US 6 junction and continue straight on 19th. After 0.1 mile turn right onto Jones Road, which is marked with a brown "Triceratops Trail" sign. Drive 150 yards, through a small apartment complex, to the end of the road, and park in the small lot marked for the trail. Be sure not to block the dumpster. From the parking area walk left (south) on the sidewalk about 150 yards to a signed gravel path on your left. This is the beginning of the 0.5-mile-long Triceratops Trail.

8

RAISING, RAZING, AND REBIRTHING THE ROCKIES

Tracing the Mountains' Ups and Downs around Golden

The abrupt transition from the seemingly endless sweep of the Great Plains to the lofty Front Range peaks is the defining characteristic of the urban corridor extending from Fort Collins, through Denver, to Colorado Springs, so much so that the metropolitan area calls itself the Front Range. More than any other attribute, it is the mountain backdrop, with its beautiful scenery and its endless recreational opportunities, that draws people to this burgeoning metropolitan area. The Front Range peaks tower 10,000 feet above the farms and cities at their feet, making this one of the most dramatic physiographic transitions in all of North America.

When and how the Front Range rampart we see today came into existence is one of the most fundamental questions one could ask about Colorado's geologic history. Surprisingly, it has proven to be one of the most challenging questions to answer (vignette 2). Although the last chapter of the scientific story has not yet been written, the rocks of Golden and Lakewood tell us the main plot of when the Rockies were first raised, during the

To reach stop 4, return to 19th Street and turn right (northeast). Follow it 0.7 mile to its end and turn left onto Belvedere Street. Park on the right at 18th and Belvedere, at the South Table Mountain trailhead. For stop 5, retrace your route to US 6 and turn left (southeast). After 2 miles exit onto CO 470 southbound. After 2.7 miles take the first exit, onto West Alameda Parkway. Turn left (east) at the top of the ramp and proceed 0.4 mile to a low road cut on the left, stop 5. Pull off onto the right-hand shoulder to park. A wooden sign identifies the rock in the road cut as the Arapahoe Formation. Stop 6 is at the Florida trailhead at the William F. Hayden Park on Green Mountain. From stop 5, continue east on West Alameda Parkway 1.2 miles to a traffic light. Turn left here, staying on West Alameda, and drive 0.7 mile to a parking area on the left signed for the trailhead.

Laramide orogeny, and what happened to them thereafter. In this vignette we poke around the rocky nooks and crannies of Denver's western suburbs following this story line. As soon as a mountain range, such as the Front Range, is raised, erosion begins tearing it down. It is in the characteristics of the sediments shed off a growing mountain range that geologists uncover some of the best clues about when the range rose (vignette 5). Thus, we cannot understand when the Rockies were raised without also understanding when and how the growing mountains were razed.

We begin at Buffalo Bill's gravesite, atop 7,400-foot-high Lookout Mountain (stop 1). From the north end of the parking lot, descend a short stairway to an overlook that possesses a large, dark outcrop. This metamorphic gneiss consists of dark and light bands formed by the intense pressure it witnessed during metamorphism. It is among the oldest rocks in the region, formed over 1,700 million years ago in a volcanic island arc and, soon thereafter, appended to North America in a tectonic collision (vignette 7). Such gneiss forms the bedrock for many Front Range peaks. Note, in particular, how hard and erosion resistant it is. This will serve as an important point of contrast with the rock we examine at stop 2. Now stroll over to the viewing platform adjacent to the museum for a panoramic view northeast over the Great Plains, which lie 2,000 feet below. Interpretive signs discuss

This 1,700-million-year-old gneiss on Lookout Mountain forms part of Colorado's original crust. Golden and North Table Mountain lie in the background.

the area's geologic history and point out major landmarks, including North and South Table mountains (stop 4), which rise more than 500 feet above Golden. From here it is evident why they are called the Table mountains.

On the short drive to stop 2, note how gentle the top of Lookout Mountain is compared to the steep grade you climbed to get here. Such gently undulating mountaintops are a common feature of Front Range foothills, with surfaces sloping gently down toward the east. Together these mountaintops represent remnants of an extensive erosion surface, called the Rocky Mountain Erosion Surface, that formed along the Front Range's eastern flank, likely during late Eocene time (vignettes 2, 11).

Although the low rock outcrop you see in the road cut west of the pullout at stop 2 consists of the same gneiss you saw at the first stop, it is anything but hard and resistant. In fact, it is difficult to recognize because intense chemical weathering has transformed it into crumbling rubble known as saprolite. Saprolite is easily eroded, which is why we didn't see any of it at stop 1. However, the Rocky Mountain Erosion Surface was subjected to such a long, intense period of chemical weathering that a particularly thick layer of saprolite formed, so erosion has not yet succeeded in removing all of it from the surface.

Now turn your attention to the panoramic view to the southeast. The most prominent feature rising from the plains is a bulky, grass-covered hump called Green Mountain, which, like South Table Mountain, stands significantly higher than the surrounding plains. Its summit rises almost to your current elevation here on the Rocky Mountain Erosion Surface. In fact, it lies just 600 vertical feet below you and is about 2.5 miles farther east. As we will see at stop 6, Green Mountain consists of a huge pile of sediment shed off the growing Rocky Mountains as the mountains were being

The panorama from stop 2 takes in Green Mountain, which consists of a huge pile of sediment shed off the growing Rocky Mountains.

eroded away. The fact that Green Mountain's summit is nearly as high as Lookout Mountain's erosion surface reveals that after the Rocky Mountains were uplifted, they were nearly buried in their own debris (vignette 2).

En route to stop 3, you descend the steep eastern flank of the Front Range, alighting once again on the plains. At the base of the mountains, just a block west of US 6, you cross the Golden fault, the mighty workhorse that uplifted this part of the Front Range on its back when it was active during the Laramide orogeny. Unfortunately, as it is pretty much everywhere along its length, the fault here is concealed beneath a mantle of loose debris and soil, so there is nothing worth stopping to see.

In a metal box at the beginning of the 0.5-mile-long Triceratops Trail, stop 3, you will usually find a helpful guide to trailside stops. Interpretive signs are mounted at each stop. The interesting features at the first station, "Duckbills, Carnivores, and Raindrops," lie at the bottom of a 40-foot-deep, 60-foot-wide trench dug by clay miners working for the Parfet Clay Mining Enterprise. The Parfet family mined clay here from the early 1900s until the end of World War II, and they are the ones who set aside this prehistoric preserve. The comparatively low-grade clay from these pits was used to make the bricks for many historic Denver buildings, including the governor's mansion, whereas the high-purity clay was suitable for tile and pottery.

The rock walls on either side of the trench consist of sandstone. Both the clay and sandstone belong to the Laramie Formation. When you look edge-on at the rocks to the right (west) of the pit, you see that the layers, which are always deposited horizontally, have been tilted to vertical. It takes a massive force to heave stacks of rock up on end like this, the kind of force that builds mountains. The Golden fault, lurking nearby under US 6, angles down into the Earth toward the west. When the forces of plate tectonics squeezed the region's crust, the block of rock west of the fault was shoved eastward and up, creating the Front Range in the process. As the western block was lifted, the force buckled the sedimentary layers, tilting them eastward and, in places like this, standing them on end. Although the Golden fault is mostly concealed, if you know where to look, its handiwork is plainly visible.

Just how far was the western fault block uplifted along the Golden fault? We can answer this question by matching up the previously adjacent rocks on either side of the fault. On the fault's west side, the rocks of Lookout Mountain are metamorphic, so they clearly don't match the sedimentary rocks east of the fault here on the Triceratops Trail. Information obtained from wells drilled near Turkey Creek Canyon, about 8 miles south of here, when combined with seismic studies, indicate that metamorphic rocks matching those at 7,400 feet of elevation on Lookout Mountain lie at about 7,000 feet below sea level on the east side of the fault. That means that the

We can deduce the history of Front Range uplift from the characteristics of the region's rock layers.

(a) About 68 million years ago the Laramie Formation sediments were accumulating at the top of a thick stack of sedimentary rocks that overlies the metamorphic rocks of Lookout Mountain and associated igneous rocks (the ancient crystalline rocks).

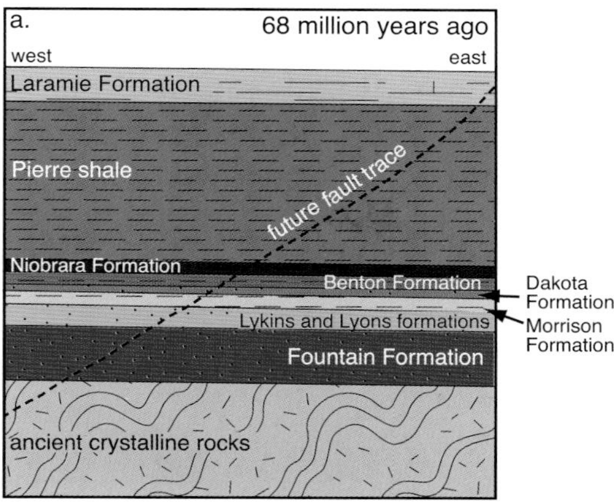

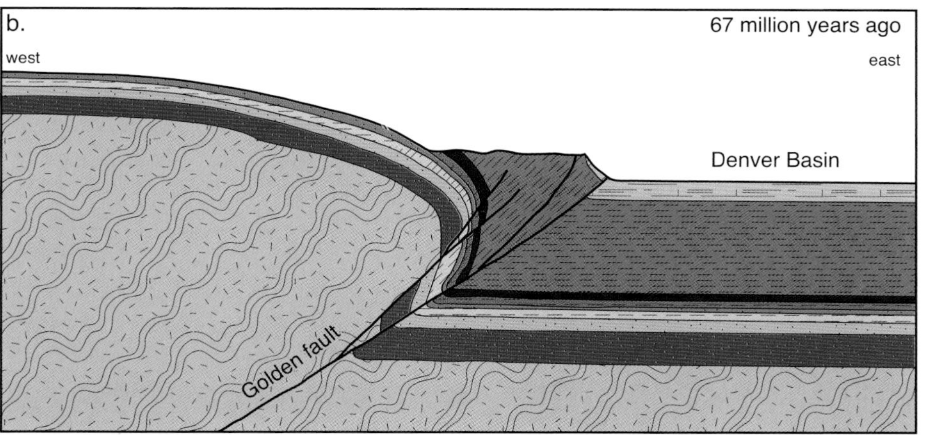

(b) By 67 million years ago, during the Laramide orogeny, the Golden fault was active; tectonic forces shoved rocks on its west side up and over the rocks to the east, creating the Front Range.

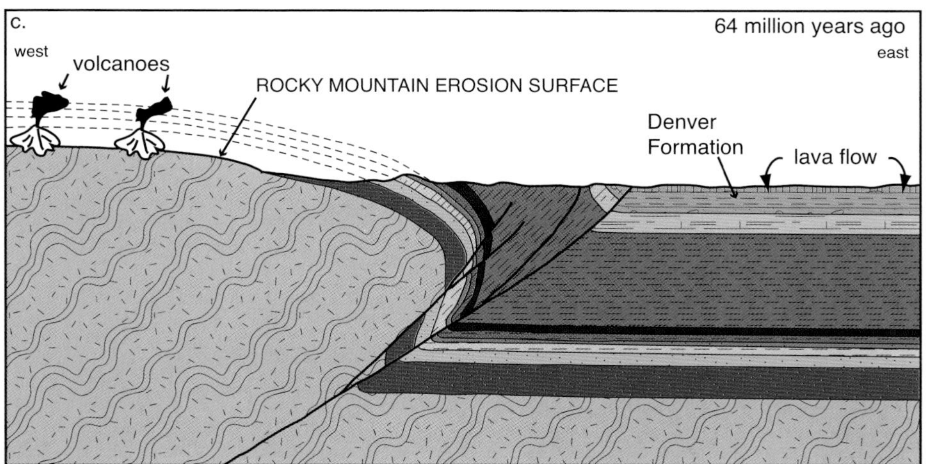

(c) The stack of sedimentary layers that was raised as part of the Front Range block was at least partially eroded by 64 million years ago, exposing the crystalline rocks below to erosion. Volcanoes crowned the Front Range at that time. Debris eroded from the mountains was deposited on the Great Plains as the Denver Formation.

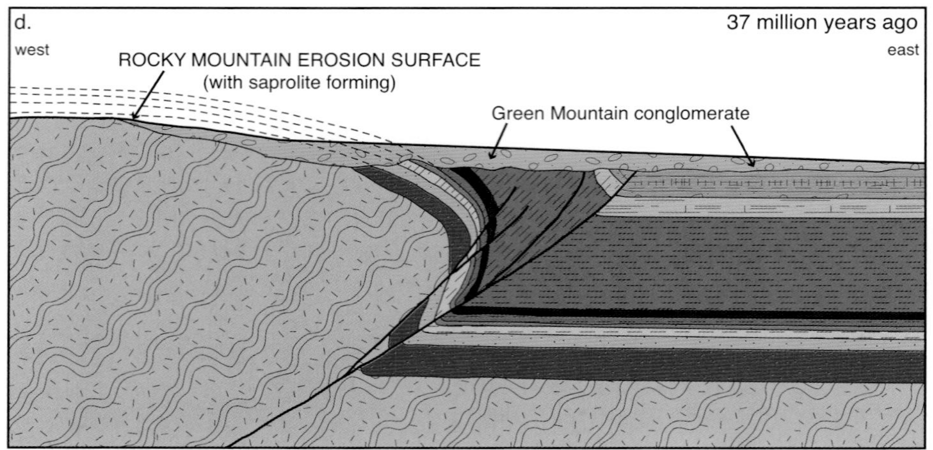

(d) By 37 million years ago the Front Range volcanoes were extinct and the Golden fault was dormant. The Green Mountain conglomerate had been deposited on the plains. The combination of mountain erosion and plains deposition removed the steep escarpment originally created by the Golden fault. The Front Range consisted of an eastward-sloping plain with no dramatic topographic boundary between the mountains and the plains.

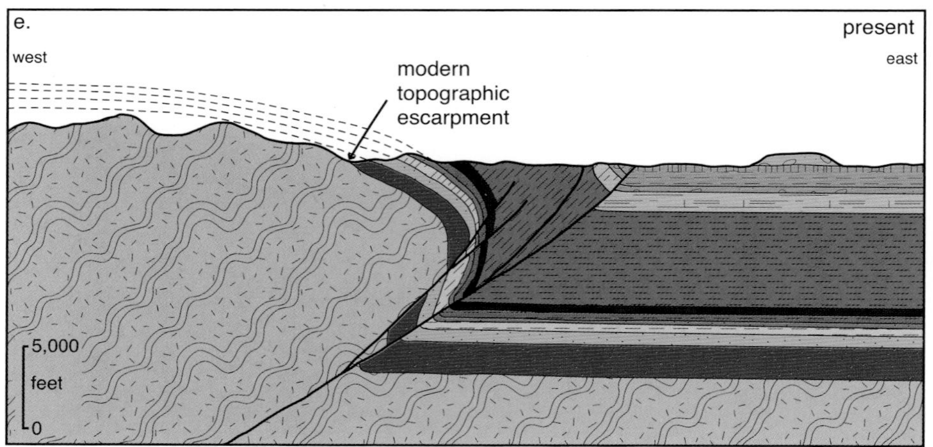

(e) Renewed erosion, possibly due to a new period of uplift or possibly triggered by climate change, reexposed the Laramide-age scarp formed by the Golden fault. This erosion resulted in today's dramatic Front Range topography. (Based on a cross section contained in Berg, 1962.)

Golden fault raised the rocks west of the fault over 14,000 feet relative to those on the east. As these rocks moved up along the fault, they were also transported eastward. Matching up the once-adjacent rocks across the fault reveals that the Front Range overrode the Great Plains by about 1.5 miles.

That's the how part of the Front Range story, what about the when? Logically, the Laramie Formation rocks tilted by the fault must be older than the motion on the fault. Therefore, if we can date the Laramie Formation, we can place a maximum age on the fault movement.

The remarkable paleontology on display along Triceratops Trail helps constrain the Laramie's age. When these rocks still consisted of freshly deposited sediment, many organisms that wandered the Golden area left impressions on the still-moist sand. Aided by small plaques affixed to the rock wall, you can find remarkably preserved dinosaur tracks belonging to both a duckbilled hadrosaur and a meat-eating, bipedal theropod. Also on display are beetle tracks and, most astonishing of all, the impressions made by individual raindrops as they impacted the moist earth millions of years ago!

Continue eastward to station 5, "Triceratops Tracks," near the far end of the trail, where you will see several tracks (the first ever discovered) made by that pugnacious, three-horned dinosaur. Thanks to the 2003 discovery of a triceratops skull by a backhoe operator excavating a north Denver house foundation, we have both tracks and bones to confirm that this dinosaur roamed the area when the Laramie Formation was deposited. The skull is now proudly displayed in the Denver Museum of Nature and Science. The nearby Fossil Trace Golf Club boasts the cast of a similar skull in its clubhouse, which is open for public examination. Triceratops and its contemporaries were among the last dinosaurs to inhabit the planet; they lived during the last 3 million years of the Mesozoic era, just prior to the asteroid impact that extinguished 70 percent of Earth's species and brought an abrupt end to the Mesozoic 65.5 million years ago (vignette 21).

The triceratops tracks help us constrain the depositional age of the Laramie Formation to a 3-million-year window. Luckily, we can narrow this range even further thanks to the presence of clay layers in this and adjacent units. Many of these were volcanic ash deposits that have been altered chemically to clay. Unlike the sandstone, ash can be radiometrically dated, producing precise ages for each layer. These dates corroborate the paleontology, yielding an age of 68 million years for the Laramie Formation.

Movement on the Golden fault must therefore have been more recent than 68 million years ago. But how much more recent? A closer examination of the Laramie Formation and adjacent layers can help us reconstruct the landscape as it looked at various snapshots in time.

Our first snapshot is from 68 million years ago. At the end of the Triceratops Trail (station 6, "Prehistoric Plants"), you will find the impressions of palm fronds and sycamore leaves, footprints of two kinds of birds, and burrows of small shrimp and worms. Similar fossils can be found in the Laramie Formation in nearby locales. A couple miles north of here, the Colorado School of Mines Geology Trail (vignette 9) preserves logs, complete with scars left by boring insects, and more tracks of comparable age. Still more tracks, including the first Mesozoic-age mammal tracks ever

Triceratops track at stop 3.

Cast of a triceratops skull on public display at the nearby Fossil Trace Golf Club.

discovered, are on display at the Fossil Trace Golf Club. This rich record of Laramie-age organisms allows scientists to reconstruct the Front Range ecosystem in considerable detail. The sedimentary characteristics of the rocks themselves complete the picture.

An interpretive sign at Triceratops Trail station 4, the "Geologic Overview," includes a diagram depicting what the Late Cretaceous Front Range looked like. It resembled the bayous of Louisiana, with a flat, subtropical, swampy plain traversed by sluggish, meandering rivers. Dank swamps covered parts of the river floodplains, as revealed by the Laramie Formation's abundant coal layers. Some 20 billion tons of coal have been extracted from the formation across the Front Range. The predominance of sand and mud, coupled with the lack of gravel, shows that river currents were lazy, indicating no large mountains stood nearby. Mountain rivers are steep and fast, capable of carrying large particles, whereas rivers in flat terrain carry and deposit much smaller particles.

Let's head now to stop 4. While some geologists now refer to the rocks on South Table Mountain by a different name (the D1 rocks), many geologists still refer to them by their original name: the Denver Formation. For convenience, we will, too. Our objective here is to capture two more snapshots of the Front Range landscape. If you have the time and energy, the hike to the top of South Table Mountain is delightful, and you will get excellent looks at the rocks discussed here. Alternatively, you can accomplish the same geologic goal by studying several massive boulders that tumbled down from above.

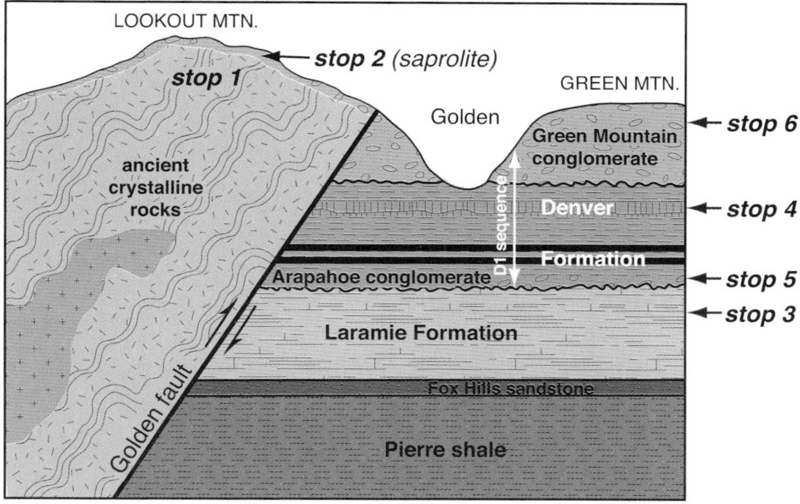

Diagram showing the juxtaposition of rock units on either side of the Golden fault in the Golden area. The stops are marked to illustrate which rocks are on display at each one.

About 50 yards up the trail you encounter an excellent interpretive sign that discusses mesa evolution. It explains that the mountain is capped by black basalt dated at 64 million years old. Here at the mountain's base, the rocks are 66 million years old. If you hike to the top, you will cross the famous, 65.5-million-year-old Cretaceous-Tertiary (K-T) boundary. Although South Table Mountain was the very first place in North America where the K-T boundary was found, locating the exact spot is tricky even for an expert. In any case, the boundary is not exposed along this trail, so if you wish to explore the K-T boundary, which marks a major extinction event, check out vignette 21.

Hike about 30 yards past the sign and look to your left for a jumble of boulders choking the gully just 20 yards off the trail. Most consist of conglomerate that contains round, fist-sized cobbles. The large size of these cobbles indicates they were transported in a steep and swift river. A sluggish, meandering river like the one we reconstructed for the Laramie Formation couldn't carry particles so large. The edges of the cobbles were rounded as they banged violently against one another in the vigorous current. The characteristics of the Laramie reveal that 68 million years ago the Front Range was flat bayou country. By 66 million years ago swift rivers transporting gravel from the mountains onto the plains had replaced the lazy bayous. This observation indicates that by 66 million years ago the Laramide orogeny had begun and the Golden fault was on the move, beginning to raise the Front Range.

Today the Front Range consists of metamorphic rocks like those we examined at stop 1, along with granite. But the Denver Formation cobbles show that such was not the case 66 million years ago. Essentially every cobble you see consists of andesite, a volcanic rock. In its infancy, the Front Range was crowned by smoking volcanoes spewing ash across the landscape. The volcanoes, having died long ago, were eroded, so none exist in the Front Range today. But they left their calling cards—the clasts—in the Denver Formation conglomerate. The magma that fed some of these volcanoes was rich in gold, silver, and other precious metals that infected a generation of Euro-Americans with gold fever (vignette 7).

We get another landscape snapshot from pieces of basalt that tumbled down from the mountaintop and lie next to the trail. About 64 million years ago one of the Front Range's volcanoes erupted a few miles north of here, at the site of today's Ralston Reservoir. The basalt lava it spewed ran southeast, down the same river valley in which the conglomerates were accumulating, where it solidified. Over time, all the Denver Formation rocks were buried beneath younger sediments. Millions of years later, when erosion resumed, it easily stripped away these sediments and the soft Denver Formation, but the old river valley, armored by its basalt cap, was spared. As erosion lowered the surrounding landscape, the ancient

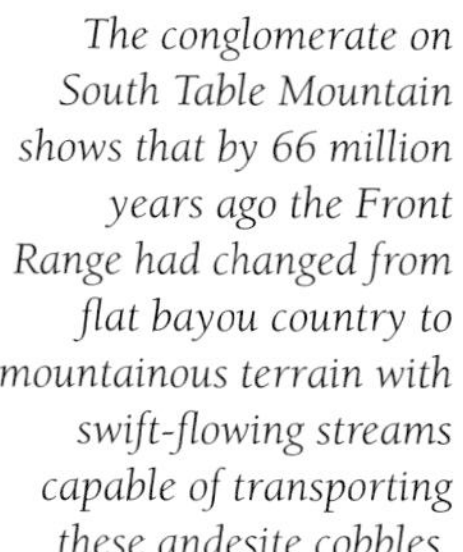

The conglomerate on South Table Mountain shows that by 66 million years ago the Front Range had changed from flat bayou country to mountainous terrain with swift-flowing streams capable of transporting these andesite cobbles.

valley maintained its elevation, becoming Golden's signature North and South Table mountains. Only Clear Creek was powerful enough to erode the basalt, which is why it has carved the small valley that separates the two Table mountains. If you have trouble finding basalt pieces here, look at the retaining wall just north of the trailhead, as it contains many pieces of this black basalt.

At this point we have been able to constrain the initial uplift of the Laramide Front Range to between 68 and 66 million years ago, an impressively tight window in the field of geology. But can we do better? Let's now move on to stop 5, an outcrop along the base of Green Mountain. A wooden sign placed by geologists decades ago announces that the rocks in the road cut north of the road here belong to the 67-million-year-old Arapahoe Formation. The rock crumbles when you touch it because it lacks the cement necessary to turn it from loose sediment into hard rock.

Two things about this conglomerate are striking when you compare it with the Laramie and Denver formations (stops 3 and 4). First, the Arapahoe Formation consists of conglomerate. That means that the Golden fault had thundered to life by 67 million years ago and was uplifting the Front Range. However, the particles here are smaller than those you saw in the Denver Formation—pebble-sized instead of cobble-sized. Based on the Arapahoe's smaller clast size, we can deduce that this part of the range had not yet grown terribly tall or steep.

The second striking observation is that the Arapahoe doesn't appear to contain any of the andesite clasts that dominated the Denver Formation. Instead, it contains sedimentary rocks, quartz, granite, and gneiss. This tells us that, at its birth, this part of the Front Range did not host any volcanoes. The sedimentary clasts tell us the range's surface was blanketed

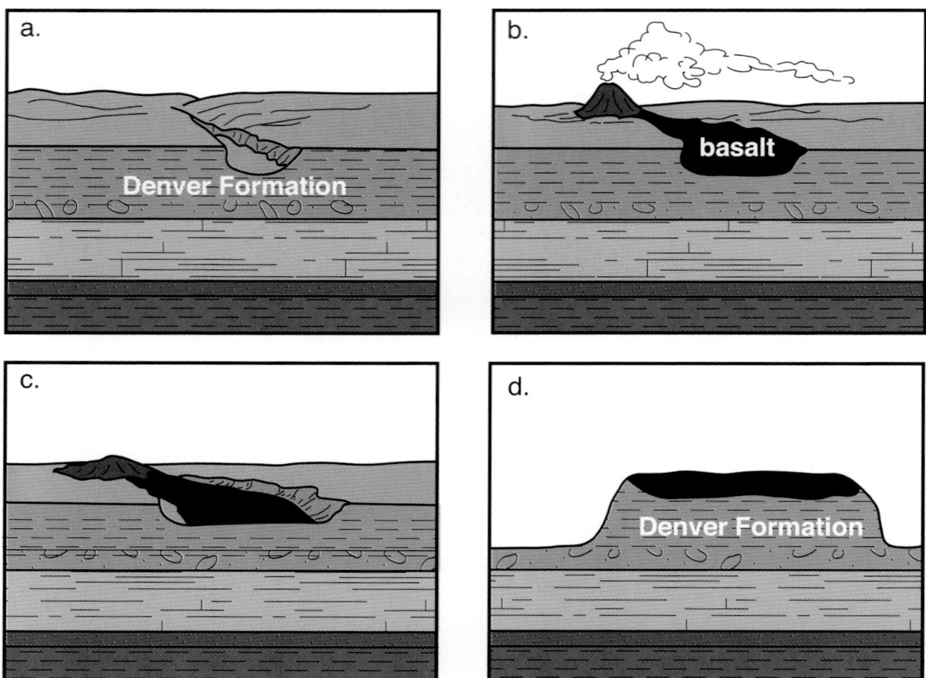

North and South Table mountains formed through a process of topographic inversion: (a) At 65 million years ago a creek draining the rising Rockies flowed southeast across the Golden area. (b) At 64 million years ago a volcano erupted near Ralston Reservoir, sending a basalt lava flow down the creek valley. (c) The basalt armored the valley, so it resisted erosion relative to the soft, surrounding Denver Formation layers. Erosion was therefore concentrated at the edges of the basalt flow. (d) As erosion continued on all sides, the basalt-capped mesa loomed ever higher above the surrounding landscape.

with various Paleozoic and Mesozoic sedimentary rocks, which used to overlie the ancient crystalline rocks (like those seen at stop 1) before they were uplifted as today's range. That blanket of sedimentary rocks remains largely intact beneath the Great Plains, where it can be more than 12,000 feet thick. Because the Arapahoe also contains granite and gneiss pebbles, we know that within the Laramide Front Range's first million years of life, some of its biggest rivers had already sliced clear through that sedimentary blanket and were eroding the range's crystalline core. Then, suddenly, a mere 1 million years later, the range was engulfed in fire, with volcanoes erupting right and left, evidenced by the volcanic cobbles in the Denver Formation.

If we can find rocks younger than those on South Table Mountain, we can investigate how long the Laramide Front Range's volcanic flare-up lasted. Fortunately, some lie nearby, at stop 6 on Green Mountain. When you

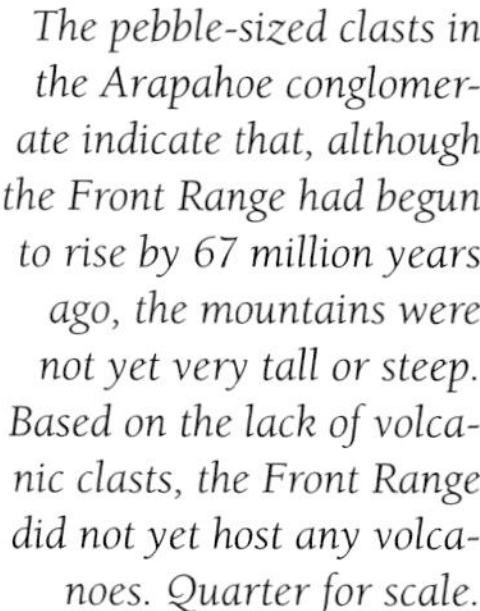

The pebble-sized clasts in the Arapahoe conglomerate indicate that, although the Front Range had begun to rise by 67 million years ago, the mountains were not yet very tall or steep. Based on the lack of volcanic clasts, the Front Range did not yet host any volcanoes. Quarter for scale.

arrive, hike along the old dirt road, now converted to a trail, that leaves the east end of the parking lot and curves around to the left (northeast), slowly gaining elevation. On the left after about 300 yards stands the first outcrop you encounter. Here, we can examine another snapshot of the ancient Front Range landscape, this one from 64 million years ago, the age of these rocks.

The telltale clasts reveal that this, too, is a conglomerate, which goes by the local name of the Green Mountain conglomerate. Like the Arapahoe conglomerate, this material is hardly rock at all due to its lack of cementation. The rounded cobbles are even larger than those you examined on South Table Mountain, indicating deposition by a very vigorous river indeed. Most of the clasts are hard granite and metamorphic gneiss, along with a few gray andesite cobbles that have been so heavily weathered they crumble at the slightest touch. The relative lack of volcanic cobbles here indicates that the volcanic activity we documented in the South Table Mountain deposits was beginning to wane. The abundant clasts of granite and gneiss indicate that by 64 million years ago rivers had begun to bite deeply into the mountains, exposing wide tracts of these older rocks.

If you have the time, hike the 1.5-mile Green Mountain Trail to the summit. To do so, continue up the road just past a deep gully to a trail junction on the ridge. Turn left and hike up the ridge. After about 0.25 mile you will encounter another trail junction at a fence. Continue straight up the ridge. After another 0.1 mile you will begin to see boulders littering the ground. At the mountain's summit there is, amidst the boulders, a bed of sandy, light gray volcanic tuff. Dated at 64 million years old, this tuff is essentially the same age as the lava flow capping South Table Mountain. Although you can't see it from here, the southern end of the South Table Mountain flow

Hikers have piled Green Mountain conglomerate boulders up to build a cairn at the summit.

lies 800 feet below you, at the elevation of the base of Green Mountain. The Green Mountain conglomerate is thus sandwiched between two volcanic layers both dated to 64 million years, meaning that its entire 800-foot thickness must have accumulated in less than 1 million years.

Logic dictates that the most vigorous river we have yet seen evidence of was needed to transport the boulders at your feet. This increase in sediment size over time—starting with the mud and sand of the 68-million-year-old Laramie Formation, changing to pebbles in the 67-million-year-old Arapahoe Formation, growing to cobbles in the 66-million-year-old Denver Formation, and culminating in the 64-million-year-old boulders you see here—documents the geologically rapid growth of the Laramide Front Range from a flat plain into very tall, steep mountains.

Boulder compositions here include reddish gray, pebbly sandstone, andesite, and exceptionally hard, bluish quartzite, revealing what the mountains were made of 64 million years ago. The sandstone boulders were eroded from the Fountain Formation, found in nearby Red Rocks Amphitheatre (vignette 9). The presence of andesite clasts indicates that volcanic activity was continuing, but because there are so many other clast types mixed in with them, volcanism didn't dominate like it had 2 million years earlier. The bluish quartzite is interesting because it could only have come from Coal Creek Canyon, halfway between Golden and Boulder (vignette 5). It clearly would require very powerful floods to transport

Looking west from the summit of Green Mountain you can see that the nearly flat tops of Lookout Mountain (identified by the tall antenna at its summit) and nearby summits all stand at nearly the same elevation. They are all part of the Rocky Mountain Erosion Surface. Green Mountain's summit (foreground) lies along the continuation of that surface, but its surface was formed by deposition of sediments shed off the nearby mountains, not by erosion.

boulders this large from the canyon, 14 miles away! (See vignette 11 for an even more amazing story involving these quartzites.) Look, too, among the boulders for smaller chips of golden brown chert, some of which display concentric, colored rings. These are pieces of petrified wood. There are, close by, even a few intact petrified logs, but they are not visible from the trail system. Like the boulders, these logs washed down the same river during a flood, probably stacking up in a logjam at a bend.

From the crest of Green Mountain, you can gaze west to Lookout Mountain, clearly visible thanks to the nest of TV antennae sprouting from its summit. Remember that Lookout Mountain's summit was part of the gently east-tilted Rocky Mountain Erosion Surface created by erosional beveling of the Laramide Front Range's crystalline rocks. It is apparent that the Green Mountain summit stands just a few hundred feet below Lookout Mountain's. But, as we have seen on our hike, Green Mountain consists of loose conglomerate shed off the mountains, not of the crystalline bedrock that composes Lookout Mountain.

Geologists connecting these dots of evidence have concluded that the Laramide Front Range was born 67 million years ago and rose very rapidly over the next 3 million years. However, by approximately 37 million years ago, the range had been so heavily eroded, and the debris shed off the

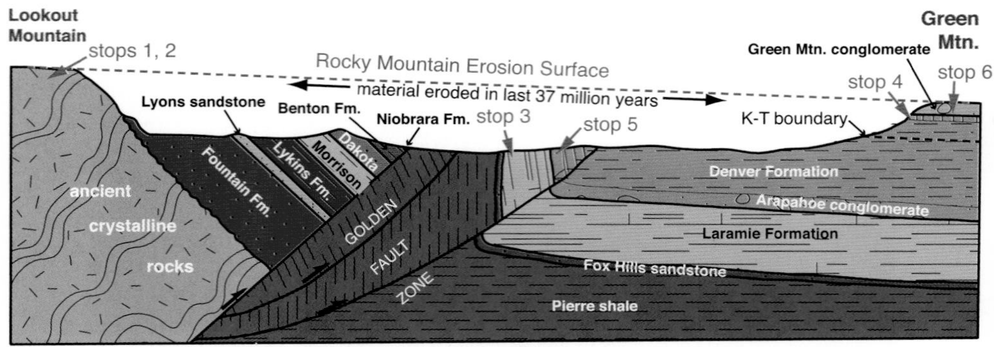

Green Mountain and Lookout Mountain were, during the Eocene, portions of the continuous, gently west-rising Rocky Mountain Erosion Surface. The valley that currently lies between them was at that time filled with sediment but was excavated during a recent pulse of erosion that began around 5 million years ago. (Modified from Weimer, 1973.)

range had filled the adjacent plains so high, that the range's steep eastern flank had been buried. The Great Plains rose in elevation gradually westward, where they merged, imperceptibly, with the rolling upland that was the Eocene-age Front Range. In vignette 2 we explore the one preserved scrap of this formerly extensive surface—the Gangplank—that still directly connects the Front Range with the Great Plains.

If the Rockies of 37 million years ago were just a gentle westward extension of the Great Plains, how then did today's dramatic escarpment form? The rocks contain no evidence of large-scale movement on the Golden fault in the last 64 million years, nor do geologists know of any other faults that could have accomplished significant uplift in the past 37 million years. The modern Front Range appears, instead, to basically be a version of the Laramide Front Range that was reborn thanks to erosion of the sediments that had previously buried it. Two hypotheses, recent broad-scale uplift and climate change, have been proposed to explain this recent erosional episode (see vignette 2 for a more complete discussion). The jury remains out on which of these hypotheses, or possibly aspects of both, best explains the development of the modern Front Range. Whatever the final consensus, future geologists will reach it through the same kind of careful observation of the region's geography and rock characteristics that we have embarked upon here. In so doing, we have witnessed the ups and downs—the raising, razing, and rebirth—of the Rockies.

9

THE WHOLE SHEBANG
Red Rocks to Golden: 1,700 Million Years of Front Range History

Etched into the rocks of the Colorado Front Range are fascinating stories about the sweeping changes this region has endured. The stones record vivid tales of mighty mountain ranges raised and torn down, tropical seas and rainforests come and gone, a vast desert of sand dunes marching to the horizon, and plants and animals that have called the region home. Usually, an area's geologic story is told in bits and pieces, in outcrops scattered hither and yon. Not so in the Golden area, where in just eight stops spanning a distance of 18 miles, spectacular exposures reveal the sweep of 1,700 million years of geologic history.

The rocks we examine in this vignette include ancient (1,700-million-year-old) metamorphic rocks overlain by a stack of brightly colored sedimentary layers that range from 300 to 64 million years old. Though originally deposited horizontally, the sedimentary layers now tilt to the east as a result of the uplift of the Rockies. This tilt allows us to work our way up through the stack, from oldest to youngest, as we travel across the Denver suburbs.

Our geologic tour de force begins at the famed Red Rocks Amphitheatre, one of the world's most stunning (and geologically interesting) concert venues. The amphitheatre is open between shows, so you can wander among the seats, enjoying the beauty of this acoustically charmed venue. A metal plaque attached to the cliff on the west side of the parking lot marks a gap in the rock record so large that it is called the Great Unconformity. Spanning 1,400 million years, nearly one-third of Earth's history, this incredible boundary angles down to the left (southeast). Left (southeast) of the unconformity lies the 300-million-year-old Fountain Formation, which consists of layers of pink sandstone and conglomerate—sedimentary rocks. To the right rests dark gray gneiss belonging to the Idaho Springs Formation, metamorphic rock that is about 1,750 million years old. It possesses

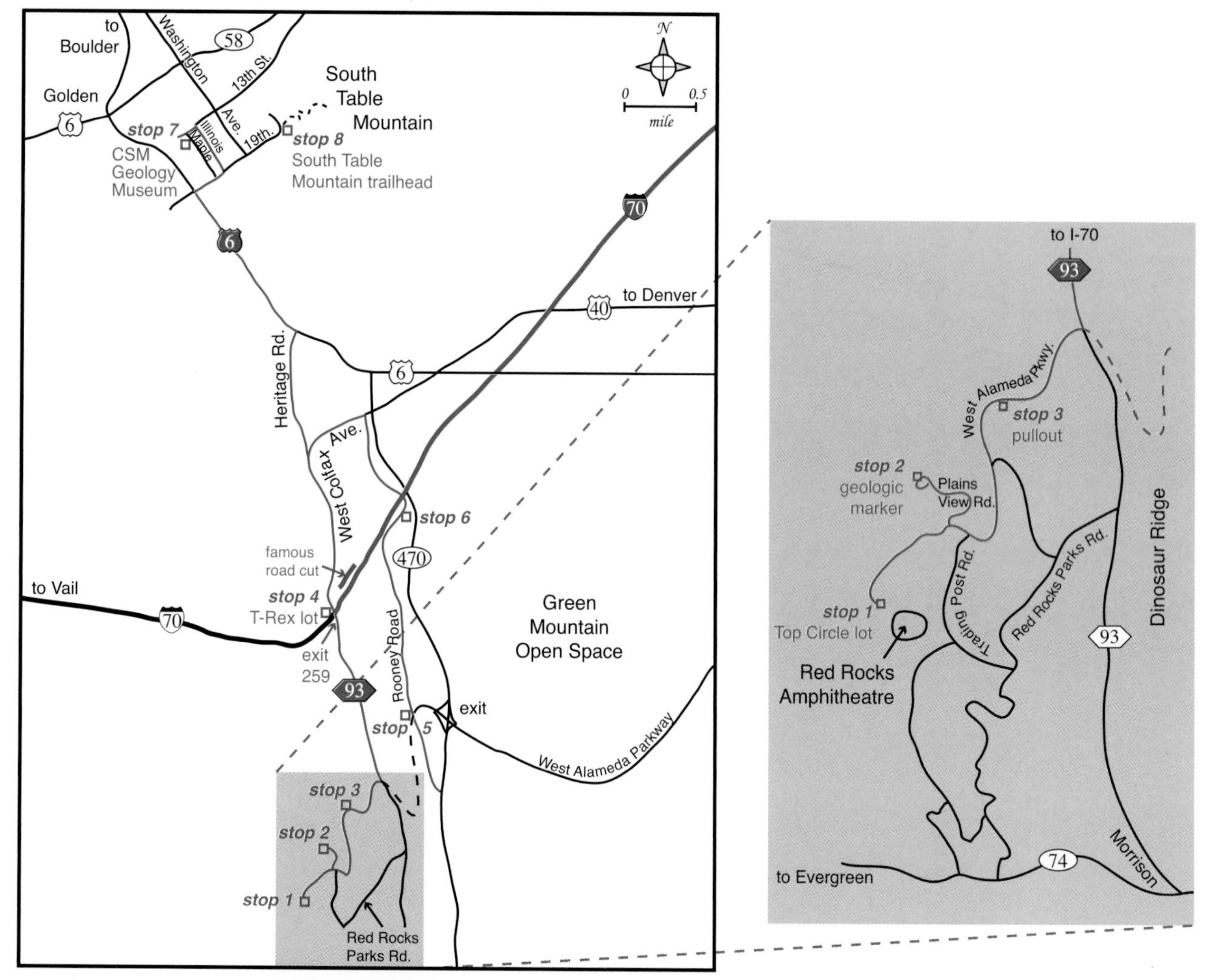
to Boulder
Golden
6
58
Washington
13th St.
Ave.
Illinois
Maple
19th.
South Table Mountain
stop 7
CSM Geology Museum
stop 8
South Table Mountain trailhead
N
0
0.5
mile
70
6
to Denver
40
Heritage Rd.
6
West Colfax Ave.
stop 6
470
famous road cut
stop 4
T-Rex lot
to Vail
70
exit 259
93
Rooney Road
Green Mountain Open Space
exit
stop 5
West Alameda Parkway
stop 3
stop 2
stop 1
Red Rocks Parks Rd.
to I-70
93
West Alameda Pkwy.
stop 3
pullout
stop 2
geologic marker
Plains View Rd.
stop 1
Top Circle lot
Red Rocks Amphitheatre
Trading Post Rd.
Red Rocks Parks Rd.
Dinosaur Ridge
93
to Evergreen
74
Morrison

GETTING THERE: Stop 1 is at the Red Rocks Amphitheatre. From downtown Denver, travel west on I-70 and take exit 259 (Morrison). Turn left (south) onto County Road 93 and drive about 1.5 miles to Red Rocks Amphitheatre Entrance 1. Turn right, following West Alameda Parkway 1.4 miles to where it ends at the Top Circle parking lot. To reach stop 2, drive 0.3 mile back on West Alameda Parkway and left (north) onto Plains View Road. Drive another 0.3 mile and park at the end of the road. Walk east 50 yards to the geologic overlook (wheelchair accessible). For stop 3, return to the junction of Plains View Road and West Alameda Parkway. Turn left (east) onto West Alameda. Drive 0.8 mile, where you will see a small wooden "Lyons sandstone" sign on the left. Park on the road's shoulder.

To reach stop 4, retrace your route to the junction of County Road 93 and I-70. Park in the T-Rex Park and Ride parking lot on the north side of the interstate. A 150-yard paved path far above the highway allows you to view the famous I-70 road cut. Stop 5 is at the east entrance to Dinosaur Ridge. Turn right (north) out of the T-Rex parking lot onto US 40 (West Colfax Avenue). Follow US 40 east for about 1.6 miles and turn right (south) onto Rooney Road. Drive 2.6 miles, crossing over I-70 en route, to the junction of Rooney Road and Alameda Parkway. Turn right (west) onto Alameda and park immediately, in front of the barrier. Walk 70 yards up the closed road to the "Western Interior Seaway" interpretive sign. For stop 6, turn left (north) onto Rooney Road and drive 1.4 miles to a wide, paved pullout at the entrance to a bike path in front of a road cut. Walk 30 yards northeast along Rooney Road to view the road cut.

To reach stop 7, the Colorado School of Mines (CSM) Geology Museum, backtrack on Rooney Road to its US 40 (West Colfax Avenue) junction. Turn left (west) onto West Colfax and go 0.5 mile, then turn right (north) onto Heritage Road. Proceed 1 mile to the junction with US 6 and turn left (northwest). Go 1.4 miles on US 6 and turn right (northeast) onto 19th street. Follow it 0.3 mile, then turn left (northwest) on Illinois Street. Here you enter the CSM campus, where you will need to pick up a parking permit from the first house on the left on Illinois Street. Once you obtain a permit, continue 0.5 mile northwest on Illinois Street and turn left (southwest) onto 13th street. Go one block to the corner of 13th and Maple, where you will see the CSM geology museum, which has a parking lot behind it. At the museum pick up an interpretive brochure with directions to the nearby CSM Geology Trail (stop 7). For stop 8, reverse your route back to the corner of Illinois and 19th Street. Turn left (northeast) on 19th and follow it 0.6 mile to its end at Belvedere, where you turn left. Park on the right side of the road at the corner of 18th and Belvedere, next to a large, open field, at the South Table Mountain trailhead.

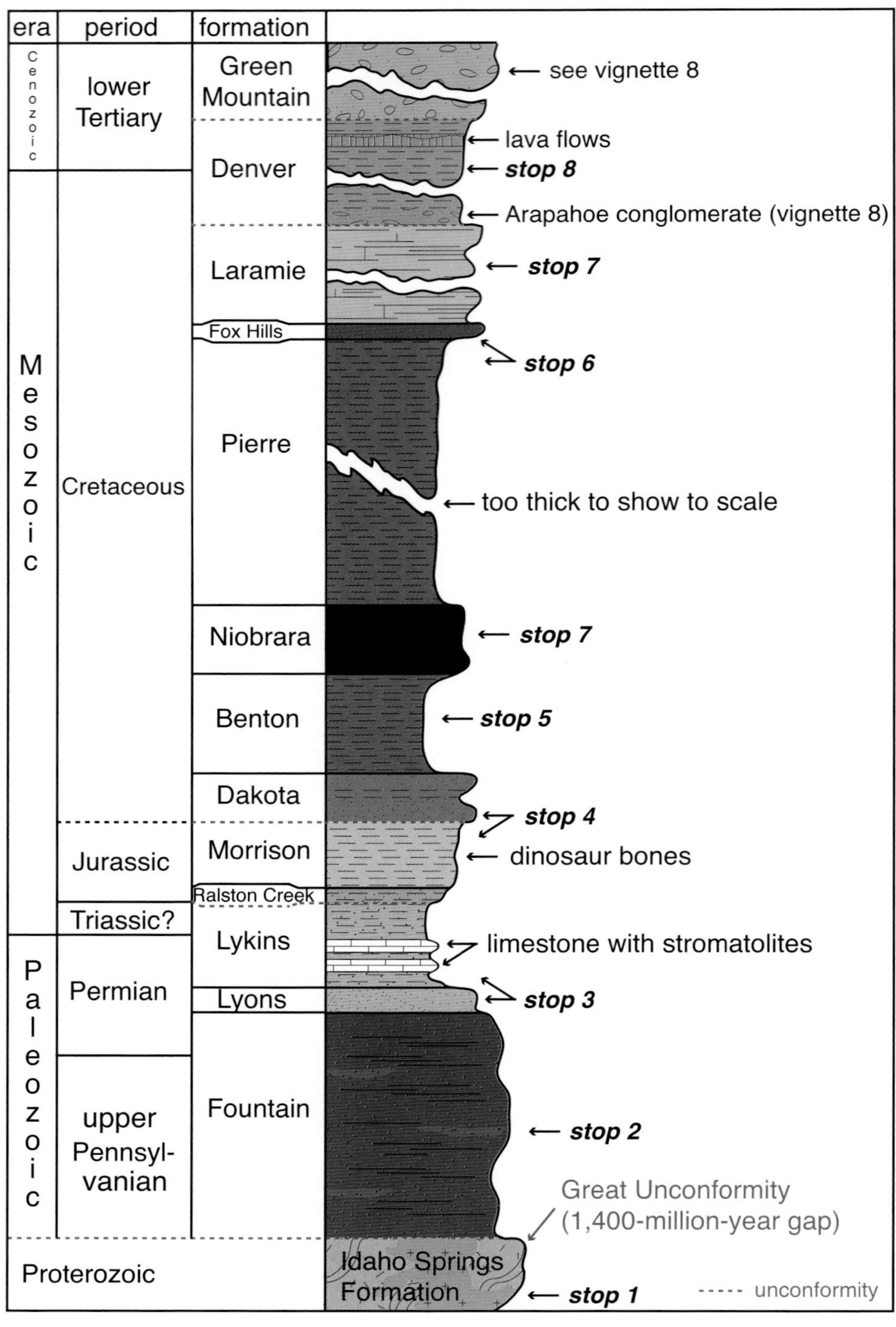

The rocks of the Front Range keyed to the stops in this vignette.

At Red Rocks you can reach out and touch the Great Unconformity, where one-third of Earth's history is missing from the Front Range rock record.

a distinct vertical "fabric" (known to geologists as foliation) formed by the parallel alignment of its mineral crystals. In places, elongate white to pink pods of granite parallel the foliation.

The Idaho Springs Formation is among the oldest rocks found anywhere along the Front Range. It and its time-equivalent sibling units form many of the Front Range's high peaks. Because they comprise the state's original crust, this family of rocks tells the story of Colorado's very origins. When they formed the world was utterly different. The continents were much smaller than they are today and were devoid of life; no plants or animals existed, only bacteria. Still, one crucial process operated the same way it does today: plate tectonics.

The theory of plate tectonics posits that Earth's surface consists of twelve major and many smaller rigid tectonic plates that move across the face of the globe, wafted about by convection currents that roil the underlying asthenosphere, which is solid but flows plastically over long time periods.

Vignette 7, which explores the birth of Colorado in more detail, also covers the basics of plate tectonics.

The characteristics of the Idaho Springs Formation at stop 1 reveal Colorado's fiery birth in a chain of volcanic island arcs. Ash erupted from the volcanoes, along with the sand and mud produced by their erosion, accumulated in layers that reached tens of thousands of feet thick. The viselike pressure exerted on this pile of material by the forces of plate convergence metamorphosed it into the hard gneiss you see here, in the process aligning all of the mineral crystals perpendicular to the direction of squeezing. Ultimately, the lower part of the pile was buried so deeply that it partially melted. This magma rose and intruded between layers of the metamorphosing rock, creating the pods of pinkish granite you see interwoven with the darker metamorphic rock. Between roughly 1,780 and 1,700 million years ago a series of tectonic collisions welded these island arcs onto the edge of North America, creating a coastal mountain range in the process. The remnants of these island arcs are the Front Range's oldest rocks.

Just like a car crash, plate collisions eventually run out of energy and grind to a halt. The coastal mountains created in the island-arc collisions quickly eroded, eventually disappearing altogether. What followed was a long period of erosion, during which the deeply buried gneiss and granite were exposed. It is certain that many exciting geologic events occurred at Red Rocks during the missing 1,400 million years of history, but we have no rock record here of what they were. In other places around the Front Range, rocks that formed during a few specific intervals within the time gap have been preserved, allowing us to reconstruct a few of those events (vignettes 1, 7, 14, 15). But what happened during the vast majority of this missing time is a mystery not only across the Front Range, but the entire American Southwest.

Following this intermission the curtain rose on the Front Range's next geologic act about 300 million years ago, with the deposition of the Fountain Formation. The Fountain's sedimentary layers all tilt down to the left (southeast), revealing that another tectonic episode occurred after their deposition. More on that later.

Some of the chunks embedded in the Fountain conglomerates here are the size of your fist ("cobble sized" in geologic parlance). In southern Colorado's Sangre de Cristo Mountains, similar rocks of the same age contain boulders three times bigger than a watermelon. It takes a very strong current to move fist- to watermelon-sized rocks around! Such swift currents are most commonly found in mountain streams. This and other characteristics of the Fountain Formation show that it was deposited on a series of alluvial fans—cone-shaped piles of sediment—that formed where swiftly flowing streams exited a mountain range, slowed down, and dropped their heavy load as they began to cross the adjacent plains. This topographic setting was strikingly similar to that of the Front Range today (vignette 6). However, the Fountain records the presence not of today's Rocky Mountains, but of an earlier range.

Because this ancient range stood in nearly the same location as today's Front Range, geologists call it the Ancestral Front Range (vignette 5). The large sediment particles embedded in the Fountain Formation are the only remaining legacy of this once mighty mountain range; had they not been preserved, we would never have known this older range existed. The pebbles and cobbles are large enough that you can identify the rock or mineral type of which they are made. The majority consist of quartz, granite, and gneiss strikingly similar to the rocks that form today's Front Range peaks. This is no coincidence; the Ancestral Rockies were composed of the same 1,800-to-1,700-million-year-old rocks that make up the current peaks. This makes sense when you consider that, as you see here, the Fountain was deposited directly on top of the Idaho Springs Formation, confirming that the land surface 300 million years ago consisted of these same Proterozoic rocks.

Artist Jan Vriesen's vision of what the Ancestral Front Range looked like 300 million years ago is faithful to the data scientists have collected from the Fountain Formation and contemporaneous rocks. —Courtesy of Denver Museum of Nature and Science

As you proceed to stop 2, all of the rocks you see are part of the Fountain Formation. From the geology lookout you have a sweeping view to the east, providing a great overview. Interpretive signs point out landmarks and discuss the area's geologic history, including all of the formations we will be visiting in this vignette. The I-70 road cut (stop 4) is visible to the north. The youngest rocks we will examine lie on South Table Mountain, the mesa capped by black rock visible even farther to the north.

North of the stop 3 pullout lies a low outcrop of blonde rock. As the sign next to it attests, this is the 280-million-year-old Lyons Formation, deposited on top of the Fountain Formation about 20 million years after the Ancestral Front Range was uplifted. The outcrop consists mainly of sand, but it also possesses a few thin, discontinuous pebble beds. There are no fist-sized cobbles like those you observed at stop 1. Compared to the Fountain, the particles in the Lyons are much smaller, indicating that the intervening 20 million years had sapped much of the energy from the once-robust rivers draining the Ancestral Front Range. The most likely explanation for this change was that the mountains had been eroded to mere stumps, greatly reducing the rivers' gradient.

The climate, too, had changed. The thick sandstone layers in front of you are the remains of ancient sand dunes. Although it is difficult to see here, the Lyons sports a very distinctive layering known as large-scale crossbedding—a direct inheritance, now frozen in time, of ancient sand dunes. If you look closely, you can discern that some layers tilt more steeply to the east than other, adjacent layers. Crossbeds are much more prominent in the outcrop of Lyons Formation that lies at the junctions of CO 74 and CO 8, in the nearby town of Morrison.

If you've ever walked in a field of dunes, you know that the downwind sides are steep enough to gallop, jump, and tumble down. In contrast, the upwind sides are much gentler. Wind blows sand up the gentle face and piles it at the dune crest, where eventually it cascades down the steep lee face in a turbulent sand avalanche. If you were able to slice through a dune to expose a cross section, layers at angles to one another—crossbeds—would be evident. Through the process of lithification, the crossbeds are locked in stone. Comparable crossbedded sandstones stretch from Montana to Arizona, indicating this desert was of Saharan proportions. The pebble layers couldn't have been deposited by wind. Their presence tells us that, while diminished, the Ancestral Front Range had not yet disappeared. The range managed to collect enough moisture to produce a few small creeks that meandered through the dunes, depositing the pebbles. Thicker, coarser-grained pebble beds exist in the Lyons Formation at Garden of the Gods (vignette 16), indicating that bigger creeks flowed in the Colorado Springs area at that time.

Artist Jan Vriesen has captured the essence of what the Front Range looked like 280 million years ago. The climate had become more arid, and sand dunes marched across the landscape. The Ancestral Front Range had been reduced to mere hills, but the few creeks that drained them flowed through the dune field, depositing pebble beds in the Lyons Formation.
—Courtesy of Denver Museum of Nature and Science

Now walk east 50 yards down the road. On your left, you will see that the blonde Lyons abruptly gives way to brick-red material that is more dirt than rock. You have reached the boundary with the Lykins Formation, the deposition of which, approximately 255 to 245 million years ago, straddled the boundary between the Paleozoic and Mesozoic eras. This was a particularly interesting time in Earth history, because the biggest mass extinction event ever took place at the era boundary, 251 million years ago. About 90 percent of all species went extinct.

The Lykins consists mainly of the soft, red mudstone you see here, interbedded with thin sandstone beds. Because it is so poorly cemented, it erodes very easily, forming valleys throughout the Front Range. A typical example is the valley immediately to your east, through which County Road 93 runs.

What does this outcrop tell us about the Front Range environment 255 million years ago? The fact that it is dominated by mudstone indicates that the Ancestral Rockies had been eroded down to a range of very low hills or had been erased completely. The rivers draining them could no longer deliver large particles to this spot. Sandstone layers are uncommon in this outcrop, but in nearby outcrops they contain symmetric ripple marks, which are only formed by currents that slosh back and forth. Typically, such currents occur along coastlines. The brick-red color is caused by the oxidation of iron the rocks contain. Such oxidation occurs most vigorously in arid to semiarid conditions, suggesting that the climate had not changed a great deal since the time during which the Lyons was deposited.

You can glean even more information about the former Front Range geography if you walk east 40 yards down the road to a second Lykins outcrop on the right (south) side, where a 10-yard-long trail leads to a long, low ridge of gray rock. The rock is much more resistant to erosion than the red mudstone and consequently forms a low ridge. It consists of limestone, the individual layers of which are thin and wavy. This rock is so distinct from the rest of the Lykins that it's been given its own name, the Glennon limestone member. The rock's most curious feature is its wavy beds.

The Glennon limestone contains thin, wavy beds that are fossil stromatolites, which lived along an arid coastline. After tidal-flat mud was stirred up by daily tides, it resettled, coating the bacterial mats. The bacteria then grew upward through the thin layer of sediment, in the process binding the particles together with their sticky secretions. As this process repeated itself through the millennia, this stack of wavy layers formed.

Unbelievable though it may seem, these are fossilized bacterial mats. When combined with the formation's dominant mudstone, its symmetrical ripple marks, and the presence of gypsum (an evaporite mineral) that is quarried north of Fort Collins, the presence of bacterial mats provides a critical clue that 255 million years ago the Denver area was an arid, hypersaline tidal flat.

Called stromatolites, these fossils are very common in sedimentary rocks older than about 550 million years. Prior to that time bacteria had the planet essentially to themselves, and their abundance in ancient rocks shows that they thrived almost everywhere. But around 550 million years ago life was undergoing very profound changes. The first complex, multicelled organisms had "recently" evolved—about 30 million years earlier. Once evolution could work on complex aggregates instead of single cells, radical innovations in body type and feeding strategy soon followed. For the first time, predators evolved that could eat the bacterial mats. In the geologic record this major biological innovation is marked by two changes: the sudden widespread appearance of complex fossils and a precipitous drop in the abundance of stromatolites. Therefore, younger stromatolite fossils are only found where conditions were extremely harsh, such as hypersaline tidal flats. Bacteria, the ultimate survivors, could thrive and form thick

Stromatolites are forming today in only a handful of places. The most famous are at Shark Bay, Australia. Hypersaline conditions in this restricted tidal bay exclude predators, allowing the anvil-shaped bacterial mats to thrive. Shark Bay provides a likely modern analogue for what the Denver area looked like 255 million years ago.

mats only where conditions were too severe for their predators. No other fossils have been found in the Lykins Formation in the area. This is a real pity, as they could provide us with clues to the cause of the Paleozoic-Mesozoic extinction event.

The short drive on County Road 93 to stop 4 takes you along the axis of the valley eroded into the crumbly Lykins Formation. From the T-Rex Park and Ride parking lot, walk a paved path along the "I-70 Point of Geological Interest" to view the next portion of the rock story, which picks up again in the Jurassic period following another unconformity. As you pass the first two signs, which describe how sediments become rocks and how layers are formed, the poorly exposed material you pass belongs to the Ralston Creek Formation, the next layer in the stack of formerly horizontal sedimentary layers, and the overlying Morrison Formation. A few ribs of light gray Morrison limestone protrude from the rubble-covered hillslope. By the time you reach the sign that describes how geologists define formations, the exposure is considerably better, with ribs of tan and red sandstone standing out amidst slopes of very crumbly red, gray, and green mudstone. During rainstorms mud weeps across the path, making it difficult in places to tell that it is actually paved. All of these layers belong to the upper Morrison Formation, which was deposited about 150 million years ago by lazy, meandering rivers that flowed over a wide plain reminiscent of today's lower Mississippi River valley. The sandstone beds are discontinuous and lens shaped because they comprise the lens-shaped (in cross section) channels of ancient rivers that filled with sand. The multicolored mudstone accumulated on adjacent floodplains. The few limestone layers formed in lakes and ponds that lay on the floodplains. Dinosaurs roamed these Jurassic lowlands, as evidenced by the dinosaur bones present nearby, at Dinosaur Ridge (vignette 10).

Between the "Morrison Formation" and the "Dakota Group" interpretive signs you cross the boundary between the Jurassic-age Morrison and the Cretaceous-age Dakota Group (a group of two related rock formations, the Lytle and South Platte formations). Another unconformity, representing a shorter time interval, exists between these layers. The uppermost Morrison bed is a maroon mudstone, and the lowermost Dakota bed consists of erosion-resistant, tan sandstone. This transition is distinctive enough that you can detect it in the matching road cut on the south side of the interstate as well.

The Dakota Group was deposited about 100 million years ago, when the Front Range lay along a tropical coastline that stretched from Wyoming to New Mexico. The many different rock types evident along the trail here accumulated in the varied environments that exist along a coast. The tan sandstone beds, some displaying prominent crossbedding (discussed on one of the interpretive signs), accumulated in rivers near the coast and as

The southern I-70 road cut viewed from the northern road cut at stop 4. The dashed line represents an unconformity separating the Morrison Formation from the Dakota Group.

beach sands. Near the path's end a few faint ripple marks, which developed as waves washed back and forth on the beach, are preserved in the sandstone. Considerably better ripple marks, as well as the tracks of dinosaurs that migrated along this beach, are on display in similar strata nearby at Dinosaur Ridge.

The next interpretive sign along the path discusses the presence of black mudstone layers, the color of which is due to the abundant organic carbon the layers contain. The carbon was derived from the bodies of countless plankton that lived and died in these coastal waters. Thanks to the low oxygen level on the seafloor, when their bodies settled to the bottom they didn't decompose, allowing the carbon from living creatures to be transferred to rock. This fossil carbon is the source material for petroleum. At the I-70 road cut it is apparent that all of these rock layers tilt down to the east. Because of this tilt, these same black mudstone layers lie thousands of feet beneath the surface just a few miles east of here. At those depths, the organic carbon is slowly cooked out of the rocks to form oil and natural gas, both of which are recovered from wells north and east of Denver. Over 800 million barrels of oil and 1.2 trillion cubic feet of natural gas have been recovered from the rocks of the Denver Basin.

Among other things, the next interpretive sign highlights the presence of valuable clay layers in the formation, several of which stand immediately behind the sign. You might think that clay could be easily extracted from any mudstone layers, such as the multicolored ones present in the Morrison Formation. But it turns out that most mudstone, including that of the Morrison, consists of a mixture of clay- and silt-sized particles. The coarser silt grains render typical mudstone unsuitable for most industrial processes. If you rub your finger on a chip of the claystone behind the sign, you will notice how smooth it feels. That is because it lacks silt. The Dakota's pure claystone layers consist of chemically altered volcanic ash. The ash, belched from distant volcanoes in what is now Utah, rained down along the former coast, where it was altered to clay by its interaction with groundwater. Because of the comparative rarity of pure claystone, Dakota clays have been mined for over a hundred years. As you travel around the Front Range, such as just north of Golden, you will see prominent white stripes on the lowest foothills. These stripes are claystone quarries.

To continue our story we need to go to stop 5, at the east entrance to Dinosaur Ridge. Once there, a walk about 60 yards up the closed road to an interpretive marker labeled "Western Interior Seaway." The dark gray rock next to the sign belongs to the Benton Formation, a brittle mudstone deposited in very thin beds only fractions of an inch thick. As we noted at the last stop, the Dakota rocks accumulated on a coastline during early Cretaceous time. Later, sea level rose, pushing the coastline west of the Front Range, into Utah and Arizona. The Benton was deposited in the shallow Western Interior Seaway, far from land. The interpretive sign here includes a map that shows the extent of the seaway.

Like the modern Black Sea, the Western Interior Seaway water didn't circulate vigorously, so the seafloor was deprived of oxygen. Therefore, as with the Dakota black mudstone we saw at stop 4, when the bodies of dead marine creatures sank to the seafloor they didn't decay, allowing considerable organic carbon to accumulate in the sediment. Pick up a shattered piece of the Benton and snap it in half. Although the outside of the rock has weathered to a light brown color, the fresh surface reveals the rock is actually dark gray, indicative of high organic content. The Benton is another contributor to the oil and gas bounty present in the Denver Basin.

Although you already examined the Dakota Group at stop 4, if you walk a short distance farther up the closed road you encounter the Dakota rocks exposed at Dinosaur Ridge, where you can see beautiful ripple marks and spectacular dinosaur footprints (vignette 10).

En route to stop 6 you cross the Golden reverse fault, but you would never know it. Major faults like the Golden pulverize the surrounding rocks during every earthquake. Shattered rocks erode much more easily, meaning soil builds up, thereby obscuring the fault. Despite its unassuming nature,

The Benton Formation consists of thin layers of dark gray mudstone that turns light brown to nearly white when weathered.

the Golden fault is a mighty beast indeed. As discussed in vignette 8, the ancient metamorphic and igneous rocks west of the fault were heaved more than 2.5 miles up and 1.5 miles over their counterparts on its east side, creating the Laramide Front Range in the process. One unfortunate consequence of movement along the Golden fault is that all surface outcrops of the next unit in our rock stack, the Niobrara Formation, have been removed.

At stop 6 the 70-million-year-old Pierre shale forms the western portion of the road cut along the south side of Rooney Road. The fact that its thin layers are standing almost on end is one clue that the Golden fault lies nearby. In fact, they tilt slightly down to the west, in contrast to the eastward tilt of all the other units we have examined. Movement on the Golden fault was so vigorous that the layers were actually overturned a bit.

The Pierre consists mainly of mudstones very similar to those we saw in the Benton, indicating that it was deposited in a similar environment. The Benton was deposited in a rising sea that peaked with the deposition of the missing Niobrara Formation, a limestone high-water mark. The Pierre was deposited as that seaway slowly began to retreat. As you walk east along this Rooney Road outcrop, you can visualize the Western Interior Seaway draining away over time. As the rock gets progressively sandier, it becomes the Fox Hills Formation. The sand indicates the seaway had nearly retreated from this region and that sand-delivering rivers were nearby. The outcrop's far eastern end consists of a snow-white lump of pure Fox

The Pierre shale was deposited in the Western Interior Seaway, which stretched from the Front Range to Illinois during Cretaceous time. The seaway teemed with fish, sharks, and giant marine reptiles, the plesiosaurs and the mosasaurs, while winged reptiles called pterosaurs, the largest creatures to ever fly, wheeled overhead.

The Fox Hills sandstone accumulated on the beach fronting the retreating Western Interior Seaway.

Hills sandstone, which marks the emergence of land—a beach—above the waves about 69 million years ago.

The end of the outcrop is not the end of our story. We'll pick up the thread a few miles to the north at the Colorado School of Mines Geology Trail (stop 7). Start at the Mines Geology Museum, which has many outstanding displays that are very much worth taking the time to tour. Our goal here, though, is to pick up a free copy of Dr. Bob Weimer's helpful guide to exploring the Mines Geology Trail, which is a self-guided tour. Walk first to the geology trail's stop 2, which examines the fascinating bedding features displayed on the west side of a sandstone ridge just west of the museum. The ridge has been tipped to vertical along the Golden fault, which lurks nearby. This sandstone is part of the 68-million-year-old Laramie Formation, a unit just slightly younger than the Fox Hills. It was deposited by rivers and in swamps that lay slightly inland from the still eastward-retreating interior seaway. The ridge's west face is the underside of one of the depositional layers, and on it you can see the incredible remains of leaves, logs, and palm fronds and the tracks of armored triceratops, all helpfully marked by blue plaques.

At the Colorado School of Mines, the 68-million-year-old Laramie Formation hosts abundant plant and animal fossils, such as this palm frond, indicating the rock was deposited along a hot, humid plain just slightly above sea level.

This vivid evidence enables us to confidently reconstruct the Denver landscape of 68 million years ago, when a flat plain just slightly above sea level sweltered under a hot, muggy sky. But big changes were about to occur that would convulse the Front Range landscape into something a bit more familiar. Before we deal with that upheaval, it is worthwhile visiting trail stop 5, just around the corner, where geologists have created a rock garden with samples of every major rock unit in the Denver area arranged in layer cake order. Here you can finally examine the Niobrara Formation, which was deposited in the Western Interior Seaway as it reached its zenith. Look for oval fossils the size of tennis balls in the hard, gray limestone. These are the shells of inoceramid clams, a large species that thrived in the interior seaway.

Head now to stop 8, where we can examine the 66-million-year-old rocks of the Denver Formation and a basalt flow—erupted during its deposition—that forms the resistant caps of North and South Table mountains. From the trailhead, follow the path about 50 yards until you reach an interpretive sign describing how the mountains formed. Another 50 yards or so beyond the sign you will see several large boulders lying in the small gully a short distance north of the trail. They are conglomerates, packed cheek-to-jowl with round, cobble-sized chunks of volcanic rock. As with the conglomerates in the Fountain Formation at stop 1, swift mountain streams deposited these conglomerates.

So, 66 million years ago a foaming river tumbled through Golden, yet a scant 2 million years earlier, the Laramie Formation was deposited on a placid plain. Clearly something big must have happened in between. That something was the beginning of movement along the Golden fault, which lifted the Front Range on its back as it tilted the rock in its path, including the Pierre and the Laramie outcrops we examined earlier, to vertical. Geologists term such a mountain building event an orogeny. They named this episode the Laramide orogeny in recognition of the fact that it was the characteristics of the Laramie Formation that revealed to them when this mountain-building episode occurred.

Erosion immediately began to tear the young mountains apart, and these conglomerates are their bones, scattered across the plains that existed at the range's feet. Almost every cobble here is volcanic in origin. This indicates that, unlike the Ancestral Front Range, this new range was crowned by smoking volcanoes. About 64 million years ago one such volcano erupted just a few miles northwest of Golden. It sent a tongue of glowing lava flowing down a river channel, in which it solidified into the hard basalt that now caps the Table mountains.

You can hike up the trail to examine the basalt caprock and treat yourself to a stunning view, or you can instead return to the trailhead and examine the basalt blocks piled on the northern side of the field, including the black

Once the land surface 66 million years ago, the Denver Formation conglomerate was buried beneath a hard cap of basalt (top of photo) that has protected it ever since, creating Golden's most famous landmarks, the Table mountains.

blocks used in the retaining wall. The basalt is clearly a much stronger rock than the crumbly Denver Formation. Therefore, after the basalt had cooled, erosion wore down the riverbanks considerably faster than the basalt-filled river channel, slowly inverting the topography. This left the old river channel high above the surrounding land, in the process forming the valley in which Golden sits (vignette 8).

So, after 1,700 million years, we have finally reached the end of our rock story here on Denver's west side. Vignettes 11 and 17 carry the state's history forward, discussing even younger units found between Denver and Colorado Springs. If you have time, it is well worth a visit to either the Denver Museum of Nature and Science to view *Ancient Denvers*, or the Colorado Convention Center to view *Ancient Colorado*. Both exhibits feature a series of dramatic paintings that bring the ancient landscapes, including those through which we journeyed, to life. The paintings of the Ancestral Rockies and of the Lyons Formation sand dunes presented in this vignette are part of that collection. A collaboration between artists and scientists, these images evoke Denver's past landscapes in rigorously accurate detail and are immensely helpful in visualizing the dramatic changes that have swept this corner of the planet through the immensity of geologic time.

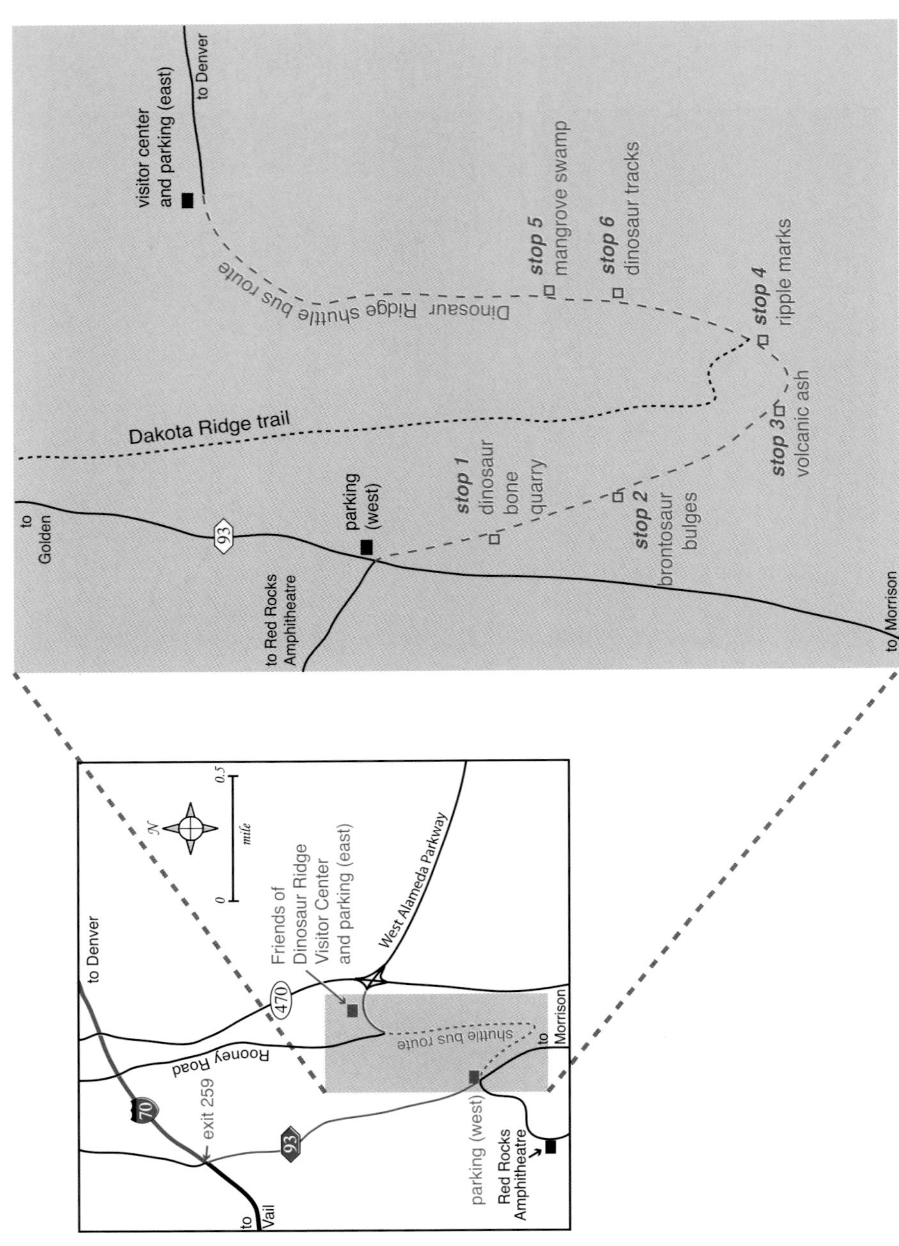

GETTING THERE: Located near the town of Morrison, Dinosaur Ridge hosts many interesting sights in a series of road cuts lining a mile-long section of Alameda Parkway. The vignette traces the ridge's features from west to east, which allows us to go from older to younger rocks. In 2009, the section of Alameda Parkway across the ridge was closed to traffic. This closure makes a visit to the ridge more pleasant than ever before, but it requires you to make a logistical decision. You can either park at the west end of the ridge, complete the vignette stops and then retrace your route back to the car (2 miles round-trip) or do a guided shuttle bus tour, which begins at the Friends of

10

DENVER'S DINOSAUR FREEWAY

Dinosaur Ridge

Dinosaur Ridge has played a pivotal role in the scientific understanding of dinosaurs ever since 1877, when Arthur Lakes, a professor at the fledgling Colorado School of Mines and a country preacher, spied a gigantic vertebra embedded in sandstone here as he returned to Golden after a day of tending to his flock. Then, in the 1930s, a spectacular set of dinosaur footprints was unearthed during road construction. Serious study of those and other nearby tracks beginning in the 1980s has kept Dinosaur Ridge at the cutting edge of dinosaur research. Thanks to the efforts of the Friends of Dinosaur Ridge, this rich scientific legacy has been preserved for us at a series of interpretive stops and in their excellent visitor center.

Arthur Lakes's bone discovery was the first ever in the Jurassic-age Morrison Formation (named for the nearby town), and the dinosaur to which the bones belonged was the largest yet known. Lakes's find immediately

Dinosaur Ridge Visitor Center located on the east side of the ridge. It is also possible to walk from the west side and pay for a shuttle ticket to return to your car. See the Friends of Dinosaur Ridge website (www.dinoridge.org) for more information. While you are in this area, another great stop is the nearby Morrison Natural History Museum (www.mnhm.org).

To reach the west parking lot from Denver, take I-70 west to exit 259 (Morrison). Turn left (south) onto County Road 93 and drive 1.2 miles to the junction with West Alameda Parkway (across from Red Rocks Amphitheatre Entrance 1). Turn left (east) onto West Alameda Parkway. Park in the small lot in front of the "road closed" barrier. Begin hiking east, up the ridge, along the paved road.

To reach the Friends of Dinosaur Ridge Visitor Center on the east side of the ridge, take the CO 470 exit from I-70 and head south 1.8 miles to the Alameda Parkway exit. Turn west on West Alameda Parkway and drive 0.1 mile. The visitor center is on your right.

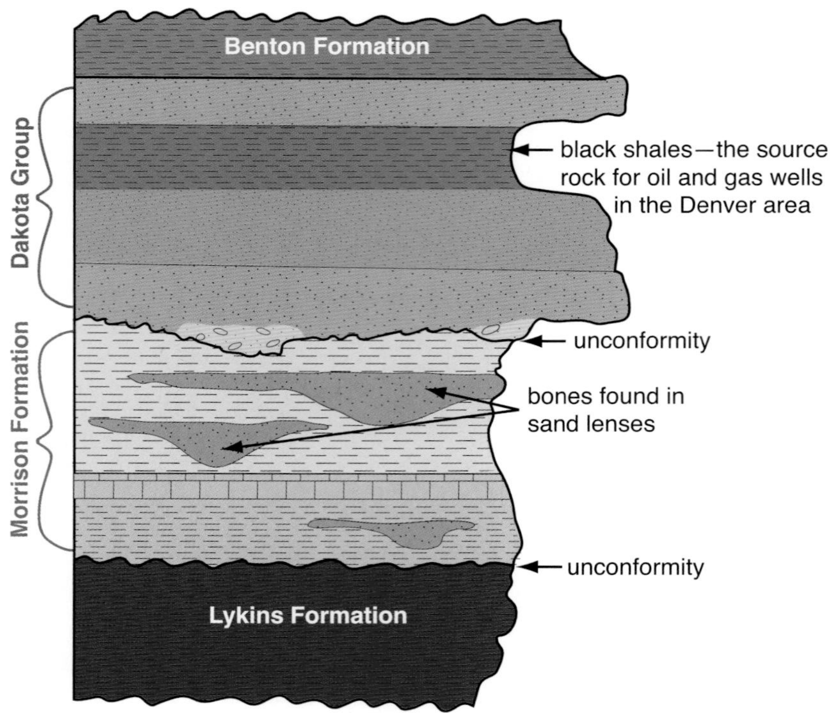

The rocks of Dinosaur Ridge.

caught the attention of both Edward Drinker Cope and Othniel Charles Marsh, two titans of paleontology who, for the previous nine years, had been engaged in bitter rivalry for supremacy in the hunt for fossil remains. The sheer size of the beast Lakes unearthed caused the two men to immediately shift the focus of their efforts to Dinosaur Ridge and exploration of the Morrison Formation elsewhere in the region, including the productive Garden Park area (vignette 19). The Morrison proved to be exceptionally fossil rich, yielding many of the rivals' most significant finds.

Stop 1 is the "Dinosaur Bone Quarry" sign, the first developed site you encounter on the west side of the ridge. While standing in this spot, it is hard to imagine that this ridge once marked the front line in a scientific battle so acrimonious that it achieved widespread infamy as the Bone Wars. Scion of a wealthy family, Edward Drinker Cope was a child prodigy who rose to prominence as the apprentice of Joseph Leidy, the preeminent American paleontologist of the mid-nineteenth century. Both were based at Philadelphia's prestigious Academy of Natural Sciences. His rival, Othniel Charles Marsh, was America's first designated professor of paleontology, a post he held at Yale. He was also the nephew of the fabulously wealthy George Peabody, the benefactor for whom Yale's Peabody Museum is named.

After a brief collaboration, Cope and Marsh became rivals who each harnessed their considerable personal wealth, titanic egos, and deep animosity for one another in an obsessive, continent-wide hunt for fossils. The two bore each other such ill will that they spied on each other's digs, stole one another's fossils, and spared no opportunity to sabotage the other's reputation in conversation and print. In their thirst for quantity, they excavated so many fossil-bearing blocks of rock that many still sit untouched in museum collections. In their haste and ardor for publications (Cope alone published over 1,200 scientific papers, a record that has never been eclipsed), they both made silly errors, in the process sullying the name of American paleontology around the world. Their rivalry reached such ludicrous intensity that Marsh dynamited one of his fossil quarries to prevent Cope from prospecting in it, and Cope, upon his death, bequeathed his skull to science with the express expectation that his brain would be found larger than Marsh's, thus proving his superior intellect.

Despite the antagonism, their efforts led to a quantum leap forward in the scientific knowledge of Earth's prehistory, and many of their theories remain important in paleontology. Boiled down to raw numbers, Cope discovered fifty-six new species and Marsh eighty-six. Those are staggering figures when you consider that only nine dinosaur species were known when the Bone Wars began. Of equal significance is the fact that their work was instrumental in making dinosaurs a national fascination for the general public; many of the species today's schoolchildren know by heart were first discovered by one of these scientific combatants, and some of the most famous were first found at Dinosaur Ridge.

Marsh hired Arthur Lakes to direct excavations in and around the town of Morrison, which Lakes did at thirteen separate quarries. The roll call of genera first discovered here includes such household names as *Allosaurus*, *Diplodocus*, *Stegosaurus* (Colorado's state fossil), and *Apatosaurus* (formerly known as *Brontosaurus*). Most of us think of these as species, but they are actually genera, the next higher taxonomic level. Genus and species are commonly reported together when paleontologists converse with each other. For instance, Marsh named the stegosaur he found here at Dinosaur Ridge (the first one ever found) *Stegosaurus armatus*, meaning "armored-roof lizard."

At stop 1 many bones are visible, still encased in their matrix of tan sandstone. These rocks were tilted sharply upward toward the west by uplift of the Rockies, so in this exposure you are looking at a cross section of the bone-bearing layer. The bones are recognizable because of their dark brown color and smooth texture. Once you tune your eye, you will see dozens of them in all shapes and sizes. Ribs, leg bones, vertebrae, and sundry fragments from a variety of different, unidentified dinosaurs are scattered around the site. Two large boulders, one on each side of the west-side steps of the viewing platform, offer a cross-sectional view of a bone where it was broken. You can even see the spongy texture of the bone's interior, produced by the many holes through which the creature's blood vessels once ran.

If you have seen a complete dinosaur skeleton in a museum, these bones may seem underwhelming. There is no allosaur ready to pounce, nor a mother stegosaur protecting her young. Instead, the bones of several different individuals lie randomly scattered. Typical of fossil localities in the

One of the dinosaur bones visible at the bone quarry. The top of this bone provides a cross-sectional look at the bone's interior, where its spongy texture is still visible.

Morrison Formation, this hodgepodge can be readily explained in the context of its deposition, which we will assess by examining the rocks along the short stroll to stop 2, which is at the "Brontosaur Bulges" interpretive site.

Before leaving the viewing platform, observe how the bones are constrained to a group of erosion-resistant, tan sandstone layers that are several feet thick. The sandstone beds are shaped like a lens, thinning upward to the left. As you walk toward stop 2, the rock along the road changes to a crumbly, multicolored mudstone. Yet when you arrive at stop 2, the impressive brontosaur bulges are likewise located in a sandstone lens similar to that at stop 1. Above the lens the Morrison once again consists of colorful and very soft mudstones. The presence of sandstone lenses encased in mudstone is a diagnostic feature of sediments deposited by lazy, meandering rivers, whose ancient channels were filled with sand (hence the lens shape), and on whose floodplains the finer-grained mudstones were deposited. The mighty brontosaurs likely left the impressive tracks here as they sauntered down to the river for a drink 150 million years ago, perhaps scanning for predators the whole way.

Why would the bones be concentrated in the river channel deposits (the sandstones) instead of the mudstones? Geologists who have studied the site believe these dinosaurs died along the riverbank, possibly after being ambushed by a carnivore. Scavengers picked apart their bones, just as happens to a lion kill on the African savannah today. Periodic floods

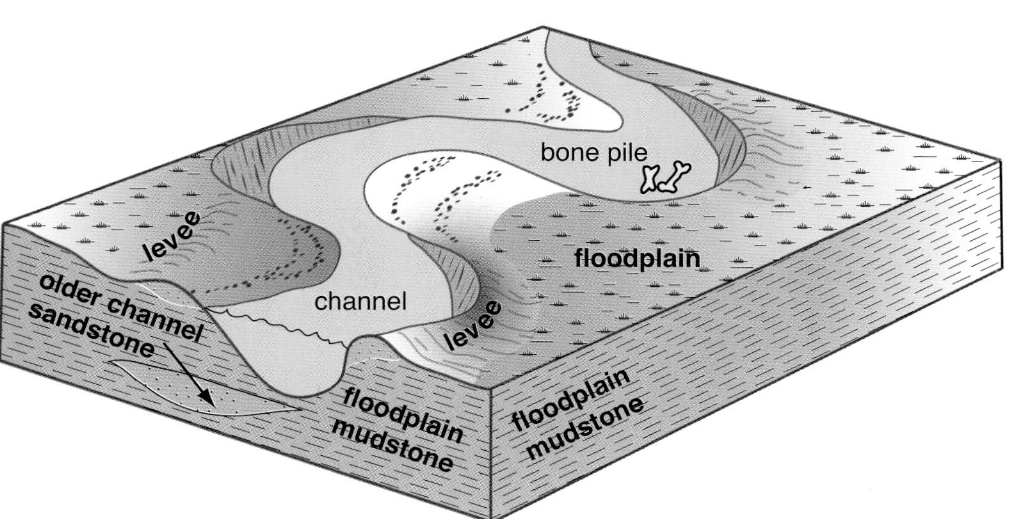

Meandering rivers like the one that flowed at Dinosaur Ridge 150 million years ago deposit sand in their channels and mud on their floodplains. When flooding occurred, the water washed the bones downstream, depositing them in an eddy where they were preserved for posterity.

then carried the bones downstream, further jumbling the remains. When the current slowed, the bones settled to the sandy river bottom, where they were entombed in the sandstone.

Assembling complete, anatomically correct skeletons from a grab bag of river-transported parts is a formidable job, and it has not always been done correctly. Marsh, for instance, attached the wrong skull to the torso of an apatosaur, an error that wasn't corrected for over one hundred years! To be sure of the reconstructions, it is invaluable to find an intact skeleton that was buried shortly after the animal died, sparing the remains from bone-scattering activities. A great example of this is stegosaurus, which was first discovered here but is best known from the three nearly complete skeletons found at Colorado's Garden Park Fossil Area (vignette 19).

While bones tell paleontologists a great deal about dinosaur anatomy, tracks provide complementary information. Stop 2's huge brontosaur bulges, which measure up to 3 feet across and 1 foot deep, provide graphic evidence of the enormous size and weight of these creatures, which tipped the scales at 30 tons. They are called bulges instead of tracks because we see them in cross section due to the eastward tilt of the sedimentary beds. From this vantage point we can see how the weight of the creature depressed the underlying sediment. The sign identifies the tracks as brontosaur bulges, but the animal that made the tracks is now called apatosaurus.

Another error Marsh made in his haste to win the Bone Wars was naming the same animal twice. In 1877 he published a very brief paper describing vertebrae discovered here at Dinosaur Ridge, naming the owner apatosaurus. Later, Marsh found the nearly complete skeleton of a huge dinosaur he called brontosaurus. This became one of the most famous dinosaurs in the world when it was put on display at Yale's Peabody Museum (it was the one with the wrong head). When paleontologists discovered Marsh's error in 1903, they designated the creature apatosaurus because it was the first name assigned to the species. Few paleontologists bothered to correct the name in the many brontosaurus displays, including at the Peabody, until the post office issued a set of dinosaur stamps in 1989. When they called the dino on the stamp brontosaurus, the hue and cry was intense!

Whether you call the animal apatosaurus or brontosaurus, it was huge, as both the bones and the tracks reveal. A good rule of thumb when examining tracks is that the height of the animal at its hips is about four times the width of its tracks, placing these giants' hips 12 feet above the ground. This information is consistent with apatosaur skeletons, helping confirm the identity of the track maker. Similarly, if you visit the nearby Morrison Natural History Museum, you can see tracks made by two stegosaur hatchlings. No baby stegosaur bones have ever been found, but analysis of their tracks reveals that they were turkey sized, about one-eleventh the height of their parents.

One apatosaur track is marked and another track occurs to its left. You can see how the underlying sediments were depressed by the weight of this 30-ton beast. An adult apatosaur was 70 feet long and 12 feet high at the hips.

Both tracks and trackways—a series of fossilized footprints made by a moving animal—teach scientists quite a bit about an organism that they can't learn from its fossilized bones. When scaled for the animal's size, the distance between tracks provides a measure of how fast it was traveling. The apatosaur that made these bulges was sauntering along between 2 to 4 miles per hour, a typical pace for these lumbering giants. Trackways also yield clues to whether a given species was solitary or social. A famous track site along southern Colorado's Purgatoire River contains over 1,300 individual footprints belonging to at least one hundred different animals. Like the tracks you see here, most belong to apatosaurs. The presence of so many parallel trackways in the same sediment layer suggests that apatosaurs traveled in herds, just like many herbivorous species do today.

Stop 3 lies near the ridge crest, 0.2 mile east of the brontosaur bulges, at the "Volcanic Ash" interpretive sign on the south side of the road. Just west of stop 3 you cross from the Jurassic-age Morrison Formation to the Cretaceous-age Dakota Group. Both consist of sandstone and mudstone.

The focus of stop 3 is a 2-inch-thick, hard, yellowish white layer of volcanic ash that drifted to the ground like snowflakes after being belched from a volcano in Utah hundreds of miles away. Unlike most sediment, ash usually can be dated radiometrically. Geologists have extracted tiny, uranium-bearing zircon crystals from this thin layer, allowing them to date it and the surrounding Dakota sediment to 105 million years ago, providing an important age constraint. The Dakota is therefore 45 million years younger than the underlying Morrison Formation. As we descend the east side of Dinosaur Ridge to the famous set of dinosaur tracks, we will gather one clue after another in order to reconstruct the Front Range landscape of 105 million years ago. As you will see, a lot can change in 45 million years.

The Dakota consists mainly of tan to white sandstone layers 5 to 10 inches thick interbedded with thinly bedded, dark gray mudstones. The sandstones aren't lens shaped like those in the Morrison, providing the first clue that the Dakota formed in a different depositional environment. Another clue is the change in mudstone color, from the Morrison's striking reds, greens, and purples to the uniformly dark gray of the Dakota. The Morrison owes its extravagant palette of colors to ash from distant volcanoes that was stirred into the mud of the river floodplains and then chemically altered by groundwater. Clearly, based on the ash bed we are examining here, the volcanoes were still erupting when the Dakota was deposited, but the ash wasn't mixed with other sedimentary components in this depositional environment like it was on the Morrison floodplains.

The dark gray color of the Dakota mudstones is caused by large amounts of organic carbon. A few miles to the east, these same rocks are buried

The Dakota Group consists of interbedded sandstone (the tan to white, erosion-resistant layers) and thinly bedded, dark gray mudstone. The white to yellow layer of volcanic ash (its right side protected behind the Plexiglas barrier) has been radiometrically dated at 105 million years.

10,000 feet below the surface, deep enough to heat them up and cook the carbon into oil and natural gas. Over 800 million barrels of oil and 1.2 trillion cubic feet of natural gas have been extracted from the Dakota and other Cretaceous-age rocks in the Denver area, making it one of the biggest petroleum fields in the United States.

The Dakota's organic-rich layers provide important information about the environment in which they were laid down. Normally, when plants and animals die, their organic carbon is recycled into new living organisms, either through bacterial decomposition or by being eaten by other animals. However, in places where the oxygen supply is limited, this decomposition becomes so slow that significant amounts of tissue are buried, placing them out of the decomposers' reach. This effectively transfers carbon from the biosphere into rocks. The black mudstone tells us that 105 million years ago Dinosaur Ridge lay in a stagnant lake or ocean embayment, a setting where oxygen is plentiful at the surface, allowing plankton to thrive, but is not circulated deeper in the water, allowing tissue to accumulate.

Stop 4 provides another significant clue to the Dakota's depositional environment. Because the rock layers here tilt up to the west, the outcrops on the ridge's east side are not cross sections through the rock stack, but rather huge slabs representing an original sediment surface, conveniently tilted for you to see. About 50 yards after you round the corner and begin your northward descent down the ridge's east flank, look for a spectacular set of ripple marks that adorn a slab of orange sandstone. These ripple marks formed when a current shaped the loose sand one day 105 million years ago.

Geologists recently realized that the magnificent preservation of these ripples was likely due to the growth of bacterial mats that bound the sediment in place after it was sculpted by the water. Because they are photosynthetic, such mats could only thrive in shallow water. One logical question to ask is, what type of current formed these ripples? Luckily, the ripple marks' geometry can reveal this. Rivers and other currents that flow in one direction create asymmetrical ripple marks that are steeper on the downcurrent side. In contrast, oscillating, back-and-forth wave motion produces symmetrical ripples that possess sides of equal steepness. If you run your finger across these ripples, you will find that they are symmetrical, revealing that gentle waves once lapped a shoreline here. Many more perfectly preserved ripple marks exist en route to the tracks (stop 6). If you test a number of them with your finger, you will likely encounter a few asymmetrical ripple marks as well, because both kinds exist here.

Taken together, these clues suggest that 105 million years ago Dinosaur Ridge lay in a coastal setting. Rivers met the shore here, impressing their asymmetrical ripples onto the sand adjacent to the symmetrical ripples of the beach. As occurs along modern coastlines, sandbars and spits separated the main body of water from a series of shallow, stagnant lagoons where dead plankton accumulated, forming the black mudstones. But did this coastline rim a lake or a sea?

You will soon pass the spectacular dinosaur tracks, but before we examine them, let's gather one more clue that will tell us whether we are dealing with the shoreline of a freshwater lake or of a salty sea. Continue down the hill to an interpretive sign labeled "Mangrove Swamp" (stop 5). The sandstone bed here is creased with the impressions of several logs. Paleontologists have matched their characteristics with those of modern mangrove trees, which only grow in tropical and subtropical seacoast settings. Mangroves are exquisitely adapted to life along the seashore because, unlike most plants, they evolved mechanisms for excreting salt through their leaves, allowing them to grow in saltwater, which is toxic to their competitors.

The rocks have thus revealed that 105 million years ago Dinosaur Ridge lay along a tropical seacoast or saltwater lake. Ample evidence gathered from rocks of similar age tells us it was a sea, known as the Western Interior Seaway, which inundated the entire Midwest. Land lay to the west, and the sea stretched eastward from here to Illinois.

Backtrack a short distance to the spectacular trackway (stop 6), where we can see that dinosaurs roamed this coastline. Here a huge slab of tilted

These symmetrical ripple marks, along with other clues, show that the Dakota sandstone was deposited along the edge of an enormous inland seaway 105 million years ago.

sandstone is covered with 335 dinosaur prints comprising thirty-seven different trackways, each made by an individual dinosaur. Two different types are apparent: a bulbous, hooflike track made by an herbivorous duckbilled dinosaur, such as an iguanodon, and a sharp, birdlike, three-toed track belonging to an ostrich-sized meat eater called ornithomimus. The interpretive signs at this stop include artistic depictions of what these two dinosaurs looked like. Crocodile and bird tracks have also been discovered on Dinosaur Ridge, but they aren't visible here. Notable for their absence are giant apatosaur tracks like the ones you examined on the other side of the ridge. The apatosaurs that made those tracks during the Jurassic had died out by the Cretaceous, when these tracks were laid down.

Although dinosaur tracks are more common than fossilized bones, only a tiny fraction escape nature's eraser. Tracks can be preserved in two different ways. The first, the cover-up method, occurs when an animal makes a print in sediment that is moist but not completely saturated. If the print dries out and hardens, then is quickly buried by an influx of sediment—say, from a flood—it stands a good chance of being preserved. In a second scenario, known as the underprint, an animal is heavy enough to make an impression not just on the surface but also in underlying layers. Already buried, these deeper imprints have a greater chance of long-term preservation.

The sandstone slab at stop 6 is festooned with trackways made by two different kinds of dinosaurs. A duckbilled dinosaur made the more-abundant tracks, and ornithomimus made the more-slender, three-toed tracks.

Even if tracks are preserved, they may never be reexposed. The sediments hosting the prints must be buried deeply enough to transform into rock, but not so deeply that they are metamorphosed. Erosion must then strip off enough overlying rock to reveal the host layer, as well as removing sand grains that originally filled the fragile prints. Clearly, with such exacting conditions, most prints never become fossils, let alone come to light.

As the posted map here illustrates, the trackway patterns reveal key aspects of dinosaur behavior that could never be learned from bones alone. If you look carefully at the hooflike trackways made by the duckbilled dinosaur, you'll see that they consist of a succession of large imprints alternating with smaller prints of the same shape. These two different print sizes were made by the larger hind feet and smaller front feet of a dinosaur who crouched while walking. Duckbilled dinosaurs have been depicted in countless books as having walked on two legs, but these tracks reveal that they sometimes moved on all fours.

The trackways of the duckbilled dinosaurs go in two different directions. Six trackways, consisting of smaller prints, all run southeast, whereas trackways of larger prints run both northeast and southwest, perpendicular to the smaller dinosaurs' path. The parallel nature of the similarly sized trackways suggests that these duckbills traveled in herds, and the segregated sizes suggest that they mainly roamed with animals of either the same sex or the same age. Based on the track spacing, none of the herbivores were in a hurry; they were moving at just 2 miles per hour. The dozen sharper, three-toed, birdlike trackways belonging to the carnivorous ornithomimus (bird-mimic) dinosaurs indicate they may have been solitary predators who were moving faster, at about 5 miles per hour.

Although dinosaur trackways have been discovered at over one hundred sites in the High Plains, Dr. Martin Lockley, one of the world's foremost dinosaur trackers, ranks Dinosaur Ridge as one of the five most important sites in the region. He makes the case that this landmark is of such global significance that it, along with the nearby Triceratops Trail and Fossil Trace track site (vignette 8), should be designated a World Heritage Site.

Of all the High Plains track sites, 65 percent are Cretaceous in age, as are the tracks at stop 6. Stretching in a line from Boulder to Tucumcari, New Mexico, these sites all have sedimentary characteristics consistent with a beach environment like the one we have reconstructed at Dinosaur Ridge. Tracks are so frequent along this 300-mile-long beach that paleontologists have dubbed it the "dinosaur freeway," and some have proposed that herds of dinosaurs migrated up and down the coast of the Western Interior Seaway.

Before you depart, make sure to stop at the Friends of Dinosaur Ridge Visitor Center, located another 0.5 mile beyond the trackway. The center has displays of interest to dinosaur enthusiasts of all ages and an excellent selection of dinosaur-related books. Another worthwhile stop is the natural history museum in the nearby town of Morrison. There you can watch paleontologists liberating bones from some of the blocks of rock that Marsh's men excavated during the peak of the Bone Wars. If Dinosaur Ridge's history is any guide, we can expect some of these bones to produce further stunning revelations about the life and times of the majestic creatures who cruised Denver's dinosaur freeway 150 to 100 million years ago.

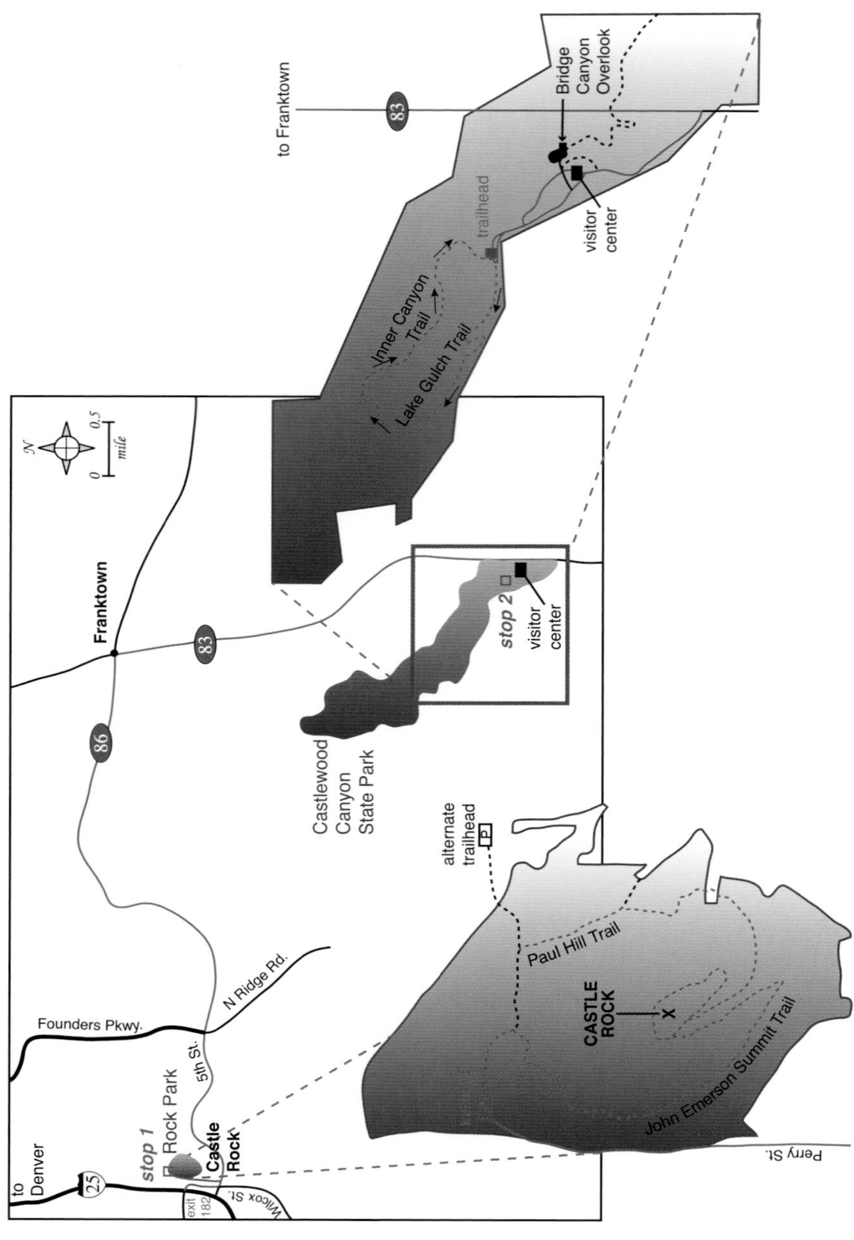

GETTING THERE: Stop 1 is in Castle Rock's Rock Park. Exit I-25 at Wolfensberger Road/Wilcox Street (exit 182). Turn left (east) at the top of the exit ramp, and once over the I-25 bridge turn right (south) onto Wilcox Street. Go 0.4 mile to 5th Street. Turn left on 5th and take the next left (0.1 mile) onto Perry Street. Follow Perry 0.5 mile and turn right (east) into the Rock Park parking lot. Follow the trail 0.1 mile to a junction. From here both the left and right (east and west) trails reach the base of a cliff in 0.5 mile, with 370 feet of elevation gain. The eastern (left) fork is a gentler hike. Once at the base of the cliff, a flat, 0.2-mile trail circumnavigates the rock exposure.

11

A LEGACY OF FIRE AND FLOOD

The Wall Mountain Tuff and the Castle Rock Conglomerate

Nestled among the peaceful pines carpeting the Palmer Divide, the high mesa separating Denver from Colorado Springs, lie two rock layers that tell extraordinary tales of this tranquil area's more turbulent past. Two vastly different kinds of devastating torrents ravaged the area 36 million years ago. The first was an ash flow spawned by a volcanic eruption whose intensity dwarfed Mount St. Helens in 1980—or, for that matter, any other modern volcanic eruption you can name. The rock layer that records this ash flow is the Wall Mountain tuff. A short time later the second kind of torrent, repeated flash floods of titanic proportions, swept the Castle Rock area. Like the eruption that preceded them, these flash floods overshadow their modern counterparts, including the one that devastated the Big Thompson Canyon west of Fort Collins in 1976 (vignette 4). The rock layer that preserves the legacy of these floods is the Castle Rock conglomerate, which overlies the Wall Mountain tuff.

Stop 2 is at Castlewood Canyon State Park. From stop 1, return to 5th Street and turn left (east). As it leaves the town of Castle Rock, 5th turns into CO 86. Continue on CO 86 for 7 miles to its junction with CO 83 in Franktown. Turn right (south) onto CO 83 and travel 5 miles to the park's entrance. Turn right and follow the park road to the entrance station and visitor center. In order to hike amidst the Castle Rock conglomerate (recommended), drive 0.7 mile to the Canyon Point parking area. Hike the Lake Gulch Trail into the canyon and return via the Inner Canyon Trail. This 2-mile loop is rated moderately difficult; the park brochure shows the route. A shorter, handicap-accessible alternative that offers good views of the conglomerate but does not allow access into the canyon is the 200-yard, paved path to the Bridge Canyon Overlook. The Bridge Canyon parking area is immediately behind the visitor center.

To fully appreciate what the Front Range landscape of 36 million years ago looked like, and how it came to be, we need to journey a bit further back in time—to the uplift of the Front Range about 65 million years ago. During a tectonic episode known as the Laramide orogeny, the range rose on the back of a reverse fault, a break in the Earth's crust that accommodates compression.

At stop 1, the hike up to the final cliff of Castle Rock ascends a cone of crumbling white sandstone that was shed northeastward off the rising Pikes Peak mountain block during the Laramide uplift. This distinctive white sandstone, traditionally called the Dawson arkose, is widespread along the I-25 corridor between Denver and Colorado Springs. It consists of hard, clear to white quartz and pink feldspar. Both minerals were derived almost exclusively from the Pikes Peak Batholith, an enormous, 1,080-million-year-old plug of granite that forms the southern Front Range (vignette 14).

Uplift ceased along the Front Range about 53 million years ago. Erosion of the newly risen peaks dominated the next chapter of the geologic story. But the extent to which these mountains were worn down is still a topic of spirited debate (vignette 2). Our inability to precisely reconstruct Colorado's landscape of 50 to 40 million years ago stems mainly from the lack of rocks dating from that time. We pick up the story's thread once again with the eruption of the Wall Mountain tuff. As the sun rose over the Front Range one day 36.7 million years ago, it illuminated a landscape of modest mountains that diminished in relief toward the east until they merged almost seamlessly with the Great Plains. Geologists commonly call this ancient topographic surface the Rocky Mountain Erosion Surface. One mountain, tucked into the folds of the highest peaks near present-day Buena Vista, was unusually restless that day. Magma had been swelling beneath it for some time, and on this day that magma reached the surface in an eruption of titanic proportions.

The volcano injected a huge plume of volcanic ash high into the atmosphere. The lighter particles were swept along by the jet stream, which carried them far to the east, until they eventually drifted to the ground like snow. In the volcano's immediate vicinity, gravity tugged the larger, heavier ash particles back to Earth. As this cloud of hot, glowing ash collapsed, it trapped beneath it a cushion of air, which allowed the ash cloud to glide over the landscape like an air hockey puck. The ash flow barreled down the mountain slopes so fast that it took just one to two hours to reach the Great Plains, 65 miles away. As the still-hot ash slowly ground to a halt, it welded together to form the Wall Mountain tuff.

Erosion began to chip away at the tuff as soon as it solidified, but remnants of this hard, resistant rock still cap scattered mesas between Castle Rock and Monument and form larger outcrops in the mountains all the way to the Sawatch Range's Mt. Princeton, where the ancient volcano once stood. These remnants are between 15 and 100 feet thick and are spread over 3,000 square miles, dimensions that testify to the vast quantity of magma and ash erupted that day. The fact that there is no abrupt step in elevation preserved in these rock scraps, where the ash tumbled off the Rockies and onto the Great Plains, also testifies that there was no sharp topographic boundary between those two provinces then, as there is today.

The tuff contains the bones of brontotheres (extinct mammals that resembled rhinoceroses but were more closely related to horses) unfortunate enough to have been grazing in river bottoms when the ash engulfed them. The bones and precise radiometric dating peg the eruption at 36.7 million years ago, in the very late Eocene epoch. To the east, the ash layer thins and large (and hence heavy) crystals are sparse, indicating the ash's eastward flow.

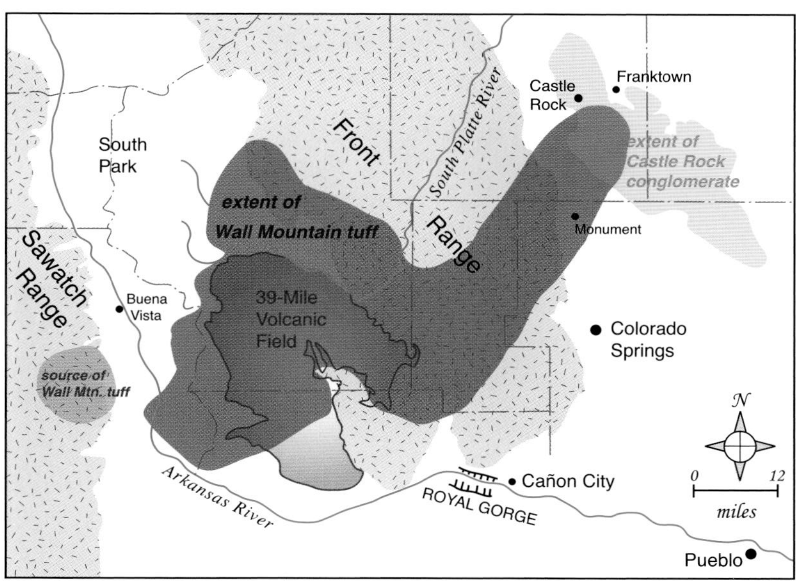

The huge extent of the Wall Mountain tuff, shown here in green, testifies to the enormous size of the volcanic eruption from which the ash emanated. The orange patch delineates the outcrop area of the Castle Rock conglomerate.

It is difficult to glimpse a true outcrop of the Wall Mountain tuff in the Palmer Divide area because the stone has either been quarried away or is privately owned. But it is still easy to examine the tuff up close at stop 1. The sheer cliff that caps the butte of Castle Rock consists of Castle Rock conglomerate. Notice the rounded cobbles and boulders composed of various rock types embedded in the walls. The biggest clasts of all are anything but round. Rather, they are jagged, angular blocks of pink tuff up to 8 feet

Many of Denver's historic buildings, including Trinity Methodist Church, are made of Wall Mountain tuff. The tuff's origin as a glowing ash flow makes it a uniform, strong, and valuable building stone.

The Castle Rock conglomerate forms a cliff that overhangs the crumbly, white Dawson arkose (dashed box shows location of inset photo). The large, angular blocks embedded in the conglomerate (inset) are pieces of Wall Mountain tuff.

long. Some of the biggest and easiest to scrutinize lie just below the overhang on Castle Rock's north side.

The eruption of the Wall Mountain tuff was the opening volley in a protracted volcanic maelstrom known as the Ignimbrite Flare-up, which engulfed the American West. The flare-up was one of the most extensive episodes of high-silica volcanism the world has ever witnessed, and Colorado was at the heart of the action, with numerous volcanoes erupting in the San Juan, West Elk, Sawatch, Never Summer, and South Park areas. Gigantic calderas, the biggest and most violent of all volcanoes, erupted throughout the American West, with seventeen of the forty biggest eruptions documented anywhere in the world having taken place during this episode. Colorado alone hosted six of these biggest eruptions, including the Wall Mountain tuff, with a volume of 240 cubic miles. The cause of all this volcanic activity is not completely understood, but it appears to be tied to a fundamental transition in Colorado's tectonic history, from a compressional setting to one of extension.

For about 200 million years, a subduction zone—a boundary where a dense oceanic plate dives hundreds of miles beneath a more buoyant plate—had existed off the west coast of North America. The Laramide orogeny was likely triggered by an unusual shallowing of the angle at which the down-going plate was subducting. The angle became so shallow that the down-going plate actually scraped along the bottom of the overriding plate, thrusting up the Rocky Mountains in the process (vignette 8). The episode of shallow-angled subduction ended about 40 to 45 million years ago, at which point the subducting slab began to sink deeper into the mantle once more. As the slab sank, hot asthenosphere replaced it, triggering partial melting of the nearby mantle and lower crust. It was the extensive pools of magma thus formed that fueled the outpouring of high-silica volcanic ash the state witnessed 37 to 24 million years ago.

So why are such large, jagged blocks of Wall Mountain tuff like those you see here embedded in the Castle Rock conglomerate? The answer is a profound shift—from torrents of ash to torrents of water—that occurred in the Castle Rock area. The presence of the tuff in the conglomerate constitutes incontrovertible evidence that the conglomerate is younger than the tuff. Thanks to the discovery of the fossilized remains of a titanothere (a mammal that superficially resembled a rhinoceros and went extinct at the end of the Eocene epoch), we know that the conglomerate was deposited sometime between 33.9 and 36.7 million years ago. Because it is younger, the Castle Rock should lie above the tuff in the rock stack, and in some places it does in fact rest directly on the tuff. At stop 1, though, the Castle Rock conglomerate lies on top of the Dawson arkose, the crumbly white rock. This relationship is actually the norm at most locations, and in places the conglomerate rests 300 feet *below* the Wall Mountain tuff. How can this discrepancy be explained?

By mapping the area, geologists have discovered that not long after the tuff encased the landscape, southeast-flowing rivers cut canyons through the concrete-like rock. These river canyons were quite deep; in many places they were carved clear through the tuff into the underlying Dawson arkose. Floods that periodically raged through the canyons undercut the nearly vertical walls, sending landslides of tuff blocks careening into the floodwaters, where the huge, jagged chunks intermingled with rocks whose edges had been rounded during their lengthy residence in the river channel. Once cemented, this gravel became today's Castle Rock conglomerate.

The best place to observe the power of these ancient floods is Castlewood Canyon (stop 2). Whether you stroll to the Bridge Canyon Overlook or descend into Lake Gulch, you will see canyon walls that consist of 10-foot-thick sediment layers that sweep across the cliff faces and are inclined relative to adjacent layers. This scalloped bedding pattern is called crossbedding. Modern settings show that crossbed layers tilt down in the direction the water flowed during sediment deposition. Note how most of the layers here tilt down toward the southeast, documenting the southeasterly flow of the river that drained this area approximately 35 million years ago.

Artist Jan Vriesen's depiction of a flood roaring through the Castle Rock area in a canyon carved through the Wall Mountain tuff. Blocks of tuff tumbled from the vertical canyon walls and became embedded in the gravel deposits of the floods. —Courtesy of the Denver Museum of Nature and Science

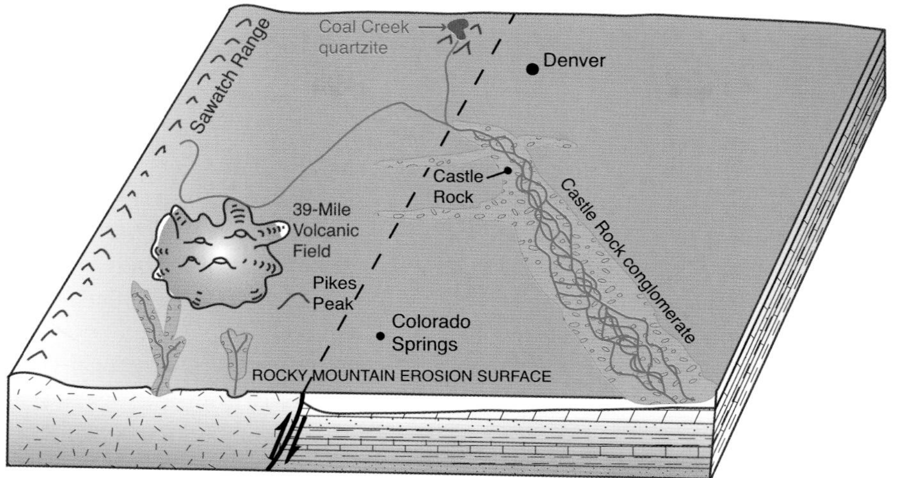

Rivers draining the upland to the west deposited the Castle Rock conglomerate. At least one tributary river had its source near modern-day Coal Creek Canyon, because that is the source for the blue quartzite clasts present in the conglomerate.

Large crossbeds in the Castle Rock conglomerate on the Lake Gulch Trail (looking northeast) show that the ancient river that deposited these sediments flowed southeast.

If you choose to descend into Lake Gulch and return to your car via the Inner Canyon Trail, you can closely examine many blocks of Castle Rock conglomerate. Here it contains rounded pebbles, cobbles, and boulders up to 2 feet across, plus larger, angular blocks of Wall Mountain tuff, all embedded in very coarse quartz sand. The rounded clasts consist of several rock types: granite, gneiss, red sandstone, and bullet-hard, smooth, bluish gray quartzite. The clasts were rounded by collisions with other rocks during floods as the raging waters transported them here from the subdued mountains to the west—the only possible source for the boulders contained within the conglomerate.

The size of the clasts is directly related to the energy of the currents that transported them. It is extremely rare to find a river deposit that contains such abundant, far-traveled (and hence well-rounded) clasts that are as big as the ones you see here. Geologists have conducted controlled flume experiments to determine just how fast a current must be to transport clasts of a given size. To move the 2-foot-diameter boulders, the water velocity must have been at least 20 feet per second (13.5 miles per hour)—a speed comparable to the 1976 Big Thompson flood, which at 20 to 25 feet per second was a catastrophe so big that it only happens every few thousand years.

While the rounded clasts embedded in the Castle Rock conglomerate traveled long distances, the still-jagged blocks of tuff came from the collapse of nearby canyon walls.

As you examine the conglomerate along your walk, take note of the rock types composing the clasts, as they reveal what rock types were exposed upstream. The brick-red sandstone clasts were eroded from the Fountain Formation, which guards the east flank of the Rockies 15 miles west of Castlewood Canyon. The granite and gneiss were derived from the mountains' crystalline core, which lies even farther away. But the most startling story comes from the bluish gray quartzite clasts. This 1,700-million-year-old rock is exposed in only one place along the entire Front Range, in a narrow strip of foothills between Coal Creek and Eldorado canyons (vignette 5), several miles north of Golden. That means that the 2-foot quartzite boulders here were transported over 46 miles from their source, and the floodwaters had to be moving at least 13.5 mph every inch of the way! Even more astounding, blocks of this quartzite up to 6.5 feet long have been found embedded in the Castle Rock conglomerate a few miles north of the town of Castle Rock, a good 34 miles downstream of their source. It takes a current moving over 27 miles per hour to move blocks that size. To put these floods into perspective, no boulders this size were carried more than a few hundred yards out onto the Great Plains by the Big Thompson flood, and no boulders of comparable size are found more than 3 miles east of the mountain front along the floodplain of *any* modern Colorado river.

What on Earth unleashed these unbelievable floods? Unfortunately, we don't really know. Geologists have found contemporaneous flood deposits with similarly monstrous boulders all the way from central Wyoming to South Park, indicating that such floods were a regional phenomenon during the latest Eocene epoch.

Two hypotheses have emerged as leading candidates. One possibility is that volcanic landslides or lava flows associated with the Ignimbrite Flare-up dammed rivers. Eventually, the dams burst, sending walls of water down the newly freed rivers. We know that such volcanic dams existed (vignette 12), but nobody has yet demonstrated conclusively that failure of those dams is what triggered the floods. One flood could not have moved the 2-foot boulders 46 miles, so if failed volcanic dams were the cause of the floodwaters that deposited the conglomerate at stop 2, the dams must have failed and rebuilt repeatedly.

The other possibility is that the same mechanism that creates most flash floods along the Front Range foothills today was also the trigger 35 million years ago. Today's dominant airflow across Colorado is from west to east, so that is the direction major winter storms sweep across the state. But because the relentless summer sunshine heats up the land in Colorado much faster than it heats up the waters of the Gulfs of Mexico and California, summer air pressure over Colorado is less than that over the gulfs. In a phenomenon known as the North American monsoon—a similar but less intense version of the Indian monsoon—this pressure difference draws moisture from the gulfs into Colorado. This combination can lead to intense, very localized storms that cause flash floods in the Front Range's narrow canyons, such as the devastating Big Thompson flood in 1976.

Bed after bed of conglomerate along the Inner Canyon Trail contains boulders up to 2 feet across. It's sobering to consider that each bed signifies the passage of a flood bigger than the Big Thompson. If monsoon storms were the cause of the floods, during the late Eocene the North American monsoon must have been vastly stronger than the one we see today, probably at least as vigorous as the present Indian monsoon.

The simple, quiet beauty that the Wall Mountain tuff and the Castle Rock conglomerate lend today's Palmer Divide belie the turbulent tales they have to tell of the far more violent and dynamic central Colorado that existed during the late Eocene. Life would have indeed been dangerous back then. Fortunately, living as we do 35 million years after the violence subsided, we can relax and enjoy the beautiful topography these cataclysmic events helped shape.

12

AN EXTRAORDINARY FOSSIL ECOSYSTEM
Florissant Fossil Beds National Monument

Your shirt is soaked with sweat as you clamber up the small granite knob rising above the north flank of the West Fourmile Creek valley. The time is 34.1 million years ago, and it is yet another in a long string of hot, humid late Eocene days. Despite the cloying heat, you press on, occasionally swatting away the pesky insects that swarm around your head. After cresting the knob you peer west, eager for your first glimpse of the towering Guffey Volcano, which has been hidden by the thick redwood forest through which you have been thrashing. Your breath catches as you spot the mountain's symmetric cone rising majestically above the forest.

All is peaceful now, but the mountain will not be quiet for long. As a time traveler, you know the mountain will soon unleash a powerful lahar, a volcanic mudflow, which will roar down this valley at speeds reaching 100 miles per hour. That lahar will set in motion a chain of geologic events destined to fossilize over 1,700 species of flora and fauna, most of them delicate, rarely preserved insects. But you don't need to be a literal time traveler to appreciate the extraordinary biological diversity of late Eocene Colorado; it is on display today and, crucially, protected from theft within the borders of Florissant Fossil Beds National Monument.

Florissant's fossil treasure trove provides an extraordinarily detailed glimpse of ancient ecosystem dynamics. Of equal importance, Florissant's fossils constitute a crucial anchor point for climate scientists seeking to pinpoint exactly when the most precipitous cooling event to sweep the globe during the last 100 million years occurred. And what's more, the fossils serve up a tantalizing clue to the uplift history of the modern Rocky Mountains. These are indeed important fossils. Let's start our exploration with a look at the volcano whose activity precipitated this fortuitous fossilization.

Physically, the valley of West Fourmile Creek has changed surprisingly little since the late Eocene. Gazing west today, up the valley from stop 1, you see a cluster of low hills. These are the remnants of the mighty Guffey

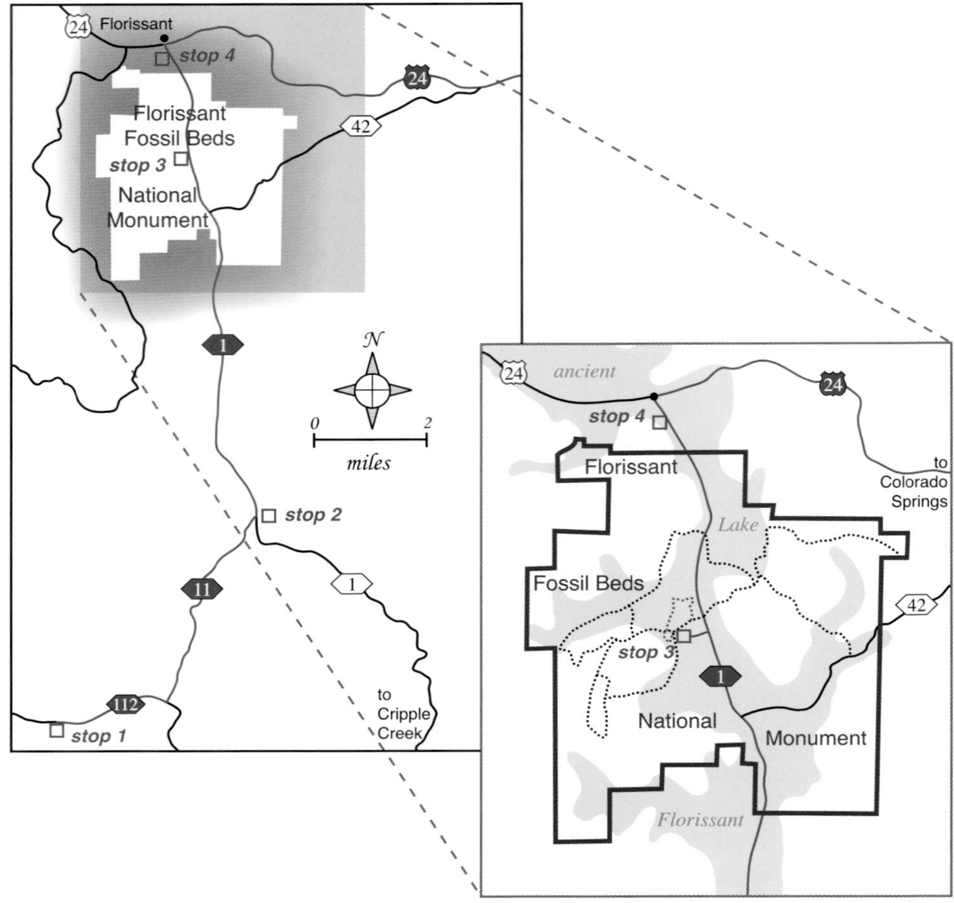

GETTING THERE: From Colorado Springs travel west about 33 miles on US 24 to the town of Florissant. To reach stop 1, turn left (south) onto County Road 1, marked as the Gold Belt Byway. Travel south for 9.1 miles, passing through Florissant Fossil Beds National Monument, and turn right (west) onto County Road 11. Follow it 4.1 miles and turn right onto County Road 112. Follow this road west up the West Fourmile Creek valley for about 2.4 miles to the Teller-Park county line, where the road name changes to County Road 102. Continue another 0.4 mile and turn left into a small dirt parking lot. Cross the road and follow a dirt path that heads north from a small, green electrical box. After 40 yards the trail descends into a small creek. Instead of descending, turn left (west) and hike 20 yards to the top of a low granite mound that offers a view up the West Fourmile Creek valley.

To reach stop 2, retrace your path back to the junction of county roads 1 and 11. Turn right (south) and after 0.1 mile turn right into Teller County's Four Mile Scenic Park. Cross the footbridge and walk across the field to County Road 1. When you reach

Volcano, a stratovolcano that loomed over this spot. Like its modern siblings Mt. Shasta and Mt. Fuji, the Guffey Volcano was tall and steep sided. Those steep slopes, along with the inherent instability of the volcanic material, caused the volcano's flanks to periodically collapse. Not surprisingly, eruptions trigger such collapses, as occurred during the 1980 Mount St. Helens eruption. But stratovolcanoes can also collapse without an eruption, for instance, in response to a mild earthquake or a heavy rainstorm. On a fateful day 34.1 million years ago, one such collapse sent a roiling torrent of mud and debris roaring down this valley toward your present location.

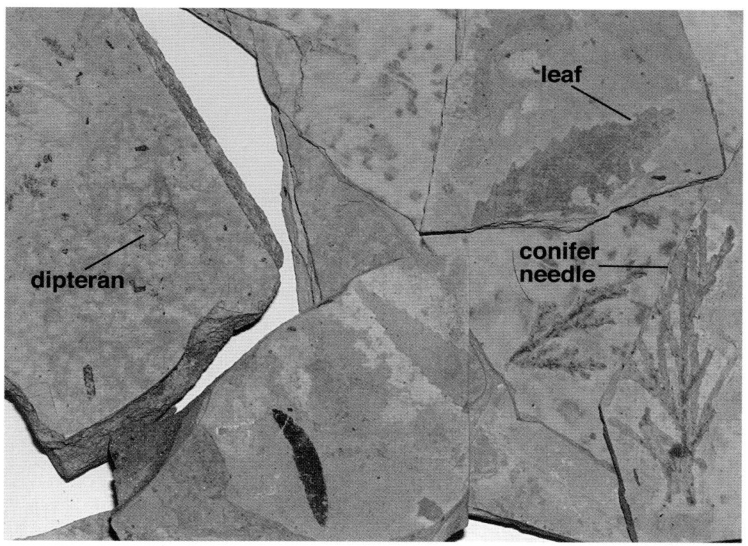

Fossils preserved on these pieces of the Florissant Formation hint at the ecological diversity on display in Florissant Fossil Beds National Monument. They include a dipteran (a mosquito relative), the leaves of several hardwood trees, and conifer needles.

it, turn right (south) and walk to the road cut exposed in a low hill. Stop 3 is at the visitor center for Florissant Fossil Beds National Monument. From stop 2 backtrack north on County Road 1 for 6.7 miles and turn left (west) onto the clearly marked visitor center access road. You reach the parking lot in 0.25 mile. An entrance fee is collected in the visitor center. Stop 4 is at the privately owned Florissant Fossil Quarry, where you must pay a fee to enter. From the visitor center, return to County Road 1, turn left (north), and travel 2.3 miles to a gated dirt road with a sign announcing this as the quarry entrance (see florissantfossils.tripod.com for more information).

The hills west of stop 1 are the remnants of the once-large Guffey Volcano.

The mass of volcanic mud and debris surged down the valley for more than 12 miles before grinding to a halt at the confluence of West Fourmile Creek and an ancient, south-flowing creek that, at the time, meandered through the location of modern Lake George and Florissant Fossil Beds National Monument, both of which are north of here. The lahar dammed the south-flowing creek, creating ancient Lake Florissant, a long and narrow lake about 1 mile wide and 12 miles long. Ultimately, over 1,700 species were embedded and pristinely preserved in the sediments that accumulated on the floor of this lake. But before we examine these, let's first head to stop 2 to take a look at the ancient lahar deposit.

Beautifully exposed in a road cut through a low, grass- and tree-covered mound, the lahar deposit displays rock chunks of many sizes embedded in a matrix of loose, crumbly mud. When the lahar was flowing, the waterlogged mud provided the support necessary to transport the big blocks of rock. Most of the blocks are angular chunks of dark andesite, the material that composed the stratovolcano. The few blocks of pink granite in the road cut were likely boulders swept up by the lahar as it roared through West Fourmile Creek valley.

Lahars triggered by flank collapse are common and recurrent events on stratovolcanoes. After Lake Florissant was formed by one flow, others

The lahar deposit consists of andesite (dark) and granite (pink) boulders embedded in a matrix of mud and sand.

followed. One lahar preserved the national monument's most visually arresting attraction: a stand of petrified stumps, which you can see along the 1-mile-long Petrified Forest Loop at stop 3. If you don't have time for the entire walk, several spectacular examples stand behind the visitor center along the trail's first 100 yards, which is wheelchair accessible.

Amazingly, the stumps stand rooted in the exact spots where the trees grew! Like most of the monument's fossil stumps, those along the trail belonged to ancient redwood trees. The dense forest that grew around Lake Florissant 34.1 million years ago contained a mixture of conifers and hardwoods, and stumps belonging to five different species of hardwood have also been discovered. The fossil redwood stumps are closely related to California's coastal redwoods, and in life they were just as big and majestic as their modern cousins. Florissant's biggest redwood stump has a titanic circumference of 38 feet!

All of the stumps are about 15 feet high, but the trees themselves, like modern redwoods, were much taller. Why did the bottom 15 feet of these trees petrify, but not the rest? It turns out that a small lahar swept down the Guffey Volcano and buried the trees to a depth of about 15 feet. Groundwater that seeped slowly through the lahar deposit dissolved shards of silica glass. That silica-rich water then percolated through the buried stumps, whose organic content altered the local chemical environment from one in which silica dissolves to one in which silica precipitates out of solution. This silica precipitation occurred so slowly that individual crystals grew to fill individual cells in the stumps, turning them to stone. This methodical replacement preserved the anatomical detail of the stumps for posterity.

From the fossil stumps, the Petrified Forest and Ponderosa loops form a triangle. Walk the eastern leg of this triangle about 30 yards, to a fork (the other leg of the triangle), and turn left. A low outcrop of mudstone

Florissant's Big Stump is one of the largest redwood stumps in the monument.

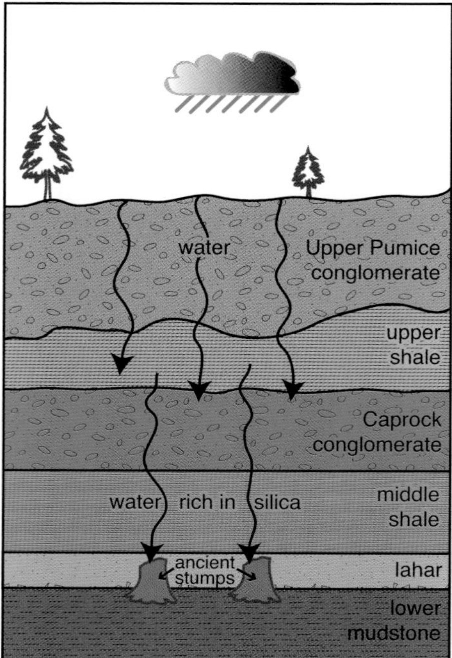

The silica of which the tree stumps are now made came from the dissolution of volcanic ash by groundwater. The silica precipitated from the groundwater and crystallized slowly in the cells of the original tree. Later erosion exposed the stumps. Many fossils are preserved in the middle and upper shales. The Caprock conglomerate is the product of a second lahar, and the Upper Pumice conglomerate consists of abundant volcanic debris that was washed into the lake during a period of more intensive volcanic activity.

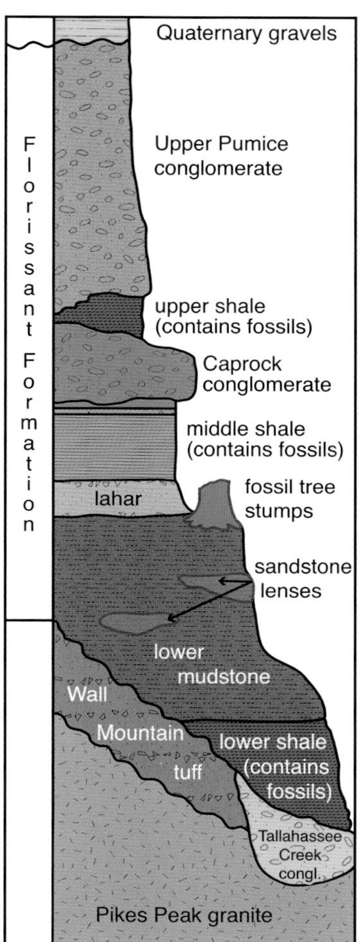

Fossil leaves and insects are concentrated in three separate shale layers within the Florissant Formation. The rocks at stop 3 belong to the middle shale unit; those at stop 4 belong to the lower shale unit. The petrified stumps lie encased in lahar muds belonging to the lower mudstone unit. (Modified from Evanoff et al., 2001; and Meyer, 2003.)

lies behind a split-rail fence on your right, at the base of a low hill. These thinly bedded sedimentary layers, part of the middle shale of the Florissant Formation, accumulated in the quiet waters of Lake Florissant. This rock is known as paper shale because each layer is barely thicker than a sheet of paper. As you will discover at stop 4, it is easy to part the rock along these layers to reveal abundant fossils. Each "sheet" of shale is actually a couplet consisting of a thin clay layer (derived from the chemical alteration of volcanic ash) bonded to a thin layer of diatoms.

Diatoms are single-celled plankton housed in protective silica shells. Ancient Lake Florissant's water chemistry was perfectly formulated to support vigorous plankton blooms consisting of billions of diatoms. Those diatoms secreted a film of sticky mucus that would have made the lake a most unpleasant swimming hole! But diatom mucus plays a prominent role in one of the leading hypotheses for how Florissant's amazing fossil trove formed. Scientists envision that leaves, insects, and spiders blown or washed into the lake were immediately enveloped by this sticky mucus, which sealed them off from the corrosive effects of oxygen and the decomposition wrought by the aerobic bacteria that breathe it. Along with their precious plant and animal cargo, the mucus blobs sank to the floor of the lake. The slow rain of sediment compressed the fossils, clay, and diatom shells into the Florissant Formation's paper shales.

Over forty thousand Florissant specimens are housed in museums around the world. Return now to the small visitor center, where you can examine a collection of these exquisitely detailed insect and plant fossils, along with a few vertebrates. You can also watch a movie explaining how they were preserved.

The diversity of Florissant's plant fossils are impressive, representing a variety of habitats ranging from moist lowlands near the lakeshore to the drier slopes of the surrounding hills. Preserved in the ancient lakebeds were the leaves, fruits, seeds, flowers, and pollen from 140 different species of plants. The flora includes eleven species of conifer trees, among them the famous redwood stumps, but over one hundred species of hardwoods dominate the fossils (five species preserved as stumps), including representatives of the elm, willow, beech, rose, and walnut families, among others. Paleontologists have even discovered palm fronds and pollen belonging to a member of the sunflower family. This sunflower pollen is the oldest fossil evidence ever found for what is today one of Earth's largest plant families, offering a tantalizing glimpse of its evolutionary dawn.

As impressive as Florissant's plant fossils are, their diversity pales in comparison to that of the insects. Because insects lack bones and other hard parts, they rarely fossilize, so to find even one is noteworthy. With over 1,500 different species of fossil insects and spiders having been described from Florissant, its record is one of the best in the world. Flying ants and beetles are especially abundant and diverse, but Florissant's ancient lakebeds also host flies, spiders, moths, butterflies, and the first fossil tsetse fly ever found. These exceptionally delicate fossils are so well preserved that exquisite details remain intact, right down to the individual lenses in a fly's compound eye!

Vertebrate fossils are comparatively sparse in the Florissant record, but they are by no means absent. Catfish, pirate perch, suckers, and bowfin, among others, swam in Lake Florissant. The skies above the lake were home to birds, including the cuckoo, the roller, and at least three other species. A diverse abundance of mammals undoubtedly inhabited Florissant's forests, but few of them were unlucky enough to fall in the lake where they could be preserved. One unfortunate vertebrate, however, was a small opossum. A few mammal fragments—of a small horse, an oreodont

A sumac leaf (Rhus) *from the Florissant Formation. Each mark on the scale is 1 millimeter. (FLFO6223b.)* —Photograph by Lindsay J. Walker, provided courtesy of Florissant Fossil Beds National Monument

Even fossil insects as delicate as this fly (Tabanus?) *are preserved in the Florissant shales. Each mark on the scale is 1 millimeter. (FLFO4039a.)* —Photograph by Lindsay J. Walker, provided courtesy of Florissant Fossil Beds National Monument

Among the fish that inhabited Lake Florissant was the pirate perch (Trichophanes foliarum). *Each mark on the scale is 1 millimeter. (FLFO497.)* —Photograph by Lindsay J. Walker, provided courtesy of Florissant Fossil Beds National Monument

(a sheep-sized browsing animal that looked superficially like a hog), and a brontothere (an extinct family that resembled rhinoceroses)—have been recovered from riverbank deposits within the Florissant Formation.

Florissant's extraordinary fossil diversity bequeaths a special significance to the site. Unlike localities with less diversity, here paleontologists can study the ecological interactions that existed between contemporaneous species 34 million years ago. Of particular interest are the abundant insect feeding-traces preserved on fossil leaves. Scientists examine the pattern of damage insects inflicted on the Florissant leaves to study how plant-insect interactions have changed over geologic time. Interestingly, many of the fossilized patterns are nearly identical to those made by the same classes of insect on modern leaves.

Another observation that keenly interests scientists is the fact that the mixture of fossil plant and insect groups does not resemble any modern assemblage. Some of Florissant's fossil taxa are closely related to species that today live only in the subtropics of Asia, Africa, or Mexico. Others resemble those adapted to cool temperate conditions like those at Florissant today. The mix of organisms that lived along the shores of ancient Lake Florissant does not seem to exist anywhere in the modern world, perhaps because identical climatic and ecological conditions no longer exist.

This uniqueness of the Florissant region's biota compels us to ask, what has changed in the last 34 million years? A primary suspect is climate. The rich floral diversity of the fossils provides scientists with a real shot at determining the paleoclimate that existed when the Florissant forests grew. However, deducing ancient climate from the plant assemblage is no easy task. The first serious attempt to extract this information was Harry MacGinitie's landmark monograph on Florissant's fossil plants, published in 1953. MacGinitie carefully classified each member of the Florissant paleobotanical community and identified its nearest living relative. He then compiled climatic data on these nearest living relatives and synthesized the information to arrive at the conclusion that the climate of the region 34 million years ago was highly seasonal, with most of the area's 20-inch annual rainfall arriving during hot (more than 80°F), wet summers. He calculated that the mean annual temperature was greater than 65°F, dramatically warmer than the modern mean annual temperature of 39°F. MacGinitie believed the former climate resembled modern subtropical areas like Mexico's Sierra Madre, northeastern Australia, and northwestern India.

In the years since MacGinitie's work, new methods for extracting paleotemperature estimates from fossil plants have been devised. More recent work has revised his mean annual temperature estimate downward to about 52 to 56°F. Nevertheless, all scientists agree that Florissant was a much warmer place 34 million years ago. Why was it so much warmer then? Two possible explanations leap immediately to mind. The first is that the geography of Florissant back then was similar to what it is today, but Earth's global climate has cooled dramatically in the interim. Given that Florissant now stands at an elevation of 8,200 feet, the other logical explanation is that it stood at a much lower elevation back then, before the Rocky Mountains were uplifted to their present, cooler elevation. Both the history of global climate and the uplift history of the Rockies are questions of keen interest to geologists, so it is clear that Florissant's fossils possess profound significance even beyond the detailed paleoecology they reveal.

MacGinitie concluded that Lake Florissant stood at a low elevation. Using his "closest living relatives" technique, he was convinced that ancient Lake Florissant formed between 1,000 to 3,000 feet, suggesting that the region has been raised at least 5,000 feet in the intervening 34 million years. Geologists know that the Rocky Mountains were first elevated about 65 million years ago during the Laramide orogeny (vignettes 8, 16), so if MacGinitie is correct, this Laramide version of the Rockies must have been almost completely eroded away, then the modern range rose later in the same location, raising the Florissant region with it. Many geologists believe this is exactly what happened. Others are skeptical, wondering what mechanism triggered the most recent uplift event (see vignette 2 for more about this debate). Regardless of how it's settled, the Florissant fossils provide a crucial piece of evidence for this debate.

Since MacGinitie's work in 1953, scientists have conducted much more research on global paleoclimate. We now know that Earth's climate is dramatically cooler today than it was 34.1 million years ago. Records from every continent and many places in the world's oceans agree that the Eocene epoch, when Lake Florissant existed, was much warmer (vignette 17). That means that the warmth-loving fossil species found in the Lake Florissant strata could possibly have lived at higher elevations at the time. Therefore, in order to use the Florissant fossil data to constrain the uplift history of the Rockies, we must first correct our data for the global cooling that has occurred in the interim. Several scientists have done just that, concluding that 34 million years ago Florissant stood at an elevation between 6,200 and 13,400 feet. If these estimates (which are not universally agreed upon) are correct, then Florissant was raised to its present elevation earlier than MacGinitie thought. The paleoelevation derived from the Florissant fossils pertains only to the immediate vicinity, but realistically, if Florissant sat at a high elevation 34 million years ago, it is very likely that the entire Front Range did, too. The conclusion would be that today's Rocky Mountains may well be the work of the Laramide orogeny after all, not the product of a separate, more recent uplift, as many geologists had concluded based, in large part, on MacGinitie's work.

Climate scientists would also dearly love to know when, exactly, the climate cooled in one region versus another. Was the cooling synchronous, or did regions cool at different rates? It is crucial to determine the timing and the pattern of global cooling if scientists are to determine what caused it. High-resolution climate records derived from seafloor sediment cores indicate that the oceans cooled dramatically right at the transition from the Eocene to the Oligocene epoch (33.9 million years ago). Did Colorado cool at the same time? Fortunately for scientists, although Florissant provides the richest trove of fossil leaves in Colorado, it is not the state's only deposit. Other excellent localities of slightly different ages exist in the Green River Formation at Douglas Pass (north of Grand Junction), in South Park's Antero Formation, in the Pitch-Pinnacle beds just west of Monarch Pass, and in the Creede Formation near the town of Creede. Results from studies of the older Green River fossils agree with those from Florissant that Colorado's climate during the Eocene epoch was very warm until 34.1 million years ago. The Antero Formation fossils, a mere 200,000 years younger than Florissant's, suggest that Colorado's climate cooled sharply sometime during the 200,000 years prior to the Eocene-Oligocene time boundary. The younger, Oligocene-age Creede fossil flora confirms that the Oligocene was a much cooler time in Colorado.

Because the Antero fossil assemblage is much less abundant and diverse than Florissant's, interpretations based on it must be made cautiously. Nevertheless, comparison of the reconstructed Florissant and Antero paleotemperatures suggests that temperatures in Colorado plunged sometime between 34.1 and 33.9 million years ago, followed very soon thereafter by cooler temperatures in the oceans and most other continental areas. Most geologists believe that multiple factors are responsible for the dramatic global cooling, but the straw that broke the camel's back may well have been the separation of Australia and South America from Antarctica due to plate tectonic movement. The physical isolation of Antarctica at the pole caused a new and very cold oceanic current to develop. The current flows completely around Antarctica, cutting it off from the influence of warm ocean currents that previously bathed the continent in waters delivered from the tropics. Prior to 34 million years ago forests had thrived on the Antarctic continent, sustained by the warmth and moisture delivered by those oceanic currents. When Antarctica was cut off, the continent plunged into the deep freeze in which it is still locked, and that cooling had repercussions around the world.

Now that you have seen some of the extraordinary Florissant fossils and traced the chain of events that preserved them, you may be eager to discover some new specimens for yourself. You can't collect any fossils in

The Florissant Fossil Quarry contains paper shales belonging to the lower shale unit of the Florissant Formation.

the national monument, but you can on private land at stop 4, the Florissant Fossil Quarry. Because the quarry lies in the lower shale unit, its fossils are a bit older than those unearthed in the national monument. The Clare family has operated this small quarry for fifty years, and for a modest fee they will provide you with a bag of paper shale and all the tools necessary to split it into sheets. Splitting the shale is both simple and fun, with every parting of the rock holding the potential to reveal a magnificent discovery. Fossils are so abundant in these rocks that, with a mere half hour of work, you are almost guaranteed to find several. The Clares are intimately familiar with the fossil species found in the Florissant Formation, so they can help you identify your finds. Leaves, needles, and fruits belonging to extinct members of the elm, beech, false cedar, and redwood families are the most abundant fossils, but ants, beetles, crane flies, and even spiders are also common. One of the few fossil birds discovered in the Florissant Formation was found at the quarry. The Clares have long had a formal partnership with the national monument, so if your efforts produce an unusual discovery, they will ask you to share it with the scientific community. If you are so fortunate, you will have made an important contribution to our ongoing efforts to better understand Colorado's ancient climate and ecosystems. Not only that, but should you discover a new species, a paleontologist who formally describes it might even name it after you.

13

COLORADO'S MOUNTAIN OF GOLD
Cripple Creek

Colorado's history has been strongly shaped by mining ever since gold was discovered on the banks of Clear Creek, just west of Denver, in 1859. Much of Colorado's mineral wealth, including that of Clear Creek, lies along a southwest-trending belt known as the Colorado Mineral Belt (vignette 7), which runs from Boulder to the San Juan Mountains. However, quite a few productive ores have been discovered outside the belt, with the Cripple Creek district being the most important. Since the discovery of gold there in 1891, the district has produced over 23 million ounces, worth more than $32 billion dollars in 2012 prices. This makes Cripple Creek far and away the richest gold field in Colorado and one of the richest strikes on the planet.

At the American Eagles Overlook (stop 1) you are, quite literally, standing atop Colorado's mountain of gold. This is the perfect location to trace the story of mining in the Cripple Creek district, from its inception to the present day. The overlook is named for the historic, underground American Eagles Mine, which was established in 1895. At an elevation of 10,570 feet, it is the district's highest mine. From the parking area, ascend the obvious stairway to the overlook, where you can wander through the mine's infrastructure and learn from the interpretive plaques about the uses of the buildings and equipment on display. To the west, the modern, ever-growing Cresson open-pit mine is visible. The stark contrast between the old mining infrastructure and the pit profoundly illustrates how the techniques of Cripple Creek mining have changed over the years.

Winfield Scott Stratton bought and developed the American Eagles with part of the $11-million windfall he obtained from the sale of a nearby mine. Like many early prospectors, Stratton knew that the riches in Cripple Creek were associated with an extinct volcano. He was convinced that these ore bodies were shaped like a wine goblet, narrowing at depth into a fabulously gold-rich stem. He put his money behind his convictions, bankrolling the deepening of this and other mines. He died in 1902, the same year the

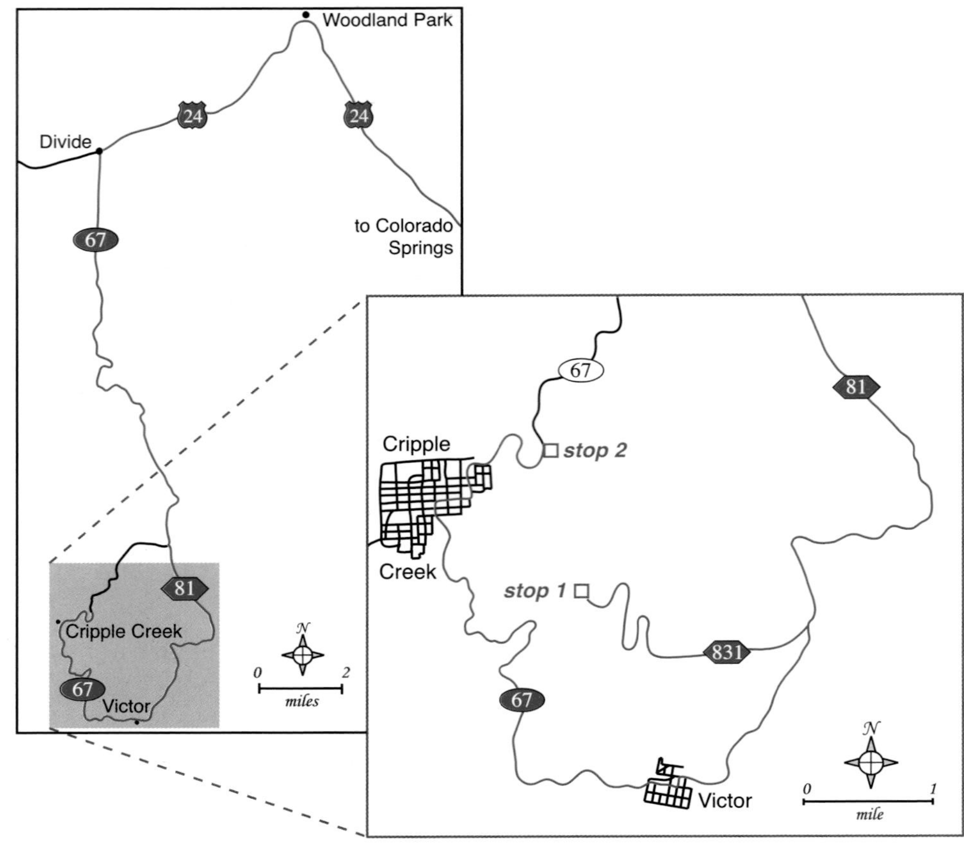

GETTING THERE: This excursion begins at the American Eagles Overlook above the active Cresson gold mine. From Colorado Springs travel west on US 24 for about 26 miles to the small town of Divide, then turn left (south) onto CO 67. Proceed 13.4 miles and turn left onto County Road 81. Follow this 5.2 miles south, then turn right onto County Road 831. You will see a blue sign announcing this as the road to the American Eagles Overlook. As you drive through the Cresson Mine, similar signs mark the way to the overlook at several road crossings, where you should be particularly attentive because mine traffic drives on the left side of the road. After traveling 1.8 miles, you reach the overlook parking area. (Mines change their road systems frequently, so check for up-to-date information and maps at www.victorcolorado.com/eagles.htm.)

To reach stop 2, retrace your route back to County Road 81, then turn right. After 1.6 miles you reach CO 67 in the old mining town of Victor. Follow CO 67 to Cripple Creek, 5.5 miles away. As you enter Cripple Creek, turn right at the first stop sign onto Bennett Avenue. Proceed 0.3 mile to a 90-degree bend onto North 5th Street (unsigned), which turns into CO 67. Follow this an additional 1.5 miles, then turn right onto County Road 82. The well-marked Mollie Kathleen Mine stands at this road junction. Here you can purchase a fascinating hour-long tour that descends the old 1,000-foot mine shaft in an authentic miners elevator (www.goldminetours.com).

Perched near the brink of a modern open-pit mine, this head frame and other assorted rusty mining equipment are all that's left to see of the historic American Eagles Mine.

The view of the active Cresson open-pit gold mine from the American Eagles Overlook is stunning in scale.

Eagles's main shaft reached its maximum depth of 1,540 feet below the surface, making it the deepest of its day. Although Stratton didn't live to see it, other mines in the district confirmed his belief that the Cripple Creek minerals continue to extraordinary depths. Throughout the first half of the twentieth century, other miners pushed their shafts ever deeper, including the Ajax Mine, the deepest in the Cripple Creek district, which was still tapping rich ores at its maximum depth of 3,350 feet—more than half a mile!—when it closed.

The tremendous depth range of these high-grade ores accounts for the Cripple Creek district's truly enormous gold reserves. To date, nearly 1,000 tons of gold have been extracted, and geologists believe that at least another 1,000 tons remain in the ground. Minerals containing gold are found everywhere in Earth's crust but usually occur in such minute quantities that they can't be feasibly mined. Ore bodies are small pockets with such anomalously high concentrations that they can be profitably extracted.

Cripple Creek's story begins 32.5 million years ago with the birth of a volcano that repeatedly erupted throughout its 2.5-million-year life span. Though the rocks from each eruption are chemically distinct from one another, they share one profound similarity: they are all unusually rich in sodium, making them what geologists term alkaline rocks. Most of the world's truly enormous gold districts are located in alkaline igneous rocks, so although geologists don't yet understand why this connection exists, the alkaline nature of the Cripple Creek volcano is undoubtedly a crucial piece of the answer to why the district is gold rich.

A second piece of the answer lies in the fact that this volcano was a diatreme, meaning that it erupted explosively when hot, rising magma encountered groundwater and instantly flashed that water into steam. The violence of such phreatic (steam-driven) eruptions repeatedly shattered the volcano's rocks. Much of the resulting rubble then tumbled back down into the partially emptied magma chamber and eventually cemented together to form an angular, broken rock called volcanic breccia. Breccia is the most abundant rock in the Cripple Creek volcano. In some shafts miners discovered charcoal from trees as much as 600 feet below the surface, showing how far material can tumble after a phreatic eruption.

The final piece of the answer as to why the Cripple Creek district is so enriched in gold stems from an event that occurred late in the volcano's life when hot, mineral-laden water welled up and percolated through the loose breccia. By exploiting the many conduits between the shattered rock fragments, this water thoroughly bathed the volcanic rocks, in the process dramatically altering their chemistry. The blue-green patches of exotic minerals as well as the general yellowish color of the many volcanic rocks lining the steps to the overlook are evidence of this pervasive chemical alteration. The most economically significant changes occurred during the

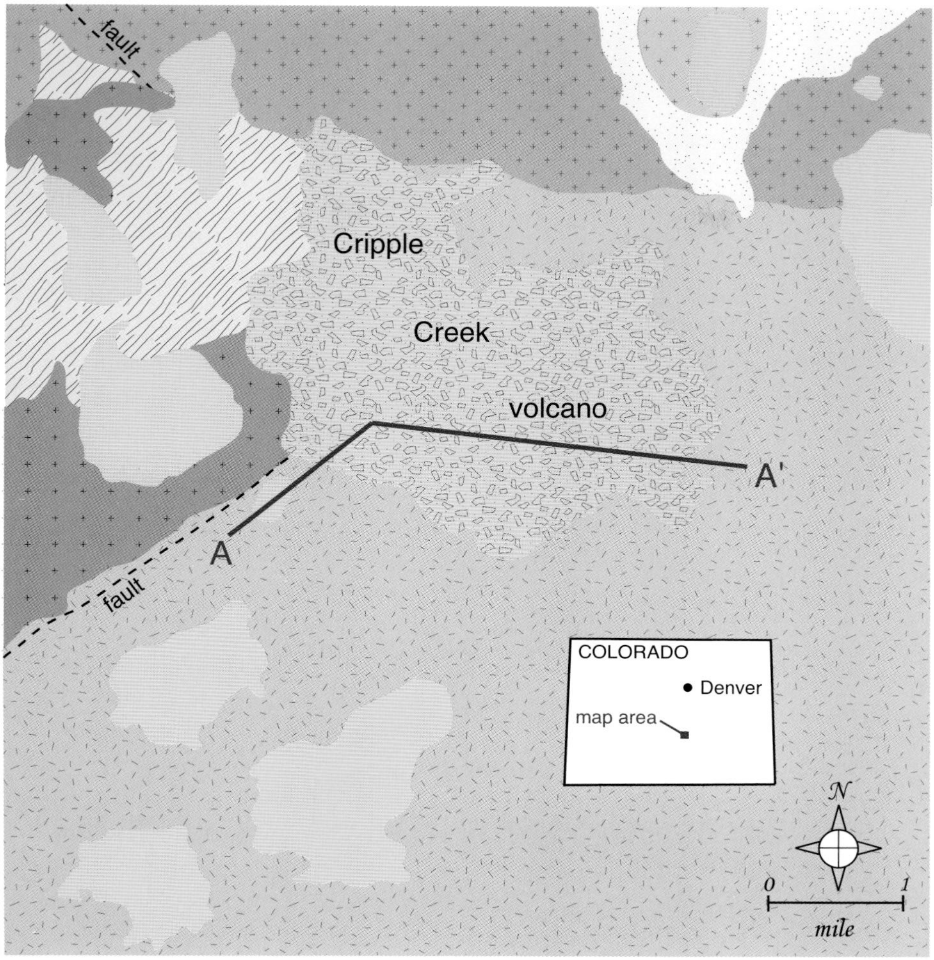

fault

Cripple

Creek

volcano

A'

A

fault

COLORADO

Denver

map area

N

0 1

mile

A

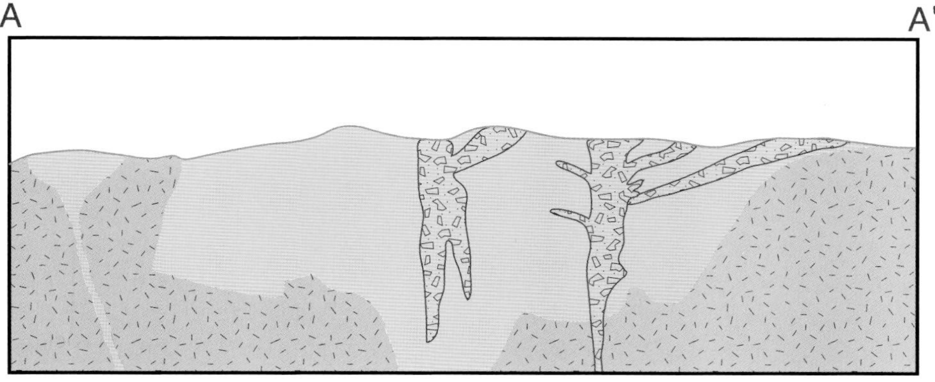

The Cripple Creek diatreme is marked by the orange outcrops on this geologic map and cross section. The plain orange outcrops consist of lava, and the patterned areas consist of breccia. The Cripple Creek volcano intruded a series of Precambrian-age (shades of gray) metamorphic (lined pattern) and igneous rocks (plus signs and hatches). The light gray, stippled pattern denotes Quaternary-age sediments. (Modified from Cappa, 1998.)

volcano's last days, when immense amounts of potassium replaced other elements. Today, potassium is more abundant than the original sodium in many of these rocks. Crucially, gold hitched a ride with the potassium and was deposited along with it. Due to the extensive network of fractures in the breccia, the gold was spread thinly and evenly amongst the volcano's rocks, amounting to about 0.03 to 0.04 ounces of gold in every ton of rock. These amounts were useless to a nineteenth-century miner, but today they are the basis of a highly profitable mining venture. Even though it took large amounts of gold to spread this small enrichment throughout the 6-square-mile volcano, there was still plenty of gold left to concentrate in narrow, 2-inch-wide quartz veins that host incredible concentrations of up to 43 percent.

One such vein caught the eye of local rancher Bob Womack in 1891 as he was herding cattle in Poverty Gulch. He quickly filed the El Paso mining claim, which developed into the highly successful Gold King Mine. Unfortunately for Womack, he sold the claim one night for $500 and a bottle of whiskey, so he wasn't the developer. Soon after Womack filed his claim, word spread and the rush was on. The Cripple Creek gold camp grew rapidly in population, wealth, and stature. By 1900, just nine years after the

The yellowish color and blue-green mineral patches of the volcanic rocks lining the steps to the overlook are signs that these rocks were repeatedly bathed in hot, mineral-rich fluids that enriched their gold content.

initial discovery, the district hit its peak gold production of 879,000 ounces. In the early twentieth century the district was home to over sixty thousand souls, and towns like Cripple Creek and nearby Victor were archetypal Wild West gold towns. The early miners chased the many vertical veins ever deeper into the Earth, to the great financial benefit of a lucky few and at the expense of the majority, who endured dangerous and backbreaking work with little reward. Labor strife was common. It reached fever pitch in 1893–1894 and again in 1903–1904. The second time, strikers resorted to using dynamite to blow up a train station and collapse a mine shaft. Thirty-three people died in the violence, and the Colorado governor sent the state militia to Cripple Creek to reestablish order.

The Cripple Creek district continued its enormous production right up until World War I. Throughout this period the ore's average grade was a highly respectable 1 to 2 ounces per ton of ore, but in mine after mine a few exceptionally high-grade veins were encountered. The most famous was the Cresson vug, a natural cavity lined with gold that was discovered in the Cresson Mine in 1914. Within weeks miners had extracted 60,000 ounces of gold from it, catapulting the Cresson up the list of the most productive mines in the district. Cripple Creek production dropped significantly after World War I due to a shortage of postwar labor and the rapidly escalating expenses associated with deepening the mines. But production continued until World War II, when an order arrived to shutter all gold mines out of national necessity. Although the mines restarted after the war's end and the gold was far from exhausted, production steadily dropped until it ceased altogether in 1961, when the last mill closed, leaving no place to process the ore the remaining miners extracted.

Things changed again in the 1970s, when the federal government deregulated the price of gold. Suddenly there was more money to be made. Coupled with advances in mining technology, deregulation led to a resurgence of interest in the Cripple Creek ores. Production remained modest until the late 1994 opening of the modern Cresson open-pit mine that you see from the overlook. The mine was named in honor of (and undoubtedly in the hopes of emulating) the fabled Cresson Mine and its ridiculously rich vug. That hope was borne out in spectacular fashion, with the mine quickly ramping up to 400,000 ounces of gold production per year—in 2012 prices, that equals over $1.5 million dollars a day.

Until the 1970s, narrow shafts penetrating thousands of feet into the Earth characterized the mining in the district. The new Cresson Mine is a very different operation. Today's miners don't toil day after day chasing a single rich vein. Rather, they are steadily turning the mountain of gold into a giant hole, carting away both the high- and low-grade ores 310 tons at a time in a steady parade of haul trucks that from here look like an army of ants crisscrossing the sprawling mine.

On your drive through the Cresson Mine to stop 1, you may well see a 310-ton haul truck up close.

The key to profitably operating this mine is volume processing. Modern miners detonate dynamite charges to blast the rock into rubble. If you scan the pit, you will likely locate the drilling rig that bores the holes into which the dynamite is loaded. Look also for the neat rows of holes that indicate an area about to be blown. Front-end loaders pile the rubble into the never-ending line of haul trucks that, twenty-four hours a day, drive a circuit from the rubble pile to the ore crusher and back. The crusher smashes the rubble into sand-sized particles, which are carried by conveyor to the Valley Leach Facility. As the name suggests, this is situated in a former valley that has been lined with impermeable plastic and filled to the brim with crushed ore. Agricultural drip lines deliver a weak sodium cyanide solution to the top of the pile. As the cyanide percolates slowly through the ore, it swaps its sodium atoms for gold, thus leaching it from the ore. The gold-bearing concentrate then passes through an activated carbon filter that strips the gold out of the cyanide solution. The solution is recycled back to the top of the leach pile, while the gold is pried off the carbon filter and concentrated using an electrolysis technique. This concentrate is then heated in a crucible to about 2,400°F. Once molten, the gold and accompanying silver sink to the bottom, while the impurities float to the surface, where they are skimmed off. The impurities solidify into slag, the glassy by-product that remains after the valuable metals have been removed, while the nearly pure gold-silver amalgam is shipped elsewhere for final refining.

The Valley Leach Facility at the Cresson Mine dwarfs an historic mine in this view from CO 67 between the towns of Cripple Creek and Victor. The black stripes running down the ore pile are irrigation drip lines that deliver sodium cyanide to the ore.

Now that you have a sense of the modern operation, head to stop 2, the historic Mollie Kathleen Mine. The drive takes you around the southwestern perimeter of the ancient Cripple Creek volcano. The Mollie Kathleen provides a rare opportunity to experience what conditions in a vertical-shaft mine were like.

Established in 1891, the Mollie Kathleen was one of Cripple Creek's earliest mines. It stands just 300 yards away from Bob Womack's original gold discovery. It is named for Mollie Kathleen Gortner, the woman who discovered gold here when she stopped for a breather while out looking for a herd of elk. Hers was the first Cripple Creek claim filed by a woman, and it was quite a productive mine, operating until 1961. From early in the Mollie Kathleen's history, miners led tourists through the tunnels by candlelight. For many years miners would dig for gold on one mine level while a tour was being conducted on another. So when gold production ceased it was natural for the operation to continue the tours, which begin with an exhilarating two-minute, 1,000-foot descent down the service shaft in an open elevator. As you descend, brief flashes of light punctuate the darkness as the elevator passes tunnels marking each mining level. The elevator finally stops at the 1,000-foot level, the lowest, where the guide leads you through a drift, a mining term for a horizontal tunnel. While in the drift the guide

The Julian Davis drift, one of the horizontal shafts you pass on the Mollie Kathleen tour.

operates several air-powered drills and you get to ride a man train, a cart driven by compressed air that runs on the same rails once used to move ore carts through the tunnels.

Earlier, we discussed the three geologic factors that enriched the Cripple Creek volcano with gold. As you stand underground contemplating the determination and grit of the miners who extracted gold more than one hundred years ago, it is fascinating to step even further back in time and ponder the events that caused a volcano to form here 32.5 million years ago. What ultimately created the riches that humans have so determinedly extracted from these modern and historic mines?

Three separate waves of volcanic activity have swept Colorado during Earth's most recent geologic era, the Cenozoic. The era opened 65.5 million years ago with Colorado in the throes of the Laramide orogeny, the mountain building episode that heaved the Rocky Mountains skyward (vignettes 8, 16). Although regionally the Laramide time is noteworthy for its relative lack of volcanic activity, the Front Range was an important exception. It hosted the northeastern end of a southwest-trending string of volcanoes and intrusions that form the rich Colorado Mineral Belt (vignette 7).

By 45 million years ago the mountain building had wound down, but these geologic fireworks were soon replaced by a second volcanic episode, this one of truly titanic proportions. Known as the Ignimbrite Flare-up, this volcanic episode was one of the most massive outpourings of silica-rich lava the world has ever seen (vignette 11). From 37 to 24 million years ago volcanoes raged from Canada to Mexico and from Colorado to Nevada. The chemistry of the magma these volcanoes erupted, which was intermediate to high in silica, leads most geologists to conclude that the flare-up marked the dying gasp of the subduction zone that had existed off the coast of California for the previous 200 million years.

The Cripple Creek volcano rumbled to life just as the volcanoes of the Ignimbrite Flare-up began to wane but before Colorado's third volcanic episode, the Rio Grande Rift volcanism, had really begun. A rift is a series of down-dropped valleys that form as Earth's crust is stretched. Colorado's crust did just that after the subduction zone off the coast of California began to die. This rift runs from Texas through New Mexico, where the Rio Grande River runs down the rift's main valley. In Colorado it is called the San Luis Valley. From Leadville to Salida, the upper Arkansas River

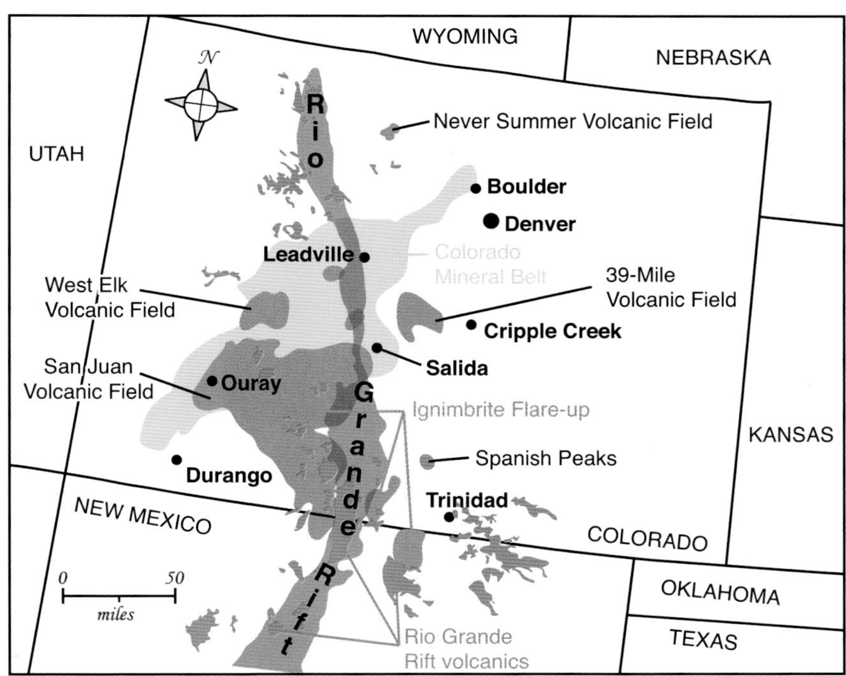

Colorado has been swept during the Cenozoic era by three waves of volcanism. The first was igneous activity (tan) related to the formation of the Colorado Mineral Belt. The second, the Ignimbrite Flare-up (brown), produced the San Juan, West Elk, 39-Mile, and Never Summer volcanic fields. The third was volcanism (orange) associated with formation of the Rio Grande Rift, which included the emplacement of the Spanish Peaks intrusions (vignette 20). The rift itself is shown in green.

flows down the rift's axis, and similar north-northwest-trending valleys dot the Colorado landscape as far north as Steamboat Springs. The faulting that created the rift was accompanied by the state's third volcanic episode (vignette 20). But most Rio Grande Rift volcanoes, the oldest a mere 4,000 years old, have a very different composition than those of Colorado's previous episodes. They mainly erupt low-silica basalt.

The Cripple Creek volcano's intermediate timing between the Ignimbrite Flare-up and the Rio Grande rifting makes it hard to determine which volcanic event it belongs to. Its magma composition makes that classification even harder still. The high potassium and sodium content of Cripple Creek's rocks is unlike that of the rocks erupted in either volcanic episode. Casting a more global net, Cripple Creek's chemically closest cousins all hail from zones of incipient rifting—locations where rifting is, geologically speaking, about to begin. Because of this chemical similarity, geologists suspect that the Cripple Creek volcano tapped a pool of magma generated deep within the mantle during the transition from tectonic compression to extension, as the subduction zone off the west coast was dying and the Rio

You pass this high-grade vein of gold ore on the tour of the Mollie Kathleen Mine.

Grande Rift was just beginning to develop. Cripple Creek's magma rose so rapidly to the surface that it melted precious little of the continental crust through which it passed, thus avoiding the contamination, or mixing, that befalls most magmas.

As you walk through the Mollie Kathleen, notice how most of the Cripple Creek gold veins are nearly vertical. The miners attacked them from below to let gravity aid them in their work. When a horizontal drift intersected a vein, the miners would quarry it out along a shaft known as a stope. The newly liberated blocks of ore would then tumble to the drift floor, where a mucker, a miner who drew the day's hardest labor, would shovel them into an ore cart. You pass several impressive stopes on the tour, as well as a pristine gold vein that is preserved thanks to the fact that it was discovered after active mining had ceased. Miners encountered this vein serendipitously while tunneling to improve the flow of tourists through the drifts. The vein helps you envision what the miners were looking for as they toiled day after day in these dark tunnels. Soon after passing the unmined vein, the tour draws to a close with the guide giving you your very own sample of Cripple Creek gold ore. Although it won't make you rich, it makes an appropriate geological souvenir that can bring back memories of your extraordinary trip through the bowels of an extinct volcano that created Colorado's mountain of gold.

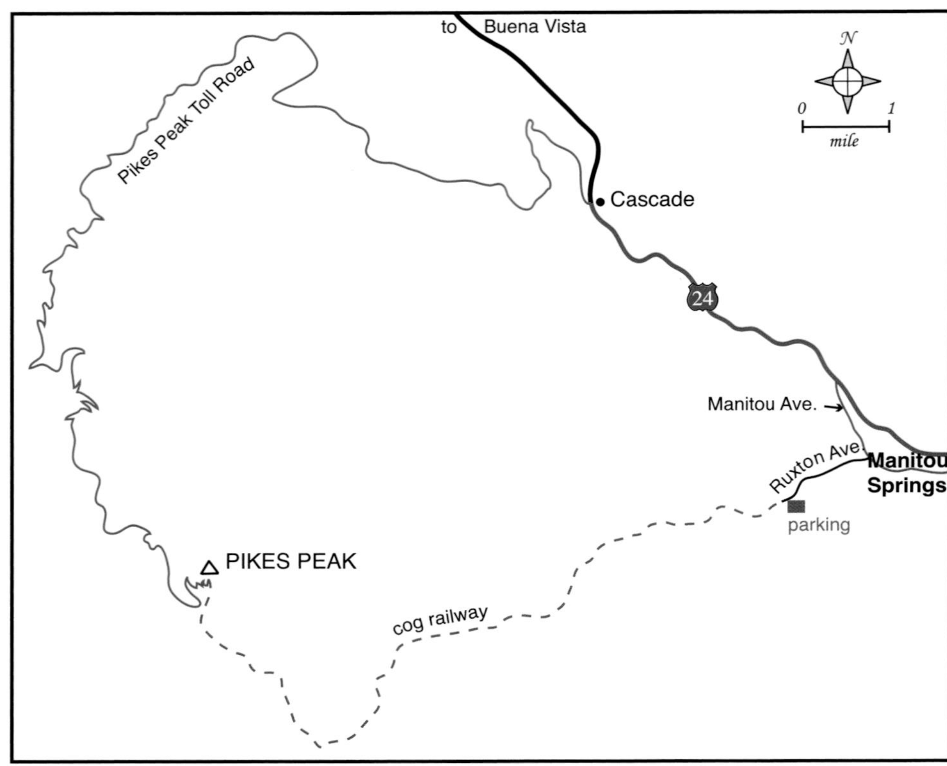

GETTING THERE: This vignette starts at the summit of Pikes Peak, which you can reach by toll road, cog railway, or trail. For any of these options, follow I-25 into Colorado Springs and exit onto US 24 (exit 141/Cimarron Street). For the cog railroad or the trail, proceed west into Manitou Springs. After 4.2 miles, exit at milepost 299 onto Manitou Avenue. Head west for 1.5 miles to Ruxton Avenue and turn left. After 0.75 mile, Ruxton Avenue ends at the cog railway parking lot. Weather permitting, the train runs several times a day year-round, and the round-trip lasts just over three hours. You can make reservations or find more information at www.cograilway.com. The trailhead for the long, steep Barr Trail is located near the railroad depot (for more information check www.trailsandopenspaces.org/trails/pike-barr-trail.htm). The cog railway also offers one-way trips for those who want to hike the mountain.

If you prefer to drive, from the I-25 exit follow US 24 for 9.3 miles to the town of Cascade. Turn left onto Fountain Avenue, following the prominent "Pikes Peak Highway" sign. After 0.4 mile veer left, following the "Pikes Peak Highway" sign. You pass immediately beneath a wooden gate. The toll road's entrance booth is 0.7 mile beyond. This 19-mile-long road stays open year-round, weather permitting. It is partly paved and partly well-maintained gravel that is fine for passenger cars. More information is available at www.pikespeakcolorado.com. However you reach the summit, you can take refuge from the chill at a small visitor center that sells curios and warm food. Altitude sickness is a concern at 14,000 feet of elevation. Headaches are common. If you experience more serious symptoms, the only cure is descent.

14

PURPLE MOUNTAIN MAJESTY
Pikes Peak, America's Mountain

For westbound travelers crossing the vast Great Plains, Pikes Peak provides the first visual relief from the days (or, in the 1800s, the weeks) of unrelentingly horizontal skylines. And what a departure it is! Pikes Peak soars more than 8,000 feet above the plains and does so in splendid isolation, without the foothills behind which most Colorado mountains commonly hide.

In 1806, Lt. Zebulon Pike, Pike Peak's namesake, led an expedition to explore the boundaries of the Louisiana Purchase. Day after long day, as his party trudged across the plains, Pikes Peak was visible on the horizon. Pike's descriptions of the peak's majesty fueled the country's imagination regarding its recent acquisition, indelibly imprinting the mountain on the public's consciousness. The peak's fame exploded again in 1859 when gold was discovered along the banks of Clear Creek (vignette 7), triggering Colorado's gold rush. The stampede of aspiring miners used Pikes Peak as their metaphorical landmark, heading west with the cry "Pikes Peak or bust!" on their lips, despite the fact that the gold was discovered far north of the peak.

Upon becoming the first Euro-American to lay eyes on the great mountain, Pike laid plans to make its ascent, which he presumed (almost surely incorrectly) would be the mountain's first. Pike was defeated by a blizzard and promptly declared the peak unscalable, a prophecy that was disproved just fourteen years later. Today, 500,000 people ascend it each year, making Pikes Peak by far the most-ascended mountain in America (and second in the world only to Japan's Mt. Fuji). Wellesley College English professor Katherine Lee Bates ascended the peak in 1893. The view from the summit inspired her to pen "America the Beautiful," our unofficial second national anthem. Thanks to that song and its close association with the opening of the American West, Pikes Peak has truly become an emblem of America.

As singular as Pikes Peak's geography is its geology. This is because it is the only big mountain in Colorado that is constructed of granite belonging

Pikes Peak, icon of the American West, as seen from Garden of the Gods.

to the Pikes Peak Batholith. This batholith—an enormous mass of once-molten rock—is by far the state's single biggest body of granite, and at 1,080 million years, its age is unique among Colorado rock formations. In fact, few rocks in the entire American West share this age, making the mountain's rocks indispensable to the geologists trying to piece together the story of North America during the late Proterozoic eon, a time of particularly dramatic geologic change worldwide.

However you ascend, your entire journey will be across Pikes Peak granite. This is because the batholith is truly gigantic: the granite is exposed across 1,200 square miles, and based on magnetic evidence, it stretches far to the east. Once you reach the summit, grab a piece of rock and examine it. Typical of granite, the constituent minerals include feldspar, quartz, biotite, and hornblende. All of the crystals are big enough to see without magnification. The only way mineral crystals can grow this large is if water-rich magma cools very slowly deep underground, where it is insulated by surrounding rock. Geologists call such coarse igneous rocks intrusive, and they have determined that the Pikes Peak granite intruded and solidified 2 to 3 miles beneath the surface. The light color of most of its minerals testifies to the high concentration of silica and confirms that this is indeed granite.

At the summit, spectacular views stretch before you in every direction. It is easy to appreciate what Katharine Lee Bates meant by "purple mountains majesty." If you have the time (and the lung capacity), roam around the summit to compare and contrast some rock samples. Depending upon where you grab the rocks from, the size of the crystals and the proportions of different minerals will likely differ, but the samples are all still granite. The reason for the variety is that the batholith was not formed from a single magma body. Instead, it is comprised of many smaller magma pods, or plutons, which intruded one inside the other to assemble the master batholith. Each pod had a slightly different chemical composition and cooling history, so the rock that solidified from each therefore has slightly different characteristics. A handful (about 2 percent) of the Pikes Peak plutons are chemically distinct. They form rock types that are not classified as granite.

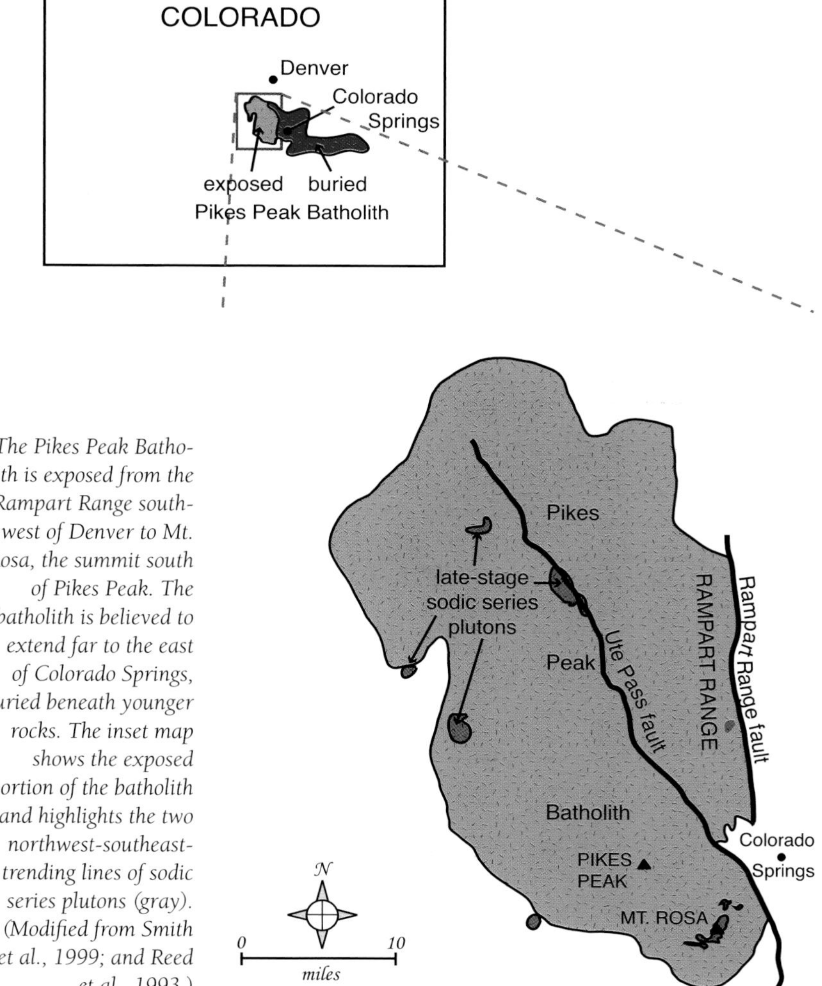

The Pikes Peak Batholith is exposed from the Rampart Range southwest of Denver to Mt. Rosa, the summit south of Pikes Peak. The batholith is believed to extend far to the east of Colorado Springs, buried beneath younger rocks. The inset map shows the exposed portion of the batholith and highlights the two northwest-southeast-trending lines of sodic series plutons (gray). (Modified from Smith et al., 1999; and Reed et al., 1993.)

These boulders of granite at Pikes Peak's summit are pink thanks to a high concentration of potassium feldspar. The granite also possesses clear quartz; shiny black biotite, which flakes like pieces of paper; and lesser amounts of black, less-shiny hornblende. The Pikes Peak granite is known for containing especially large crystals, which are prominent in this rock.

Although these sodic series rocks will play an important role as we decipher the peak's geologic history, you won't see any of them on or near the summit.

If you pause during your descent to examine the rocks, you will see that from the mountain's top to its bottom the granite's gross characteristics remain the same. This observation would hold true if you ventured across the batholith's entire 1,200-square-mile exposure. This uniformity raises an interesting question: what geologic process injected such an enormous volume of chemically homogenous magma into Earth's crust in just a few million years? In order to answer that question, we need to explore the differences that exist between two types of granite: orogenic and anorogenic.

Most granites form where tectonic plates crash into one another. During such collisions, areas of the crust and/or mantle are heated to the melting point of their most silica-rich mineral constituents, while their less silica-rich minerals don't melt. This partial melting produces granitic magmas. The molten rock then intrudes the chains of mountains that rise parallel to the plate boundary in response to tectonic compression. The construction of a mountain range by compressional stacking of crustal slabs, one atop the next, along thrust faults is known as an orogeny. Although most granites form in these tectonic settings, there is an important exception. Geologists have identified a subtype with a chemistry that strongly suggests it did not form in a compressional mountain range. This subtype is known as A-type granite, with the *A* standing for *anorogenic*, meaning "in the absence of orogeny."

Colorado hosts many examples of granites typical of orogenies, but they all formed long before the Pikes Peak granite, about 1,700 million years ago when Colorado's continental crust was born (vignette 7). When the Pikes Peak granite formed 600 million years later, Colorado was not home to thrust faults and its rocks were not experiencing regional metamorphism, demonstrating that the Pikes Peak granite was not produced during an orogeny. In fact, the chemistry of the Pikes Peak granite is considered a world standard by which the class of A-type granites is defined.

Most geologists believe that A-type granites form either at hot spots, where massive plumes of hot material rise to the surface from deep in the mantle, or where the crust is being pulled apart—a rift. The Yellowstone hot spot beneath Yellowstone National Park is a good modern example of a hot spot, and East Africa's magnificent Rift Valley is a good example of a modern rift. In both geologic settings, the absence of tectonic compression means that thrust faults aren't forming in the surrounding rocks, nor is the region experiencing widespread metamorphism, two distinctive hallmarks of an orogeny. The granite that develops at hot spots or rifts constitutes the remains of magma chambers that fed surface volcanoes. At Perry Park, north of Colorado Springs, geologists have found chunks of light-colored volcanic rock embedded in the younger Fountain Formation. The fragments are of comparable age and composition to the Pikes Peak granite, though they formed during a volcanic eruption. These fragments suggest that the Pikes Peak magma chamber did indeed feed surface volcanoes.

The Yellowstone hot spot has remained stationary deep in the mantle for millions of years while the overlying tectonic plate has migrated westward, slowly shifting the center of volcanic activity at the surface (and the granite bodies that solidify in the magma chambers) from west to east. Yellowstone's magmas have the same A-type chemistry as does Pikes Peak granite, and because no tectonic compression is occurring in the Yellowstone region, no regional metamorphism is happening and no thrust faults are forming. The characteristics of this setting sound strikingly similar to those of the solitary, eastward-trending blob of Pikes Peak granite, making the conclusion that a similar hot spot underlay Colorado 1,080 million years ago, when the granite formed, a plausible one.

What about the rift idea? How does a comparison with today's East African Rift stack up? Rifts generate A-type granites, so no problems there. But can a rift explain the batholith's isolation, with no rocks of similar age

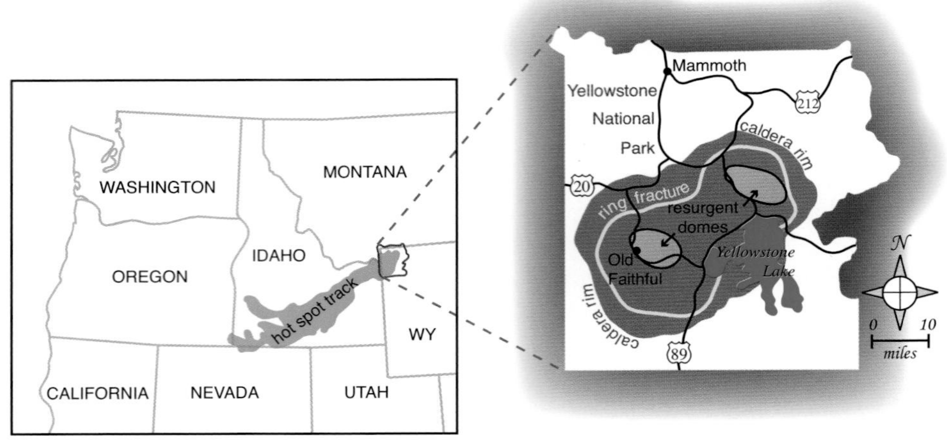

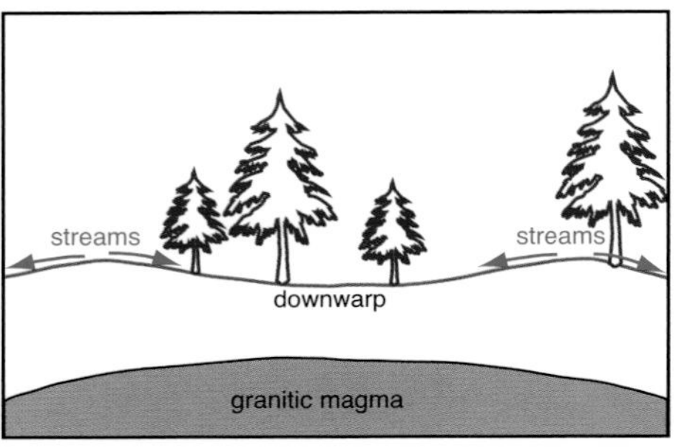

Potential modern analogues for the setting in which the Pikes Peak granite formed are the Yellowstone hot spot and East African Rift Valley. The Yellowstone hot spot has burned a track across southern Idaho as the North American Plate migrated over the hot spot. A series of granite intrusions likely underlies this track. The hot spot has formed the active caldera (area inside the ring fracture) that occupies much of Yellowstone National Park and, as seen in cross section, a pod of granitic magma likely underlies the active caldera. The resurgent domes are small volcanoes that erupted after the huge explosion that formed the caldera. As the magma shifts beneath the caldera, it leads to surface bulges and downwarps, which cause stream courses to shift through time.

The East African Rift is in the process of tearing a large chunk of crust off the African continent. Divergence between tectonic plates begins with the formation of a rift valley (gray, hatched lines and cross section A-A′). The thinning of the crust as it is stretched and the eruption of basalt causes the land in the rift to subside. New oceanic crust forms from the basalt, creating a narrow ocean basin (cross section B-B′, with new oceanic crust shown in black). The Red Sea is at that narrow ocean-basin stage of rifting. As the plates continue to diverge, more oceanic crust forms and the ocean basin grows (cross section C-C′), eventually becoming a mature ocean.

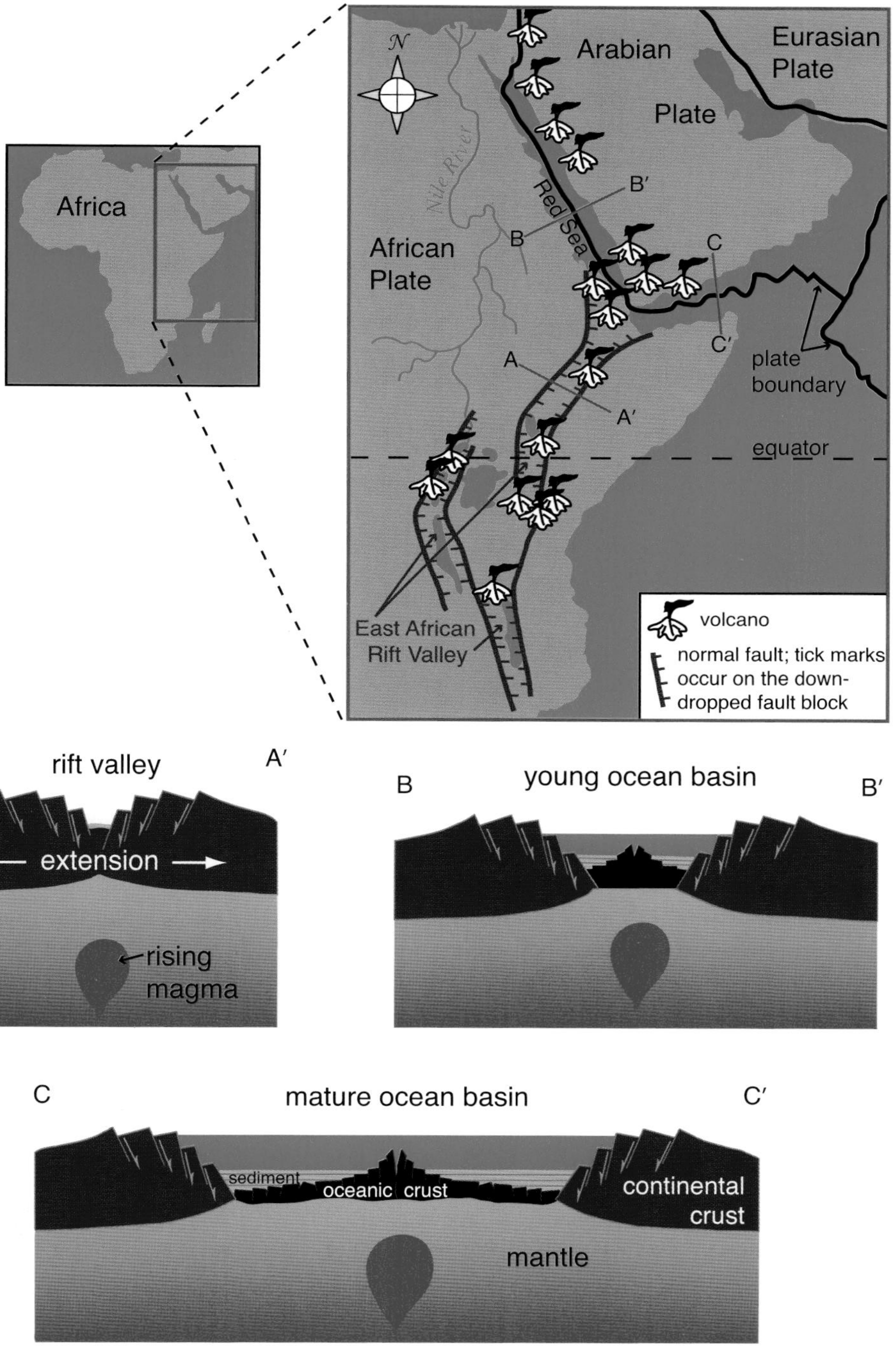

Africa
N
Arabian
Plate
Eurasian
Plate
Nile River
Red Sea
African
Plate
B
B′
C
C′
A
A′
plate
boundary
equator
East African
Rift Valley
volcano
normal fault; tick marks
occur on the down-
dropped fault block

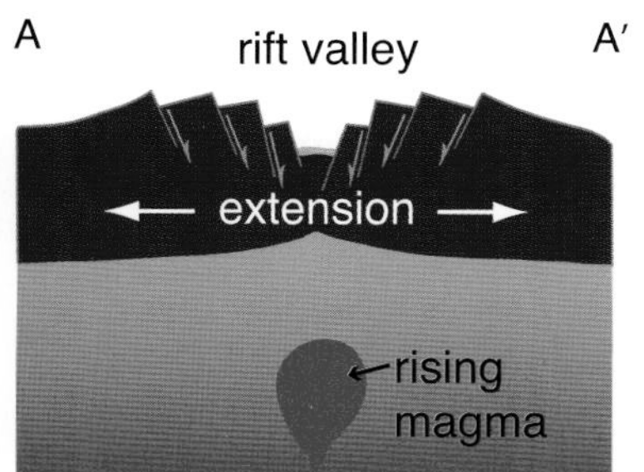
A
rift valley
A′
extension
rising
magma

B
young ocean basin
B′

C
mature ocean basin
C′
sediment
oceanic crust
continental
crust
mantle

and composition surrounding it? Unlike an isolated hot spot, rifts form narrow, elongate bands of crustal tearing perpendicular to the direction of plate stretching. There are no obvious ancient rifts near Pikes Peak. Another apparent problem with the rift idea is that rifts generate much greater volumes of dark-colored, low-silica (basaltic) magma than they do the light-colored granitic material that comprises Pikes Peak. The magma that feeds the vast majority of the East African volcanoes consists of dark basalt. When it solidifies underground, this magma forms the intrusive rock gabbro. Almost no 1,080-million-year-old gabbro exists in Colorado, seemingly arguing against the rift hypothesis.

But what if we dig a little deeper into the details and consider the characteristics of the few North American rocks that are contemporaneous with the Pikes Peak granite? The geologists who have spent the most time and effort looking at the late Proterozoic (1,100- to 1,000-million-year-old) rocks of North America strongly believe that, like Africa today, North America was trying to rip itself apart at that time. If so, how does Pikes Peak fit in?

First, let's reexamine the batholith's geometry. Recall that the batholith is composed of many individual, smaller magma bodies that intruded one into the next. Do these intrusions follow any geographic pattern? The answer is hard to determine because, as you've seen on the ascent of the peak, the different granites so strongly resemble one another. But recall that 2 percent of the batholith's rocks are not granite. Because these sodic series rocks are easily distinguished from the surrounding granite by their chemical composition, their pattern (or lack thereof) can be determined with far greater precision. The intrusions line up in two parallel lines that trend north-northwest to south-southeast. These trends parallel a family of major fractures in the Colorado crust that geologists suspect were active at about the same time. Nobody is certain if these fractures are faults, but it's possible they were normal faults—the type that accommodates crustal stretching triggered by continental rifting—during the time the Pikes Peak granite was crystallizing. Two of the biggest such fractures *were* active as thrust faults (the Rampart Range fault and the Ute Pass fault) during the Laramide orogeny, when the modern Rampart Range and Pikes Peak mountain blocks were raised up along them (vignette 16), but it is quite possible that they began their life during the Proterozoic as normal faults.

Things get more interesting when we consider the record of similarly aged rocks from adjacent areas. Three other granite exposures in western North America share an age with the Pikes Peak, including the Llano granites near Austin, Texas (best exposed at Enchanted Rock State Park), Texas's Franklin Mountains, and scattered granite bodies in northwestern Sonora, Mexico, near the town of Caborca. These rocks share many of the Pikes Peak granite's chemical characteristics, and their origins are equally enigmatic.

But where are the abundant dark gabbros (the intrusive rock equivalent to basalt) that we expect to find in areas of continental rifting? Gabbro is a particularly dense, massive rock type, so where large quantities of it lie buried, the Earth exerts a slightly stronger gravitational tug than in adjacent areas. Geophysicists routinely measure Earth's gravitational signature. When geophysicists first performed such a survey across North America, they were surprised to discover that a truly enormous body of gabbro lies beneath the middle of the continent, snaking like an inverted question mark from Michigan to Ontario, Canada, then bending southwest from Minnesota to Kansas. This gabbro pokes its nose above the surface at a few locations in Minnesota and Ontario where the Pleistocene ice sheets stripped away the overlying rocks. The gabbro is nearly identical in age to the Pikes Peak granite. The only tectonic setting where such a long and narrow but truly massive pile of gabbro can form is a rift, so geologists call the whole pile the Mid-Continent Rift. Another big body of contemporaneous gabbro, the dot at the bottom of the inverted question mark, is exposed along the Pecos River valley in New Mexico and Texas. Dikes of gabbro and basalt of the same age and geographical trend also exist in the Grand Canyon and California's Mojave Desert, supporting the hypothesis that the continent was actively pulling itself apart 1,080 million years ago.

When gravity surveys are conducted across Colorado, the Pikes Peak Batholith, like the Mid-Continent Rift, shows up as a place of unusually high gravity. Granite is actually less dense than the average crust, so the batholith's high gravity must be due to the presence of especially dense rocks beneath it. Gabbro is the most likely culprit. Intrusion of a gabbroic magma body would likely partially melt the surrounding continental crust, thereby producing a magma body large enough to form the Pikes Peak granite. Either a hot spot or a rift could have created such a pod of dense magma, but given the nearby presence of the Mid-Continent Rift, it is likely that rifting was involved.

Interestingly, many hot spots lie along rifts (many geologists believe that rifts form where several hot spots are "stitched" together), so it is conceivable that both hypotheses for the Pikes Peak granite could be true. Possibly, a hot spot lay at the location of Pikes Peak during an episode of rifting that stretched Colorado's crust in a northeast-southwest direction. This stretching accounts for the northwest-southeast trend of the mapped crustal fractures and the parallel alignment of the Pikes Peak Batholith's sodic series plutons. However, if Colorado's crust was stretching, it certainly was not doing so as intensely as it was 300 to 400 miles farther east, where gabbro is more abundant.

The modern rift in East Africa traces a wandering path similar to that of North America's Mid-Continent Rift. Several isolated volcanoes, including Kilimanjaro, the highest peak in Africa, rise hundreds of miles away from the rift's main axis; they are called off-axis volcanoes. Kilimanjaro may be a modern analogue for a volcano that towered above today's Pikes Peak granite.

The hypothesis that North America was being seriously stretched 1,080 million years ago and that Colorado, though not on the axis of the rift, was being thinned enough to produce some volcanism is plausible. But there is one hitch. Geologists fully expect the stretching along the East African Rift to continue until the east side is ripped from the continent, forming an intervening ocean. This scenario has already taken place to the north, where the Arabian Peninsula has been torn from Africa, leaving behind the long, narrow Red Sea. But North America remains intact today, more than 1 billion years after the mid-continent rifting. Why did North America not split in two?

This is another question for which we don't have a definitive answer. Although Colorado was not directly involved in an orogeny 1,100 million years ago, a huge mountain building episode, called the Grenville orogeny, was taking place to the south and east. The orogeny built a thrust-faulted

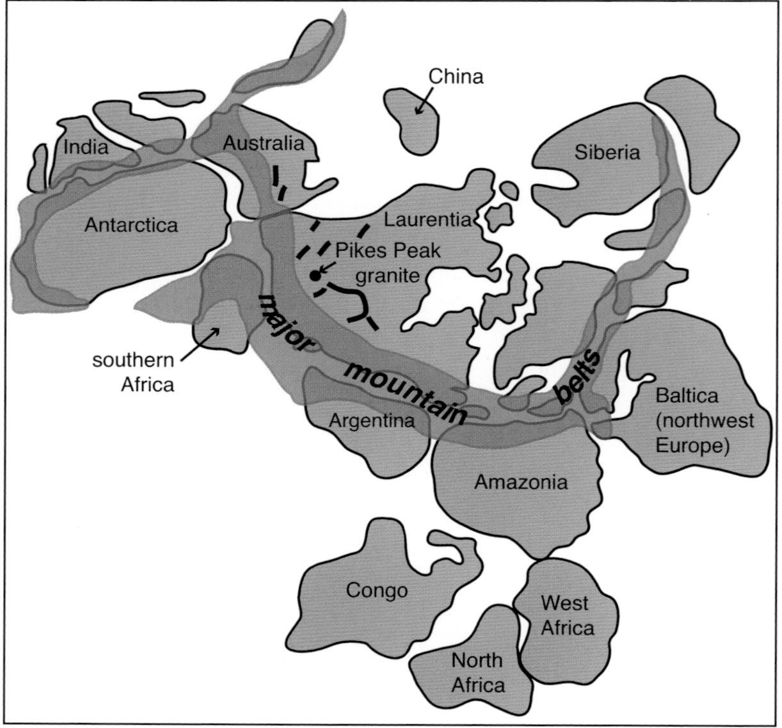

The Pikes Peak granite intruded the crust of proto–North America (Laurentia) during the assembly of the supercontinent Rodinia, about 1,100 million years ago. Major mountain belts formed where the continents collided, and rifts (black lines with tick marks) formed behind the collision zone.

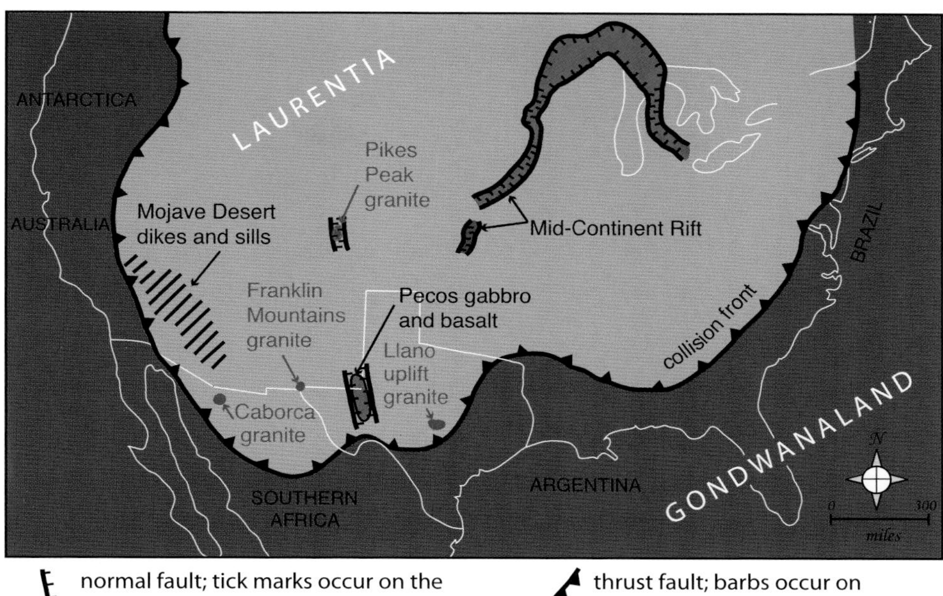

The ancient continents of Laurentia and Gondwanaland collided to form the supercontinent Rodinia. (Laurentia was thrust up and over Gondwanaland.) The overlay of the modern U.S. coastline and the ancient locations of other modern geographic features are provided for geographic reference. During the supercontinent's assembly, gabbro and basalt formed along the Mid-Continent Rift and in the Pecos River valley and Mojave Desert–Grand Canyon areas, all of which lay perpendicular to and behind the collision front along which North America was welded to southern Africa and Argentina. The Pikes Peak, Llano, Franklin Mountains, and Caborca granites were also intruded behind the collision front, in areas of extension.

mountain range that snaked along the trend of the modern Appalachians, from New York's Adirondack Mountains to Alabama, then veered west to Austin, Texas. Many researchers believe that this ancient mountain belt extended through Mexico into Antarctica and Australia, suggesting that those presently far-removed continents were, in the late Proterozoic, Colorado's near neighbors. The Grenville range was far longer than the current Himalayas and was created by a continental collision of titanic proportions.

It's now common knowledge that the configuration of continents we see today is temporary, and that the continents are always on the move. Due to this continental drift, all of the modern landmasses were welded together approximately 300 million years ago, forming a gigantic supercontinent known as Pangaea. Pangaea broke apart 200 million years ago, and its fragments have been drifting across the globe ever since. Although many people are familiar with this story, they often don't realize that the assembly and destruction of supercontinents is a cyclic phenomenon that has happened repeatedly throughout Earth's history. Tectonic reconstructions that predate Pangaea are fraught with uncertainty, but geologists agree that a global supercontinent preceded Pangaea. Called Rodinia, it formed about 1,100 million years ago. The Grenville orogeny was the final, titanic collision event that assembled Rodinia. The Pikes Peak granite provides Colorado's only rock record from that tremendously important chapter of Earth's geologic history.

The Mid-Continent Rift and the Pikes Peak Batholith both formed during the latter stages of supercontinent assembly, and they did so along a trend that is crudely perpendicular to, and behind, the line along which the continents were sutured (the collision front). The best modern analogue to the Grenville orogeny is the collision between India and Asia that is uplifting the mighty Himalayas. The Himalayan collision front is oriented east to west. But to the north, beginning in Tibet and continuing to Siberia, stretches a series of rifts, including the one filled by Siberia's famous Lake Baikal. These rifts are oriented roughly south to north. This geometry is strikingly similar in both orientation and scale to the relationship between the Grenville collision front and the Mid-Continent Rift.

Many geologists believe that the collision of India with Asia generated forces so immense that not only have the Himalayas been heaved upward, but the Asian continent has fractured. Though the Baikal Rift is geologically significant, nobody anticipates that it will continue growing unchecked, splitting Siberia and Tibet in two. Like head-on car crashes, plate collisions possess a certain amount of energy. When the frictional forces that crumple the crust (or the car hood) have dissipated, the collision ceases. Geologists hypothesize that the Himalayan collision is slowing down, and sometime in the not-too-distant geologic future it will halt. If this hypothesis is correct, then today's Baikal Rift is likely analogous to the Mid-Continent Rift, which was created during the Grenville collision but wasn't destined to form a new ocean basin. The Pikes Peak Batholith, in this model, formed in a magma chamber that fed an off-axis volcano, possibly centered over a hot spot, west of the main Mid-Continent Rift.

The Pikes Peak Batholith might never have been exposed were it not for the uplift of the Rocky Mountains during the later Laramide orogeny (vignette 16). Two reverse faults, the Ute Pass and the Rampart Range faults, cleaved the batholith in two and heaved the western portion skyward. The newly elevated terrain was then wracked by intense erosion, which stripped off the overlying rock and exposed the granite below. Where the thrusting lifted the hard, pink granite the highest, this powerful erosion hewed the rock into a solitary, precipitous mountain, and Pikes Peak—America's mountain—was born.

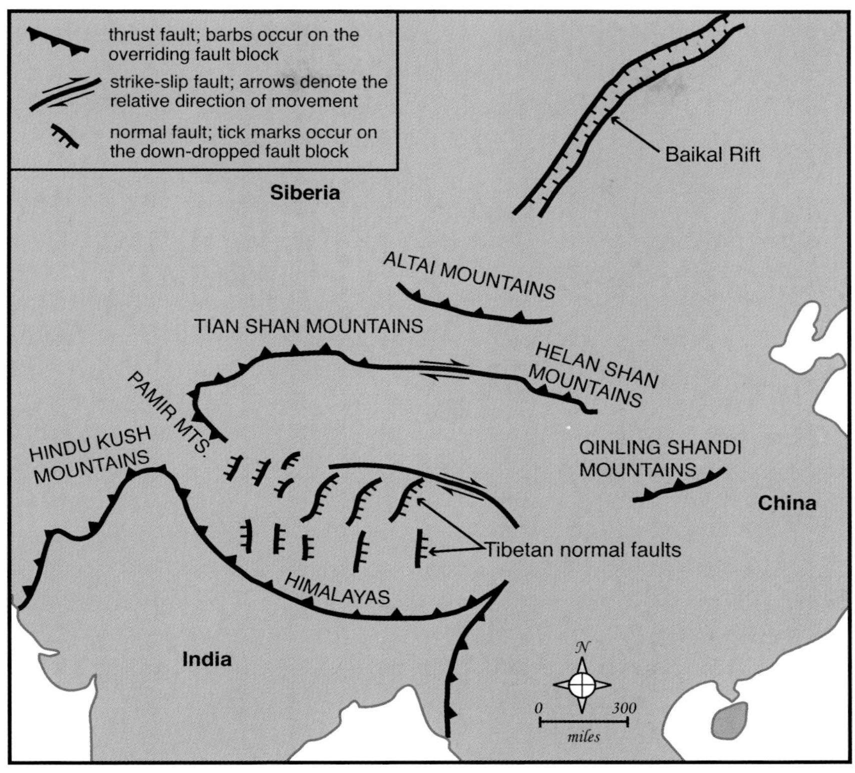

The geography of Asia today bears a resemblance to that of North America 1,100 million years ago. The Himalayas have been uplifted along the front where India and Asia are colliding. Rifts have formed in Tibet and Siberia's Lake Baikal area, and basalt has erupted in these rifts. (Modified from Smith et al., 1999; Condie, 2001; Molnar et al., 1973.)

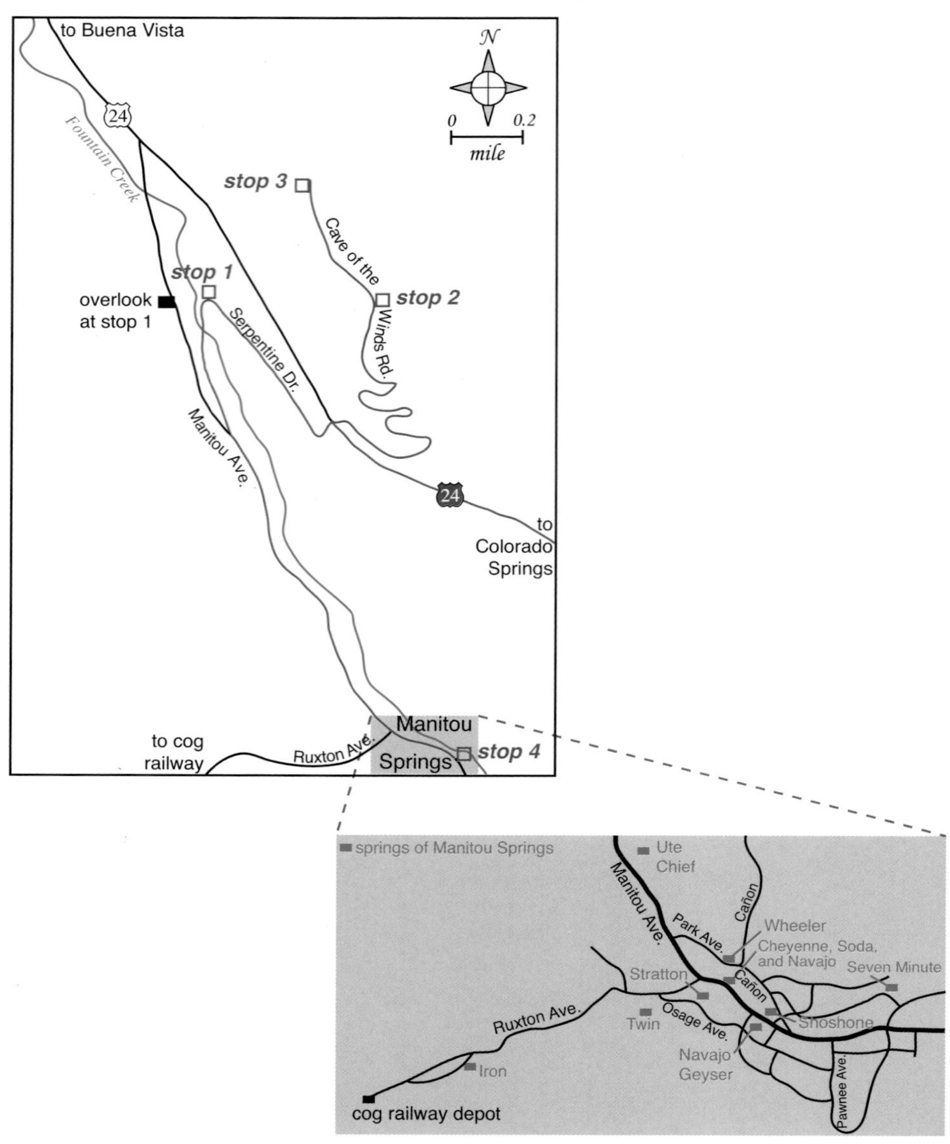

GETTING THERE: From exit 141 (Cimarron Street) of I-25 in Colorado Springs, travel west on US 24 for 5.7 miles. Turn left onto Serpentine Drive and follow it for 0.3 mile down a steep hill. Stop 1 is a small gravel parking area (and historic marker) on the right at the hairpin curve. To reach stop 2, retrace your route to the junction with US 24 and cross it to follow Cave of the Winds Road. Stop 2 is a small pullout on the right 0.6 mile from the junction. The fossils are best seen at the south end of the retaining wall, especially the second block from the end. Stop 3 is Cave of the Winds, which is another 0.4 mile up the road. Guided cave tours run frequently throughout the day and last about forty-five minutes. The path is lighted and the walking is not difficult. The temperature

15

SPELUNKING IN AN ANCIENT SEA
Cave of the Winds

As the Cambrian period dawned 542 million years ago, the world was in the midst of one of the most profound revolutions ever to unfold on its surface. Life, which for the previous 3,000 million years had existed exclusively as bacteria composed of, at most, a few cells, had recently (about 40 million years previously) developed the important evolutionary innovation of cooperation—cooperation between millions of cells. This synergy, and the cellular specialization that came with it, yielded the planet's first multicelled organisms. The inexhaustible variety of forms these new creatures could assume led to such a rapid profusion of new species that paleontologists have dubbed this period of evolutionary development the "Cambrian explosion." Evolutionary selection pressures immediately began to winnow out the less-useful body plans, triggering a never-ending chain of succession of one species by another, which ultimately led from these Cambrian pioneers to every species that exists on Earth today.

One important evolutionary innovation was the development, for the first time ever, of hard shells. Shells are fossilized comparatively easily compared with soft tissues, so extensive fossil beds—the earliest of such accumulations—appear in Cambrian formations around the world. The introduction of shells greatly enhanced our record of early multicellular creatures, and the accumulation of their forms in oceans around the world led to thick stacks of limestone and dolomite.

in the cave remains a constant 54°F year-round. Information concerning hours, prices, and geologic information about the cave are available at www.caveofthewinds.com. To reach stop 4, retrace your route to stop 1 and continue on Serpentine Drive for another 0.3 mile to its junction with Manitou Avenue. Turn left (east) onto Manitou Avenue and proceed 0.4 mile to downtown Manitou Springs. Park where convenient and stroll through downtown, visiting the springs en route. You might want to bring along a water bottle or cup so you can taste the variations between the springs' waters.

Late in the Cambrian period a shallow, tropical seaway was encroaching on Colorado. That seaway ebbed and flowed across the area for the next 200 million years. First, sand accumulated along the seashore. As the sea progressively deepened, billions upon billions of the newly evolved shells slowly accumulated on the seafloor and were cemented into rock, forming a stack of limestone layers that, 500 million years later, nature hollowed out to form the beautiful Cave of the Winds.

The cave was surely discovered centuries ago by Native Americans. But since its rediscovery in the early 1870s by either Arthur B. Love or the young Pickett brothers (accounts vary), tens of thousands of adventurous individuals have ventured into the cave to admire its natural beauty. We'll begin our exploration on the banks of Fountain Creek (stop 1), down the hill from the cave itself. A historic marker at the parking area announces

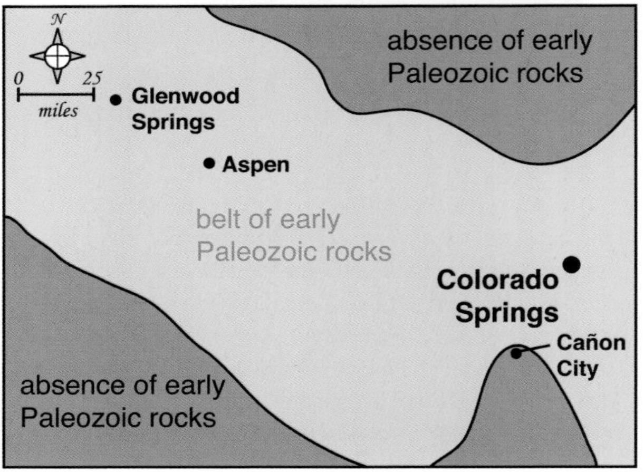

The Colorado Springs area is one of the few Front Range locations where rocks that record events during the early Paleozoic era are preserved. As global sea level rose during the Cambrian period, a seaway flooded Colorado's midsection. Crossbeds visible in the Sawatch Formation (photo) at stop 1 testify to the former presence of strong tidal currents that flowed back and forth from northwest to southeast. (Bottom illustration modified from Myrow et al., 1999.)

that this spot lies along the old Ute Pass, the first wagon road built to the gold fields of Cripple Creek west of Pikes Peak (vignette 13). Follow the dirt road northwest, up the creek, about 50 yards. The rock face on your right consists of eastward-tilting beds of quartz sandstone and brown dolomite (a magnesium-rich limestone). Together these layers make up the Sawatch Formation, which was deposited about 500 million years ago during the Late Cambrian period.

About 20 yards west of where you parked, a salmon pink rock completely devoid of layering begins to peek out of the ground below the Sawatch Formation's layers. The farther west you walk, the taller this cliff of pink rock rises, until the Sawatch layers stand above your head. The large, interlocking pink (potassium feldspar), clear (quartz), and black (biotite) crystals and the overall light pink color of the unlayered rock indicate that it is granite—here the Pikes Peak granite, the remnants of a magma chamber that slowly solidified about 3 miles below the surface 1,080 million years ago (vignette 14). The sharp boundary between the granite and overlying Sawatch Formation represents a 580-million-year gap in the rock record known as the Great Unconformity. Many profound geologic events undoubtedly transpired in Colorado during this missing time, but because no rocks record those events, most remain shrouded in mystery.

The Great Unconformity is also clearly visible along the US 24 access road to your southwest, across Fountain Creek. If you have time, take the short drive to that spot, where you gain a panoramic overview of the rock outcrop you are currently examining.

We do know that as Proterozoic time gave way to the Cambrian, Colorado (and, based on similar rock sequences across the continent, most of North America) consisted of a low-lying plain that lay slightly above sea level. The 3 miles of rock that lay on top of the Pikes Peak granite when it formed had eroded away during the time gap, thereby exposing the granite at Earth's surface. It is very difficult to accomplish 3 miles of erosion without some sort of uplift event, so it is likely that at some point between 1,080 and 500 million years ago the Colorado Springs area was wracked by a mountain building episode. When it happened and why remain uncertain because the rock clues that would have told the tale were eroded away before the Sawatch Formation was deposited.

Intense tropical weathering during the Cambrian slowly decomposed the granite that formed the surface of this plain. As the Cambrian period progressed, rising global sea level caused a shallow sea to encroach on the area, depositing beach sands and other sediments along its rising shore. The layers tilt eastward, so as you walk back to your car, each bed you pass is younger than the last, thereby allowing you to observe the geographic changes that swept the area as the Cambrian period progressed. The lowest 12 feet of the Sawatch Formation consists of beach-deposited sandstones.

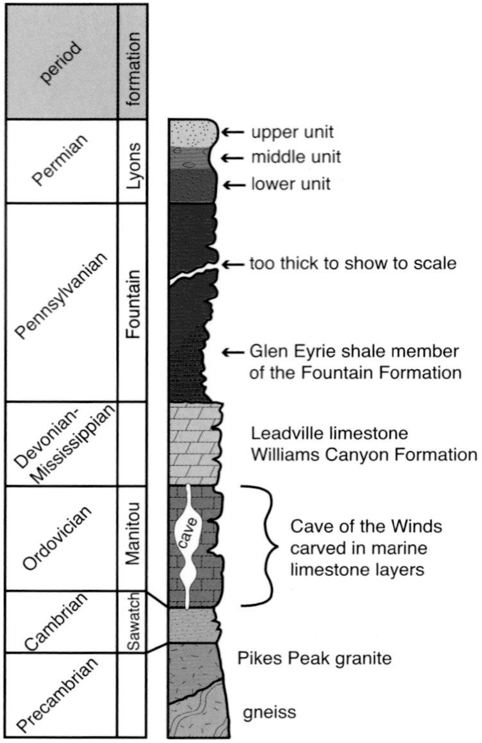

The sequence of rock units exposed near Cave of the Winds.

The top of this unit consists of an unusual, 4-inch-thick zone that is stained deep red by iron. This iron staining records a retreat of the sea, which exposed the newly deposited sand to weathering under unusual chemical conditions. Blocks of this red layer litter the roadside, in which you can see shells belonging to some of Colorado's earliest pioneer invertebrate organisms. During the interval of unusual chemistry the shells were replaced by the minerals pyrite and chert.

The upper layers of the Sawatch Formation, above the iron-stained bed, consist of dolomite alternating with sandstone that in places has a green hue imparted by the mineral glauconite. The presence of glauconite, which only forms in shallow marine conditions where sediment accumulates very slowly, marks the beginning of another encroachment of the shallow sea from the west. It also indicates that no large landmass capable of delivering abundant sediment to this patch of seafloor lay nearby.

The main sedimentary layers tilt down to the southeast (toward Serpentine Drive), but groups of layers in the dolomite-sandstone unit actually tilt in the opposite direction, sweeping down to the left. These are what

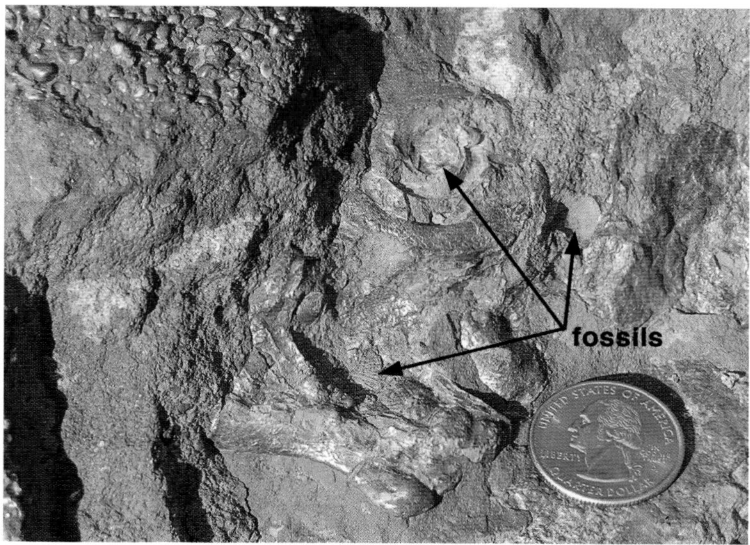

A variety of invertebrate shells and shell fragments are preserved in the red-stained layer of the Sawatch Formation. Look for shells (pointers) above and left of the quarter.

geologists call crossbeds. Here they come in groupings up to 10 feet thick, indicating they were deposited in tall sand dunes. The rock's constituent marine fossils demonstate that these were undersea, not desert, dunes. Strong tidal currents pushed these dunes across the shallow seafloor. The inclination of the crossbeds, down to the northwest, indicates the strongest currents moved from the southeast to the northwest, depositing layer after layer of sand at an angle.

Sea level dropped yet again at the end of the Cambrian period, causing the shallow sea to drain away from this area. But slightly later, about 480 million years ago, during the Ordovician period, the sea returned, depositing limestone of the Manitou Formation as it rose. We know that no rocks exist here from the time of the Cambrian-Ordovician boundary because fossils of that age are missing from the rock sequence. The Manitou Formation is of particular importance for our story because it is the layer in which most of Cave of the Winds was carved. It consists of the thinly bedded, yellowish rock at the cliff top. The outcrop itself is inaccessible, but you can easily examine blocks that have fallen off the cliff. Two such blocks lie next to the gate that blocks the dirt road. The blocks along the road are white because floods coursing down Fountain Creek washed off the yellow surface stain that is produced by chemical weathering.

There is one final feature of this outcrop that is worth noting. A prominent diagonal crack runs up and left across the rock face, and the layers to

Unlayered, pink Pikes Peak granite rises above the dirt road at stop 1 as viewed from the US 24 access road. Brown beds of Sawatch Formation sandstone and dolomite overlie it, separated by an unconformity, which the authors' children are pointing to in the inset photo (dashed box marks location of inset photo). Crossbeds that tilt down to the northwest, opposite the main tilt of the sedimentary layers, are prominent in the Sawatch. Thinly bedded, yellowish sedimentary layers at the top of the cliff belong to the Manitou Formation. Rock layers are displaced across a crack that angles up and left across the cliff face. This is a thrust fault, which has shoved the layers on the right up and over the rocks to the left.

the right (southeast) of it have been displaced up and over the rocks to the left (northwest). This is a small thrust fault. The crack is reasonably easy to spot from stop 1, but the displacement of layers is not. This layer offset is much easier to spot from the higher vantage point along the US 24 access road on the other side of the creek. The eastward tilt you have noticed in the rock layers here was accomplished along similar faults during the Laramide orogeny. That eastward tilt has been an important factor in the formation of Cave of the Winds.

Blocks of the Manitou Formation have tumbled off the cliff at stop 1, allowing for easy examination of their thin limestone beds.

At stop 2 you can see the Manitou Formation in outcrop (the rock wall to your left) and also enjoy a sweeping view of picturesque Williams Canyon. Cave of the Winds is situated below the visitor complex buildings perched on the canyon's western rim. From this vantage point you can easily see that the canyon's sedimentary layers tilt southeastward. Because of this tilt, the result of the uplift of the Rampart Range to the north (vignette 16), Williams Canyon's western walls are composed of Manitou limestone from the bottom to nearly the top, but the eastern wall consists of Manitou only to midheight. The upper east wall consists of the Devonian-age Williams Canyon Formation and, above that, the Mississippian-age Leadville limestone. Each of the limestone units on display in this canyon was deposited during a rise in sea level, and unconformities exist between them. Each unconformity marks a time when sea level fell—times during which no sediment accumulated and the top sediment layers were mildly eroded.

Together the three formations form a 300-foot-thick stack of limestone layers, exactly the raw material necessary to form a cave. There are two reasons for this. First, the limestone beds contain abundant pore spaces (high porosity), and those pore spaces are well connected to each other (high permeability). Groundwater can easily flow through such highly permeable

Stop 2 provides a sweeping view of Williams Canyon, with the Cave of the Winds visitor center perched on its western rim. The canyon's western walls consist of beds of the Manitou Formation that dip to the southeast. The eastern walls display the entire stack of Colorado's late Paleozoic rock layers. The black bars denote the section of cliff composed of each rock formation.

rock layers. Second, limestone is made of calcium carbonate, a chemical compound that dissolves readily in acid. Most groundwater is slightly acidic, so as it percolates through the limestone it dissolves the material, hollowing out caverns.

Three later geologic events, combined with the presence of limestone, produced the perfect setting for cave formation. The first was the accumulation of shale on the seafloor about 315 million years ago, during the Pennsylvanian period. This is the Glen Eyrie shale of the Fountain Formation, which does not transmit groundwater well. The second event occurred between 65 and 54 million years ago, when the modern Rocky Mountains were uplifted. Here in the Colorado Springs area, great blocks of crust were heaved up along two major faults. The Pikes Peak massif was raised along the Ute Pass fault, which parallels Fountain Creek and US 24 just west of here. The Cave of the Winds area was uplifted and tilted down to the southeast along the Rampart Range fault, as is evident in the walls of Williams Canyon. Rainwater began to percolate into the tilted limestone rocks where they were exposed at the surface in the foothills of the Rampart Range, to the north. Water from deep in the Earth seeped along the Ute Pass fault, picking up dissolved minerals along the way as it reacted chemically with the Pikes Peak granite. All the groundwater is forced to flow through the limestone because it is sandwiched between the low-permeability Pikes Peak granite and the low-permeability Glen Eyrie shale. Because the layers are tilted down to the southeast, the groundwater flows that direction.

The third and final key event that set the stage for the creation of Cave of the Winds was the cutting of the canyon of Fountain Creek and those of its tributaries, such as Williams Creek. Once the canyon had breached the limestone, its floor provided a place where the groundwater could escape back to the surface. Today that point of emergence is a series of springs along the banks of Fountain Creek in downtown Manitou Springs (stop 4). But the inconspicuous veneer of river gravel that crowns the mesa top east of Williams Canyon reveals that today's springs constitute a fairly recent escape valve for the water. Fountain Creek deposited the gravel, which is called the Nussbaum alluvium, about 1.5 million years ago. Today the mesa stands 600 feet above the creek, thereby documenting that Fountain Creek and its tributaries have carved their canyons 600 feet deeper since that time. That means that the entire canyon before you at stop 2 was carved during the last 1.5 million years, and the springs lining the banks of Fountain Creek in downtown Manitou Springs were situated above Cave of the Winds 1.5 million years ago, where the river bottom then stood.

As we shall see at stop 4, the properties of the modern Manitou springs indicate that two sources of water are mixing in them. The first source is abundant rainwater and snowmelt that penetrates a few hundred feet into the ground and reemerges a short time later at a spring. The second source is water that has circulated deep in the Earth, where it has been heated. Hot water is very effective at dissolving minerals, so this water emerges at the springs full of iron, manganese, and other minerals that earned it a reputation for being therapeutic and fueled Manitou's fame as a health resort during the late 1800s to early 1900s. The deep water is also charged with carbon dioxide, which makes it highly acidic and hence extremely corrosive to limestone. Cave of the Winds formed between about 4.5 and 1.5 million years ago, the time interval when this corrosive groundwater-mixing zone underlay the springs of Fountain Creek when it flowed near Cave of the Winds. As Fountain Creek and its tributaries carved their canyons deeper, the groundwater-mixing zone dropped in elevation along with them. The mixing zone now lies beneath downtown Manitou Springs, where it is dissolving limestone to form a new cave.

From stop 2 it is just a short drive to the cave itself (stop 3). The visitor center has a few small exhibits about cave formation processes and the history of the cave, but the main attraction is a guided tour of the cave

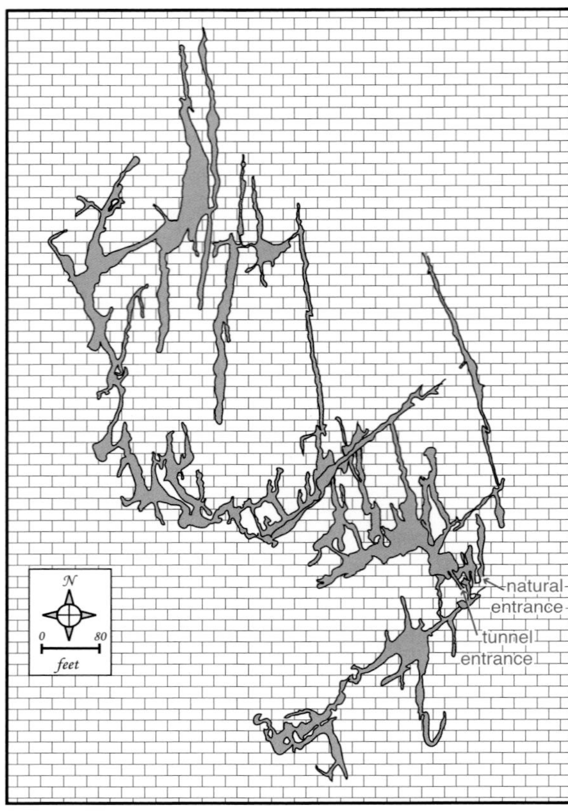

Cave of the Winds, like most caves, consists of a gridwork of passages etched out of the limestone along bedding planes and joints. This is what the cave would look like, in map view, if the layers of rock above it were removed. (Modified from Luiszer, 1999.)

itself. Guided tours traverse only a small fraction of the 2 miles of passages discovered so far, but they visit rooms that contain many of the finest decorations the cave has to offer. A map of the cave highlights its grid of passages. This geometry is typical of caves because the corrosive groundwater that dissolves cave passages migrates along the paths of least resistance. Bedding planes and planar rock fractures known as joints, which are commonly subvertical (nearly but not quite vertical), provide those paths.

You enter the cave through a manmade tunnel that opens onto a natural gallery decorated with stalactites and stalagmites. Stalactites form when solid calcium carbonate, which forms the mineral calcite, precipitates from water drops on the cave ceiling. As the water seeps out of the cave roof, carbon dioxide trapped in the water is able to escape due to the release of pressure. This process is nearly identical to the escape of carbon dioxide from a carbonated soda when you crack open the can, thus releasing the pressure. The escape of carbon dioxide drives the chemical reaction that precipitates the solid calcite (which is what forms limestone rock). All stalactites begin as thin tubes of calcite, called soda straws, which form around the edges of individual water droplets. Over time soda straws become plugged with

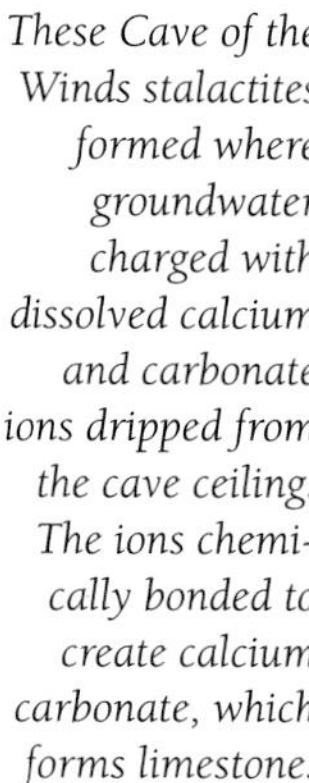

These Cave of the Winds stalactites formed where groundwater charged with dissolved calcium and carbonate ions dripped from the cave ceiling. The ions chemically bonded to create calcium carbonate, which forms limestone.

calcite, forcing water to flow down the outside of the straws, where it precipitates calcite, in the process forming a bulkier stalactite. A stalagmite forms beneath a stalactite, where water dripping from the stalactite drops its load of calcite upon the cave floor. Given enough time, a stalactite and stalagmite will eventually grow together to form a pillar.

When your tour is done, head back down the hill to stop 4 for a tour of the modern springs that gave Manitou Springs its name. Eleven different springs are located within the town, with most of them separated by a short, pleasant stroll through the picturesque town. A brochure and a map of the springs are available at the visitor information center.

For centuries before the arrival of European settlers, Native American tribes used the springs for medicinal purposes. They felt that the natural carbonation was the breath of the Great Spirit Manitou, and they considered the springs sacred. Settlers soon shared this enthusiasm for the springs' healing powers, and by the late 1800s Manitou was known for its health spas. By the middle of the twentieth century the spa culture was in decline and the springs fell into disrepair, but a major renovation effort was begun in the 1980s, and now each spring flows from a clean drip tube into an artistically designed basin. Each is marked with a plaque that includes a brief history of the spring's human use and a chemical analysis of its dissolved minerals. Be sure to bring a cup with you so that you can taste the waters' natural carbonation.

The water of Shoshone Spring is naturally carbonated. The water loses carbon dioxide to the air, which drives a chemical reaction that precipitates a crust of white calcium carbonate (limestone) on the fountain.

If you have time to visit only one of the downtown springs, Shoshone Spring, near the corner of Manitou Avenue and Otoe Place, is a great choice. The spring is housed in a circular stone building with a fountain built into the outer wall. You can easily taste the natural carbonation, and the white crust on the rocks the fountain is constructed of is further testament to the presence of carbon dioxide. The crust consists of newly created limestone that forms when carbon dioxide in the water is released to the air.

Carbon dating has shown that the water coming out of Shoshone and the other downtown springs has remained underground for about 30,000 years. This age represents mixed water. Studies have shown that water percolating down from the surface (meteoric water) spends only a few months underground, whereas water from deep in the Earth wells up slowly, over many millennia, along the Ute Pass fault system. Shoshone Spring has the highest manganese content of any Manitou spring, which provides further evidence that its water comes from the mixing zone. Meteoric water alone would not be able to pick up such mineral content after such a short time beneath the surface.

Very near the cog railway station stands the Iron Spring Geyser. Its water comes exclusively from the Ute Pass fault system; it doesn't mix with

Iron Spring Geyser's water contains abundant dissolved iron, which bonds with oxygen when it reaches the surface, forming rust.

meteoric water. Because it has traveled so slowly through the Pikes Peak granite, it is loaded with dissolved iron. When the water reaches the surface, the iron combines with oxygen to form iron oxide, or simple rust, which coats the spring's Basin.

The early-Paleozoic-age limestone rocks found in Manitou Springs exist in only a handful of other places along the Front Range. It is fortunate they have been preserved here, because they tell us, through their fossils and sedimentary characteristics, about Colorado's earliest inhabitants: creatures who swam in a shallow sea that inundated the area soon after the Cambrian explosion had populated the world with its first complex organisms. The vast accumulation of shells those early invertebrate Coloradans left behind was cemented into the limestone that, 500 million years later, corrosive groundwater etched out to form Cave of the Winds. That water then decorated the cave with stalactites and stalagmites, to the great delight of the cave's many visitors. It is mind-expanding to go spelunking in an ancient sea, all the more so when you finish the day by sipping mineral water from a soda spring and contemplate the unexplored cave that is forming beneath your feet at that very moment. In fact, you can taste a little of the 70 tons of limestone the mineral water dissolves out of this growing cave annually with every sip!

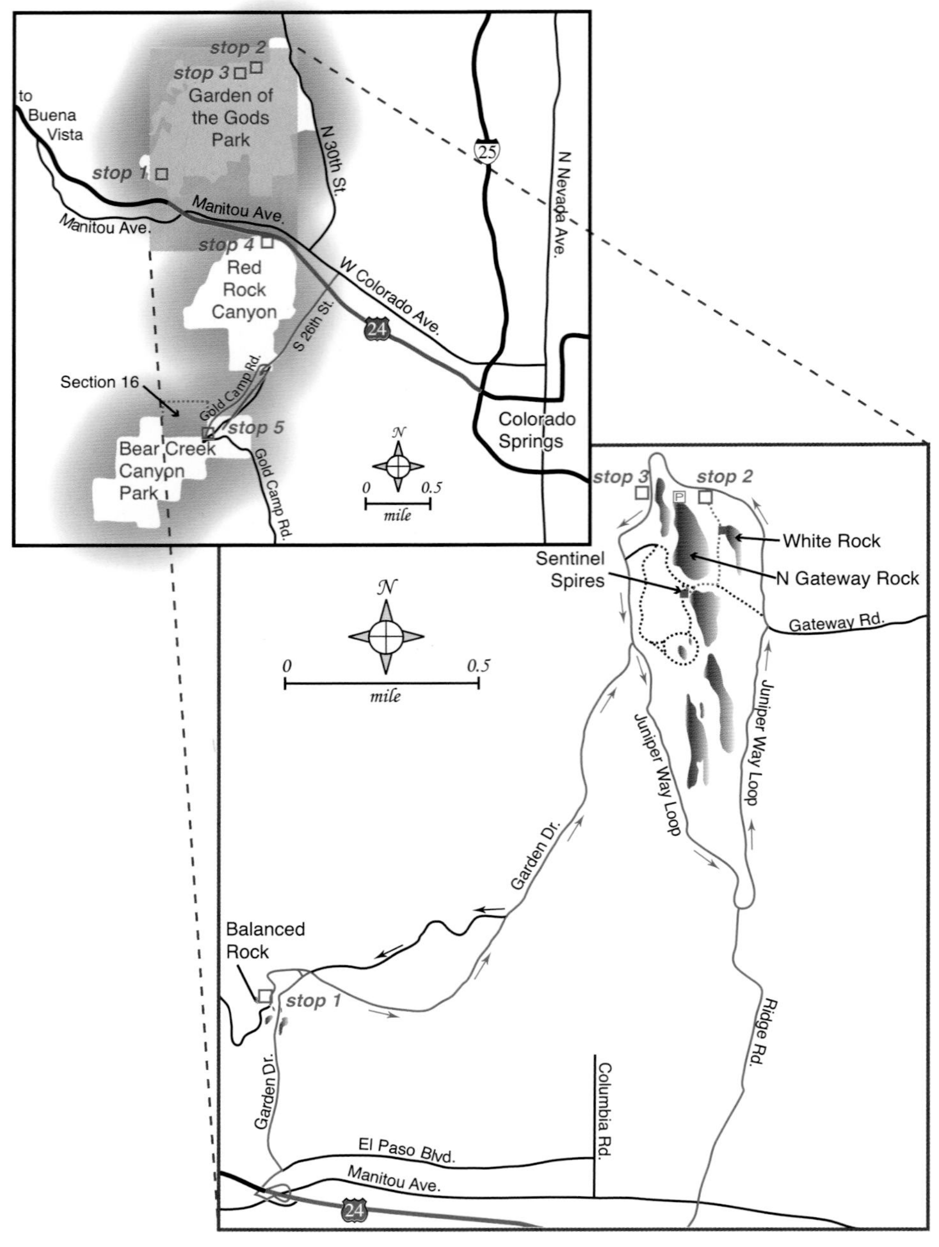

GETTING THERE: Stop 1 is Balanced Rock, an easily recognizable feature in Colorado Springs's beautiful Garden of the Gods Park. From Colorado Springs travel west on US 24 to exit 24 (Manitou Avenue). As you exit, the ramp curves under US 24 and deposits you on Manitou Avenue. After passing under the highway, turn right at the traffic light, following a sign to Garden of the Gods. This road ends at a T-junction after 0.2 mile. Turn right onto El Paso Boulevard. Follow this back under US 24 and take the first left onto Garden Drive (also signed for Garden of the Gods). Follow Garden Drive to the clearly marked Balanced Rock parking area, 0.6 mile from US 24.

16

BUILDING A GARDEN FIT FOR THE GODS

Faulting and Fins at Garden of the Gods and Nearby Parks

Even amongst the Front Range's geologic largesse, western Colorado Springs is something special. Ferdinand Vandeveer Hayden, a famous geologist who in 1867 was appointed director of the Geological and Geographical Survey of the Territories, summed it up best when he said, "I do not know of any portion of the West where there is so much variety displayed in the geology as within a space of 10 miles square around Colorado City" (the original name for Colorado Springs). This amazing diversity is most spectacularly displayed at Garden of the Gods Park, where great sandstone fins jut more than 300 feet into the air. The park acquired its name when surveyor Rufus Cable first laid eyes on these spectacular rocks, in 1859, and exclaimed, this "is a fit place for the gods to assemble!" In this vignette

Stop 2, a collection of several sites we'll explore in the main portion of the park, is best accessed from the Garden of the Gods' North Main Parking Lot. From stop 1, continue northeast on Garden Drive for about 1.5 miles to the one-way Juniper Way Loop, where you must turn right. At the junction with Ridge Road (0.7 mile after you begin the one-way), turn left to stay on Juniper Way Loop. At the junction with Gateway Road (another 0.7 mile) continue north on Juniper Way an additional 0.4 mile to the North Main Parking Lot.

Stop 3 is at the scenic pullout on Juniper Way Loop 0.3 mile beyond the North Main Parking Lot. To reach stop 4, continue south on the loop for 1.1 miles to the junction with Ridge Road. Turn right (south) and follow Ridge Road to US 24. Cross the highway and take the first left onto West High Street, a short spur road that accesses the Red Rock Canyon Open Space. Park at the end of the road in the easternmost parking lot. To reach stop 5, return to the US 24/Ridge Road junction. Head east 1.1 miles on US 24 to 26th Street and turn right (south). Proceed 1.5 miles on 26th, then turn right onto Gold Camp Road and follow it 1.2 miles to the Bear Creek Canyon Park's Section 16 trailhead parking lot.

Garden of the Gods, seen here from stop 3, is home to spectacular pink and white spires of vertically tilted Lyons Formation. Cheyenne Mountain looms in the distance.

we will explore the sequence of geologic events responsible for this amazing scenery.

Balanced Rock (stop 1) is the perfect place to begin our exploration. This precariously perched boulder consists entirely of the Fountain Formation, a sedimentary rock composed of sand and gravel shed off the Ancestral Front Range as it began to rise between 315 and 300 million years ago. Notice the large size of the particles within the formation; there are cobbles up to 10 inches across at eye level on Balanced Rock's pedestal. Streams can't transport such heavy particles very far from their mountain source. This evidence suggests that Colorado Springs lies at what was once the toe of this ancient mountain range (artist Jan Vriesen's painting on page 133 gives you a visual image of what this range might have looked like).

From similar observations throughout the area, geologists have learned that the Ancestral Front Range stood in approximately the same location as the modern Front Range (vignette 5). Yet in the Colorado Springs area scientists have found Fountain Formation gravel and sand interbedded with mudstone and limestone containing marine fossils. The marine mudstone and limestone comprises the Glen Eyrie Member of the Fountain

Balanced rock consists of slightly east-tilted layers of Fountain Formation sandstone that contain pebbles and cobbles.

Formation. The fact that conglomerate and sandstone interfingers with the marine mudstone and limestone reveals that, unlike the modern Front Range, the ancient mountains stood in a shallow, tropical sea.

Geologists once thought the Ancestral Front Range was one large, southeast-trending island that stretched clear across Colorado from Wyoming to New Mexico. However, thanks to recent, detailed work performed here in western Colorado Springs, they have deduced that 315 million years ago the Ancestral Front Range actually consisted of a series of mountainous islands. The south shore of one island lay north of Colorado Springs, in the modern Rampart Range. Farther south, where Pikes Peak now stands, rose another island, called the Ute Pass uplift. Back then, the US 24 corridor between Pikes Peak and the Rampart Range was also lower in elevation, as it is now, and formed a narrow strait connecting larger seas to the east and west. The Glen Eyrie Member was deposited in that strait.

Both mountainous islands were composed of the Pikes Peak granite, a 1,080-million-year-old, hard igneous rock (vignette 14). Vigorous mountain erosion wore this rock away and dumped the debris into the strait, where it accumulated on a series of alluvial fans to a thickness of over

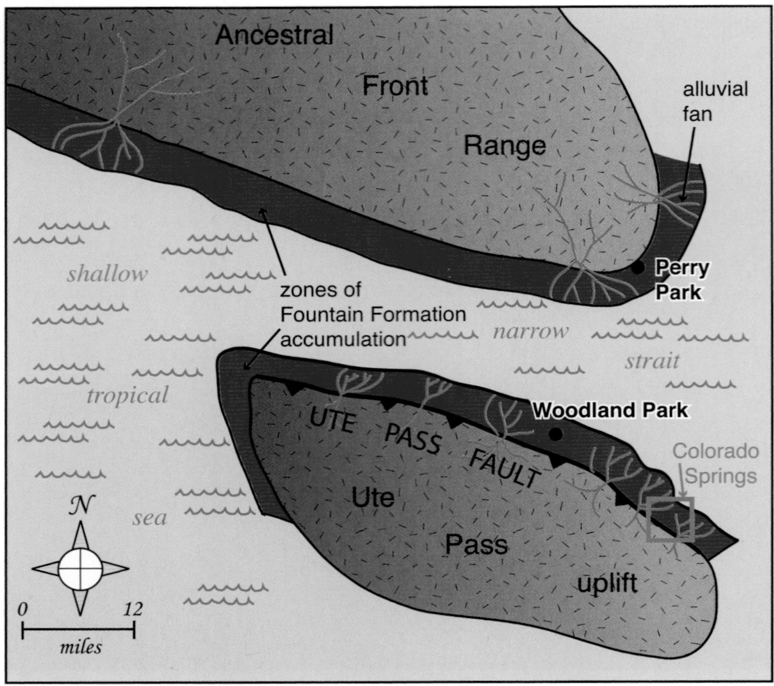

Today's US 24 corridor was, 315 million years ago, a narrow strait that separated two mountainous islands of the Ancestral Front Range. (Modified from Sweet and Soreghan, 2010.)

4,000 feet. By 300 million years ago so much sediment had accumulated that the alluvial fans coalesced and filled the strait all the way up to sea level. With the two islands merged, no more Glen Eyrie marine sediment accumulated, only conglomerate and sandstone of the type you see here at Balanced Rock.

The Ute Pass uplift was raised along the Ute Pass fault. Faulting in the same area later raised Pikes Peak during the Laramide orogeny. The Ute Pass reverse fault runs north along the eastern flank of Cheyenne Mountain, then bends northwestward to parallel US 24 through Manitou Springs and beyond. The fault is located at the break in slope where the mountain walls become noticeably steeper. The Ute Pass fault has seen some activity during the Quaternary period, but we know it was also active during the uplift of the Ancestral Rockies, in part because its movement slightly folded the then newly deposited Fountain Formation, but these folds are absent from younger formations.

Geologists don't know how high the Ancestral Rockies rose but have long assumed they reached modest elevations of only a few thousand feet above sea level. Given that they rose out of a tropical sea, the presumption has been that they enjoyed a warm climate. However, globally, the average climate during the Ancestral Rockies' heyday was quite cool. Glacial sediments from places like Australia and Africa show that the planet was locked in the grip of an ice age even more intense than the more recent and better-known Pleistocene (vignette 3). We know that during the Pleistocene (and even today) ice caps on high tropical mountains, such as Africa's Kilimanjaro, grew and descended to lower elevations. Could the Ancestral Rockies, despite their tropical location, have been high enough to support freezing temperatures, or even glaciers?

Alas, geologists today lack tools to directly measure the elevations of the Ancestral Rockies, so their former height is a matter of spirited debate. Recent work, though, has led some geologists to conclude that the Ancestral Ute Pass uplift was high enough to endure freezing temperatures, and the Balanced Rock area has provided key evidence. To examine the evidence yourself, walk west about 50 yards from Balanced Rock and cross the gravel Rampart Range Road (you can also drive here, but there isn't a good place to park). Look in the western road cut for a pattern of polygons composed of white sandstone amidst the Fountain Formation's more typical pink sandstone. Sand cracks create this polygonal pattern. They look just like mud cracks, which form because mud expands when wet and shrinks when dry. But sand doesn't similarly expand and shrink, so sand cracks can't form through this process.

Similar sand cracks are found today in cold climates, where sand alternately freezes and thaws. Some scientists have concluded that the Fountain's sand cracks formed the same way, thereby recording at least occasional freezing temperatures in the ancient Ute Pass mountains. Based on independent evidence, these same geologists even speculate that the Ute Pass uplift actually hosted glaciers. They estimate these rivers of ice flowed down to about 5,000 to 6,000 feet of elevation, meaning the ancestral peaks above Colorado Springs must have stood considerably higher.

Before leaving stop 1, we need to make one last important observation. Notice that the sedimentary layers at Balanced Rock tilt down to the east at a gentle angle of about 15 degrees. File this fact away for comparison with the layers at stop 2, where we will now head.

From the parking lot at stop 2, walk south on the paved, wheelchair-accessible Perkins Central Garden Trail to the Sentinel Spires. During this short stroll you find yourself surrounded by the Garden of the Gods' signature rock spires. To your left (east) a fin of white sandstone called White Rock rears skyward, while to your right (west) looms an even larger wall of pink sandstone known as North Gateway Rock. These rocks lack the pebbles and cobbles so abundant at Balanced Rock. Despite their color

Some scientists conclude that freezing and thawing of Fountain Formation sand in a cold climate during the Pennsylvanian period caused these polygonal fractures to form and fill with white sand.

difference, both walls consist of the Permian-age Lyons Formation, which was deposited after—and therefore on top of—the Fountain.

After the path bends west, look to the right for an interpretive plaque titled "Time Frozen in Stone" next to the Sentinel Spires, whose rock layers have been tilted nearly vertical, forming two impressive fins. As the plaque describes, the Sentinels consist of two different types of rock, one white and one pink. The Sentinel Spires lie in the transition zone from the Fountain Formation to the Lyons Formation. Viewed from the plaque, the Sentinels appear to be the edge of a sandwich, with white "bread" layers encasing a pink "filling." The white layers contain small pebbles embedded in sand. In this sense they resemble the Fountain Formation you observed at Balanced Rock, except the pebbles here are considerably smaller. The intervening pink layers, by contrast, closely resemble the typical Lyons Formation you saw on North Gateway Rock in that they consist of pure sand devoid of pebbles.

Locate a wavy pattern in a white pebbly bed at eye level on the rock's west face, about eight steps north of, and across the sidewalk from, the plaque. These waves are ripple marks sculpted by a river current as it flowed across the landscape one day some 285 million years ago! The small size of the pebbles tells us that by the time these sedimentary layers were being deposited, the Ancestral Rockies were no longer being uplifted vigorously along the Ute Pass fault. These were the Ancestral Rockies' final days; as erosion inexorably diminished their stature, the rivers that drained them became progressively less energetic and therefore transported much smaller particles than they had during the mountains' heyday, when the material that forms Balanced Rock was deposited.

Not only do the pink sand layers lack pebbles, but the sandstone is homogenous. If you have a magnifying glass or a hand lens, you can see that each grain has a smooth, round shape and is nearly identical in size to its neighbors. These are characteristics of sand deposited by wind to form sand dunes. Wind sorts sediment by size much more efficiently than does water, and the numerous high-energy, grain-to-grain collisions that occur during wind transport rounds the grains.

When the sediment that composes the Sentinel Spires was being deposited, sand dunes were beginning to blow across the increasingly arid

Sentinel Spires are composed of pebble-bearing, white sandstone layers interbedded with pink sandstone layers that have all been rotated vertically by activity on the Rampart Range fault. The ripple marks and pebbles are visible on the rock's left skyline, as shown in the inset (dashed box marks location of inset photo).

landscape. A few creeks and rivers managed to straggle across the sandy plain, draining the nearby low hills that were all that remained of the once mighty Ancestral Rockies. The Sentinels' pink layers are what remains of those very first dunes; their white, ripple-marked layers were left by the creeks. The Sentinel Spires' interpretive plaque includes a painting by artist Jan Vriesen that will help you visualize this scene (painting reproduced on page 135).

Another telltale characteristic of dune-deposited sandstone is the presence of large-scale crossbedding. This pattern comprises layers in the rock composed of thin sand beds that intersect the overall orientation of the layering of the Lyons Formation. Some of the crossbeds approach angles of 30 degrees to the horizontal. All of the pebble-free layers here in the central Garden of the Gods contain such crossbedding, but later events obscured it. We'll examine crossbedding at stop 4.

Soon after the sediments of the Sentinel Spires had been deposited, much larger dunes engulfed the region. You can examine the rocks of this period on your stroll back to the car. Pause first at North Gateway Rock, whose pure, pebble-free sandstone is the legacy of that Permian sand sea. It consists of the Lyons Formation's lower sandstone member. Creeks draining the nearby hills made a brief comeback a short time after the lower sandstone had been deposited, likely in response to a wetter climate. These creeks deposited beds of sandstone and pebbly conglomerate (the Lyons's middle member) that resemble the Sentinels' white layers. Because of its poor cementation, this material was quickly eroded. It forms the grassy corridor you walk through between North Gateway Rock and White Rock. As the climate dried out, once again the dunes returned, forming the well-sorted, well-rounded sand grains that compose White Rock, which is made of the uppermost of the three Lyons sandstone members (see the figure on page 216).

Recall the gentle eastward tilt of the layers at stop 1. Compare that to the layers at stop 2, which have all been stood on end. Why are these rocks standing vertically while the rocks just 2 miles to the southwest are barely tilted? The extra-wide wheelchair pullout near the restroom facility provides a vantage point from which to examine White Rock closely. A web of light-colored deformation bands, each less than 0.25 inch thick, crisscrosses the rock's face. These bands are characteristic of deformation in high-porosity sandstones such as the Lyons. Their abundance tells us that a fault lies nearby. In fact, it runs right under your feet. This is a reverse (compressional) fault that shoved the white rock of the upper Lyons Formation westward, over the pink rock of the lower Lyons, in the process rotating the adjacent rock layers to vertical.

Because the Lyons Formation, which was deposited 280 million years ago, has been tilted by fault motion, the fault must have moved more

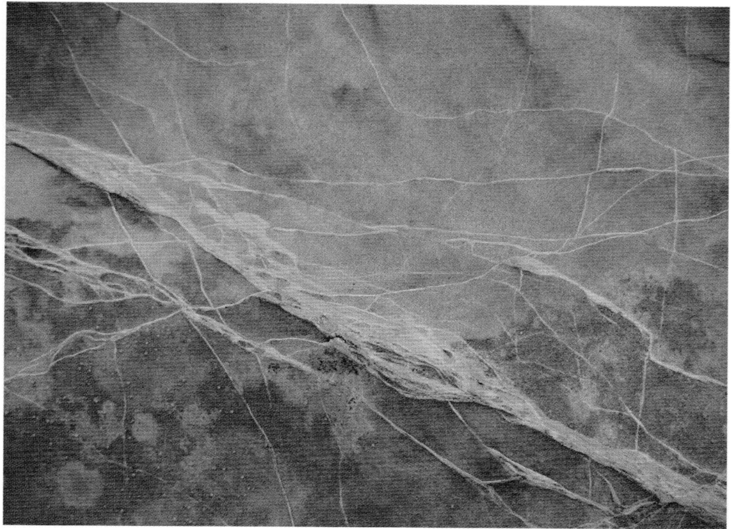

White deformation bands crisscross White Rock. Such bands are abundant in the vicinity of large faults, such as the Rampart Range fault that you examine at stop 3.

recently than that. We can further narrow the time of fault movement if we detect any younger rock formations that have also been tilted. Between here and the Garden of the Gods Visitor Center, several smaller, vertical fins of rock exist, all younger than the Lyons. In fact, every rock layer in the Colorado Springs area deposited prior to 64 million years ago has been tilted. It is based on such evidence that geologists have determined the timing of the Laramide orogeny, the mountain building event that uplifted the modern Rocky Mountains (vignette 2).

At White Rock we can see the deformation bands that are associated with fault movement, but we can't see the fault itself. The Tower of Babel, the tallest and most spectacular portion of North Gateway Rock, provides us with an intimate glimpse of an actual fault. To reach it, walk to the northwest corner of the parking lot. A dirt path begins just beyond a split-rail fence; follow it southwest for about 100 yards to the tower's base.

When viewed from the north, the Tower of Babel's sheer wall of Lyons sandstone rises directly above a mass of low, lumpy rock that appears to consist of similar layers. However, the rocks at the tower's base consist of the Fountain Formation, as revealed by their telltale pebbles. The Lyons sandstone above is separated from the Fountain rock by a planar crack that angles down to the east. This is a fault plane. The younger Lyons Formation has been moved up and over the older Fountain Formation. Reverse faults typically shove older rocks over younger ones. That typical age progression

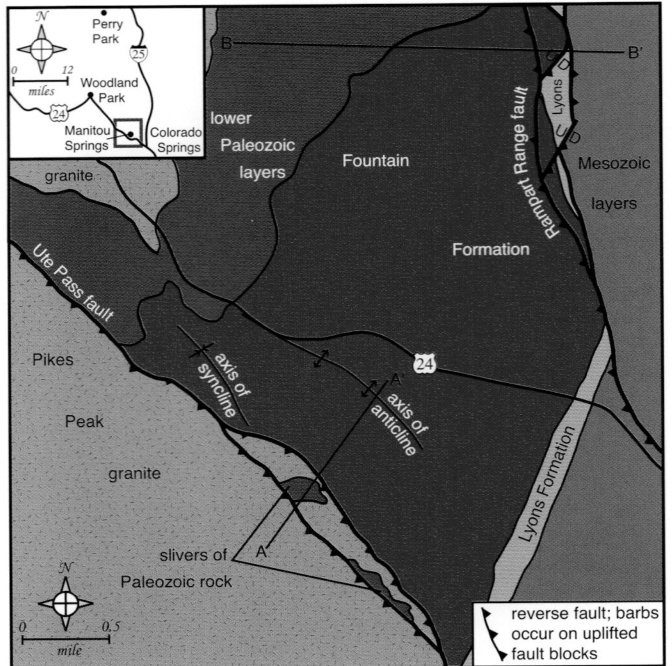

Geologic map and interpretational cross sections showing the geology of the Garden of the Gods and surrounding region. (Modified from Morgan et al., 2003; Sweet and Soreghan, 2010.)

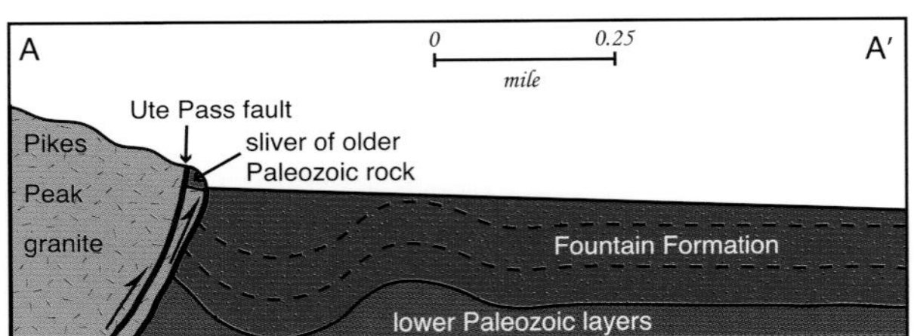

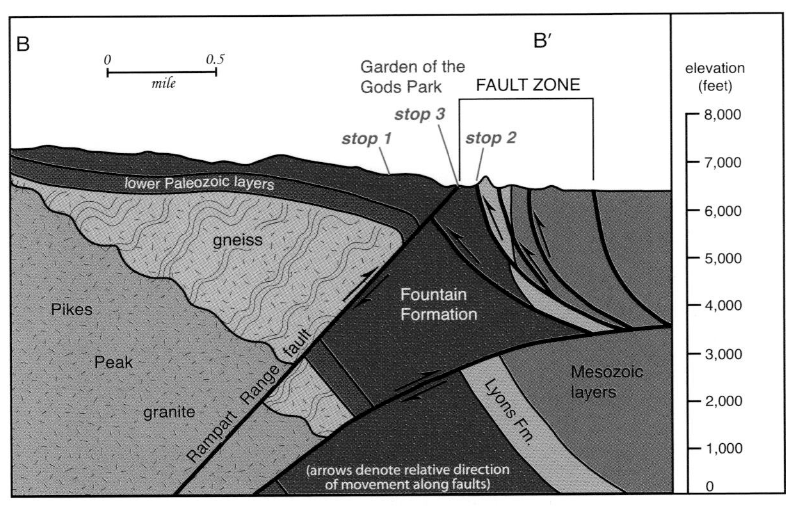

The Tower of Babel (looking south) is a spire of Lyons Formation sandstone that has been thrust to the west, up and over the Fountain Formation.

is inverted here because the up-and-west rock motion along this small, subsidiary splay fault is the opposite of the up-and-east rock movement along the main strand of the Rampart Range fault, which you will observe at stop 3. That main strand is the area's master fault, but like most major faults, the Rampart Range fault splits into multiple strands (splays) near the surface, forming a fault zone. The subsidiary strands, such as this one, can and commonly do move in the opposite direction of the master fault.

Immediately below the fault plane the otherwise vertical Fountain layers have been bent toward the west. Called a drag fold, this bend formed when the Lyons rocks above the fault were forcefully shoved to the west, bending the underlying Fountain rocks in the process. The violent cracking, deformation bands, and rock tilting on display at stop 2 all testify to the immense power unleashed through faults by plate tectonics. It is sobering to consider that the fault you have examined here is merely a small branch of the major fault that shaped Garden of the Gods.

The view from stop 3 is breathtaking, particularly in the afternoon light. Vertical rock fins rear up from the patchwork of forest and grassland

The Fountain Formation beds in the Tower of Babel were bent in response to the westward movement of the Lyons Formation rocks over them.

Looking south-southeast from Red Rock Canyon Open Space (stop 4), the south-trending ridges of Lyons Formation are truncated by Pikes Peak granite, which moved up and toward the camera along the Ute Pass fault. This truncation is also visible in the distance from stop 3.

blanketing the foreground valley. Pine-clad Cheyenne Mountain, with its crown of communication towers, is the highest, bulkiest massif on the skyline. The Ute Pass fault lies at the change in slope where Cheyenne Mountain and the other foothills peaks rear up at a noticeably steeper pitch. If you look carefully at the grass-covered landscape below the peaks, you can detect several southwest-trending ridges that abruptly end at the break in slope. These ridges are southward extensions of the vertical rock layers of Lyons Formation. The Precambrian-age Pikes Peak granite, which comprises the steeper terrain above the break, was faulted up next to the sedimentary rocks along the Ute Pass fault, thereby truncating the ridges.

Stop 3 is an excellent place to examine not only the handiwork of a large fault at the landscape scale, as we have with the distant Ute Pass fault, but also what a large fault looks like up close and personal. Notice that the material in the road cut directly across the road consists of a jumble of loose particles ranging in size from boulders to mud. As you head south from stop 3, the road curves to the west. All the cuts between stop 3 and the turnoff to the disabled parking area consist of the loose jumble of particles. If you were to walk across this area, you would find that the jumbled zone is not random, but rather forms a northwest-southeast line about 300 feet wide. This line of loose debris is the calling card of the Garden of the Gods' biggest fault, the Rampart Range reverse fault.

Named for the Rampart Range, which it heaved skyward on its back during the Laramide orogeny, the fault runs along the break in slope at the eastern toe of the Rampart Range. It extends from Perry Park in the north, through the Garden of the Gods, to an intersection with the Ute Pass fault south of US 24. Here, the fault separates the slightly east-tilted rock we saw at stop 1 from the vertical rock fins of stop 2, and it is primarily responsible for standing the Garden of the Gods' rocks up on end. Like most major faults it is not an obvious feature because it hides in the crushed rock formed by its own movement. This pulverized rock enhances soil formation and vegetation growth, further obscuring the fault.

Stop 4 is located in the Red Rock Canyon Open Space, which protects the southern extension of the rock layers that compose the Garden of the Gods' vertical rock fins. Because the Rampart Range fault didn't move nearly as much at stop 4 as it did in the Garden of the Gods, the rocks have maintained more of their original appearance. One benefit of this cleaner appearance is that the Lyons Formation's characteristic large-scale crossbedding, a hallmark of its upper and lower members having been deposited in sand dunes, is on excellent display. Look for it on the delightful 0.5-mile hike up the Red Rock Canyon Trail. If you are up for a slightly longer excursion, continue up the same trail (a 0.85-mile walk) to visit the Kenmuir rock quarry, which began operations in the 1870s. Blocks of Lyons sandstone quarried here were shipped as far away as Texas, and

The Rampart Range fault has pulverized the rock at stop 3, creating a 300-foot-wide line of debris.

The Lyons sandstone at stop 4 includes a lower set of beds deposited at a 30-degree angle relative to the overlying set of beds. This large-scale crossbedding is characteristic of sand that accumulated in a sand dune.

The Dakota Group layers at stop 5 were rotated to vertical by fault movement during the Laramide orogeny.

Kenmuir stone was used in the construction of several historic Denver buildings, including the Molly Brown House.

Before you leave the Red Rock Canyon Open Space, take a moment to examine the rock cut that rises above the lower parking area. This is an excellent exposure of steeply tilted red and pink layers belonging to the upper Fountain Formation. Several layers near the cut's western end have been displaced along a planar crack that angles down to the east. The planar crack is yet another small thrust fault that shoved the rocks above the fault plane up and west relative to the ones below.

At stop 5, in Bear Creek Canyon Park, we will walk across the Ute Pass fault. In fact, our starting point sits directly on the fault zone. From the parking lot for the Section 16 Trail, walk back north along the road (toward town) 500 feet to the prominent road cut. Here Gold Camp Road was blasted through vertically tilted beds of the erosion-resistant, Cretaceous-age Purgatoire Formation and Dakota Group. A southern continuation of this ridge is visible across the canyon of Bear Creek. Now walk back to the parking area and head south for 500 feet to the next outcrop. This rock is completely different from the layered sedimentary rock nearby. It is Precambrian-age Pikes Peak granite.

The juxtaposition of the sedimentary rocks and granite reveals that somewhere on our short stroll we crossed the Ute Pass fault. Like the Rampart Range fault and most other large ones, the fault plane is not visible. The telltale feature revealing the fault is the abrupt truncation of the south-marching sedimentary ridges at a wall of Pikes Peak granite (and the Lyons Formation ridges we observed from stop 3, which ended abruptly at granite). During the Laramide orogeny the sedimentary beds were first tilted to vertical, then the Ute Pass fault lifted Pikes Peak granite up against the younger sedimentary units.

Here in western Colorado Springs, the Rampart Range and the Ute Pass faults have stood a 7,000-foot-thick stack of sedimentary layers up on end, making it possible to traverse their 500-million-year history with just a short hike. Framed against the backdrop of Pikes Peak and a cobalt blue sky, the pink and white rock fins indeed make a garden fit for the gods.

17

HALLMARKS OF A HOTHOUSE WORLD
Paint Mines Interpretive Park

About 55 million years ago Earth's climate suddenly went haywire. Our planet warmed as much as 18°F in just a few thousand years—the geological blink of an eye. Because this temperature spike occurred near the boundary between the Paleocene and Eocene epochs, geologists have named it the Paleocene-Eocene Thermal Maximum (PETM). The rock record reveals that the PETM was a time of ecological chaos on land and at sea, including North America's greatest-ever turnover in mammal faunas, a huge influx of invasive plant and insect species, and the extinction of 40 percent of shelled deep-sea microorganisms. The PETM is also associated with significant changes in atmospheric and oceanic circulation. Given the rapid warming the planet has experienced during the last two hundred years, many scientists suspect that we may be on the path to an encore performance of this hyperthermal event. They therefore look to the ecological consequences of the PETM for guidance regarding what a worst-case ecological scenario might be as Earth continues to warm.

The hallmarks of this hotter world are colorfully displayed on Colorado's High Plains at El Paso County's Paint Mines Interpretive Park, the best place in Colorado to see the Paleocene-Eocene transition. Here, a 30-foot-thick section of soft mudstone, artfully splashed with pigments of red, pink, yellow, and purple, is sandwiched between layers of hard white sandstone deposited by rivers draining the newly risen Rocky Mountains.

The Front Range was uplifted during the Laramide orogeny by a series of faults that run along the toe of the modern mountains. As soon as the peaks were raised, Mother Nature began to break them down. The mountains west of Paint Mines consisted (as they do today) almost exclusively of Pikes Peak granite (vignette 14), the weathering of which produces abundant crystals of quartz and feldspar. Rivers draining the mountains spread layers of quartz and feldspar sand, called the Dawson arkose, across the adjacent portions of the Great Plains, creating the white sandstones that sandwich the colorful mudstones.

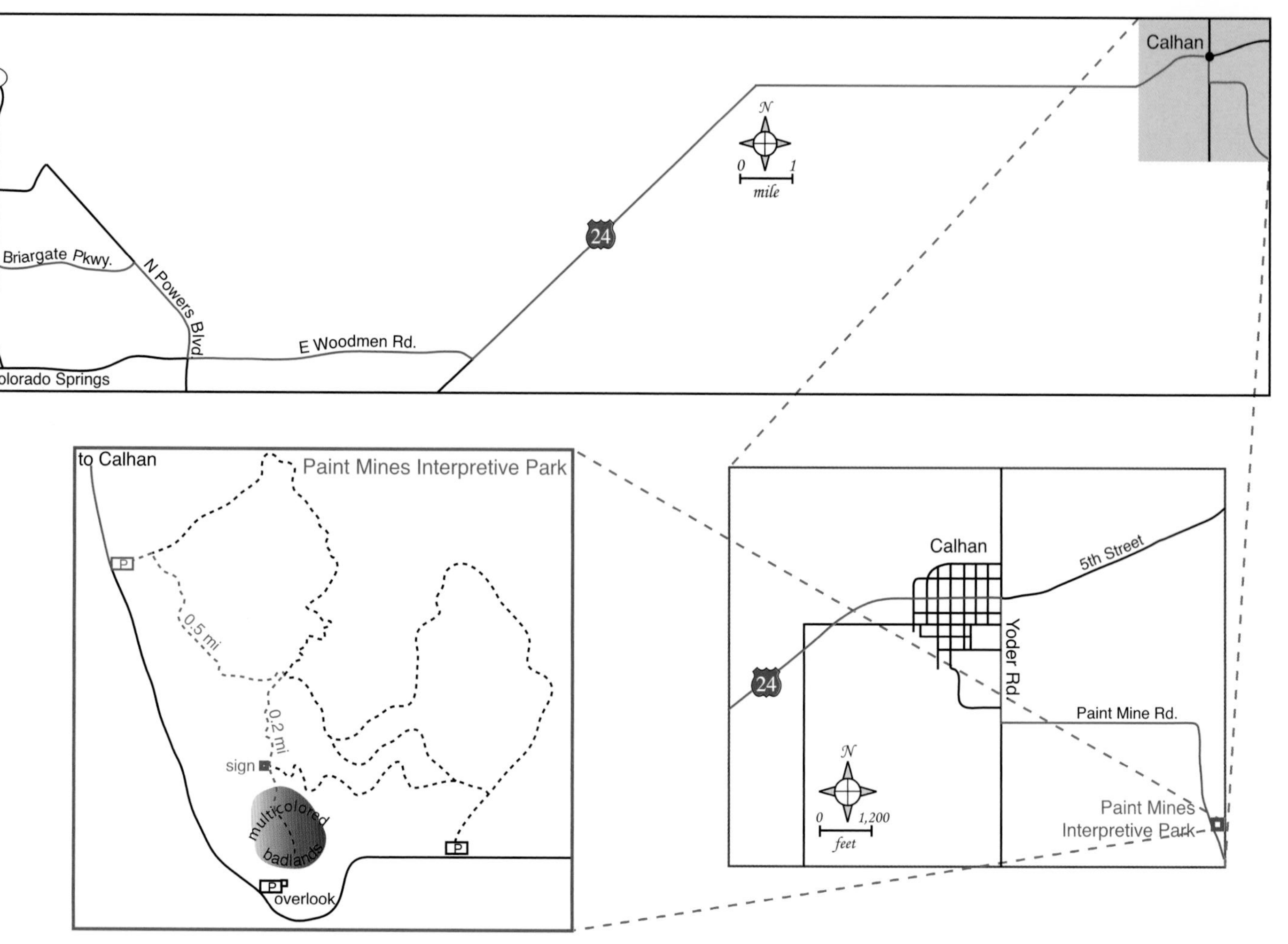

83
25
exit
151
Briargate Pkwy.
N Powers Blvd
E Woodmen Rd.
to Colorado Springs
24
N
0
1
mile
Calhan
to Calhan
Paint Mines Interpretive Park
P
0.5 mi
0.2 mi
sign
multicolored
badlands
overlook
Calhan
5th Street
Yoder Rd.
Paint Mine Rd.
Paint Mines
Interpretive Park
1,200
feet

GETTING THERE: Paint Mines Interpretive Park lies just southeast of the town of Calhan. To get to Calhan from Colorado Springs, travel east for 30 miles on US 24. From Denver, travel south on I-25 about 60 miles to exit 151 (Briargate Parkway). Follow Briargate east for 3.6 miles and turn right onto North Powers Boulevard. Continue 2.4 miles and take the East Woodmen Road exit. Turn left (east) onto East Woodman Road and drive 6.5 miles to the junction with US 24. Turn left onto US 24 and travel 18.8 miles to Calhan. From Calhan turn right (south) onto Yoder Road at the east end of town. After 0.6 mile turn left (east) onto Paint Mine Road (good gravel). After 0.9 mile Paint Mine Road executes a 90-degree right turn. Park in the clearly signed lot on the left 0.5 mile beyond this turn.

At the trailhead there is a metal sign that shows park trails and points of interest. You want to head to the map's Point 6. To get there, follow the obvious trail 200 yards east to the first junction. Turn right (south) on a wide gravel trail and follow it for 0.5 mile to the next junction, which is in the park's deepest wash. Turn right and follow a sandy trail up the wash. As you walk the wash, look for layers of dark gray lignite in the low cliffs that line the east bank. After walking 0.2 mile up the wash you reach an interpretive sign describing the park's rock formations (Point 6 on the park map). From the sign continue up the wash a few hundred yards. Here you will be surrounded by the white, purple, red, and tan badlands that are the focus of this vignette.

Alternatively, if you prefer to view the geology from above, continue driving along Paint Mine Road another 0.5 mile beyond the main parking lot to the overlook parking area on the left. A casual 200-yard walk along a wheelchair-accessible gravel path leads to an excellent overlook of the same badlands.

The eye-catching mudstones, however, formed quite differently. They are the product of intense chemical weathering of the sediment layers, which formed soils. Such ancient soils are fittingly called paleosols. The park earned its name because Native Americans who have lived in the area for nine thousand years collected the vibrantly colored paleosols for pigment in pottery and ceremonial paint. Euro-American settlers have also harnessed these colorful clays to make bricks and ceramics from pioneer times to the present day.

From the main parking area, proceed past the first and second trail junctions and up the wash. As you walk, you will see several dark gray layers interbedded with the thicker, more abundant tan sandstone in the low cliffs east of the wash. These gray layers consist of lignite, soft coal beds that are the preserved remains of ancient swamps. Chemically, swamps are exceptionally good at preserving whatever happens to fall into them. These layers are no exception, as we discuss later in the vignette.

Cenozoic era			
period		**epoch**	**age** (millions of years ago)
Quaternary		Holocene	0.0117
		Pleistocene	2.6
TERTIARY	Neogene	Pliocene	5.3
		Miocene	23
	Paleogene	Oligocene	33.9
		Eocene	D2 sequence
			55.8 ←paleosol
		Paleocene	
			65.5 D1 sequence

Timescale for the Cenozoic era. The PETM occurred 55 million years ago, near the boundary between the Paleocene and the Eocene epochs. The rocks at Paint Mines belong to the D1 and the D2 sequences, whose ages are plotted on the timescale.

The variegated badlands sandwiched between white sandstone layers are ancient soils that formed during the PETM. The multiple, colorful soils are also separated from one another by white, river-deposited sandstone, telling scientists that periods of soil formation alternated with those of stream deposition.

Coal (lignite) seams like this one in the Paint Mines wash are the remains of ancient swamps, which often preserved leaf fossils.

As you continue up the wash past the coal seams, you are soon enveloped by multicolored badlands carved out of the 30-foot-thick paleosol-bearing rock unit. *Badlands* is the term used to describe a terrain of soft rocks that lacks vegetation and has been extensively gullied. As you walk amongst them, you can see how badlands quickly and easily crumble away. The Paint Mines badlands owe their continued existence to the protection provided by several erosion-resistant, white to tan sandstone layers above them.

The capping sandstones have been dated at 54.3 million years old, placing them in the earliest Eocene epoch. In the local geological terminology, they are part of the D2 sedimentary sequence. By contrast, the sandstones below the paleosol unit are nearly 10 million years older, dating to 64.1 million years ago—the early Paleocene. They belong to the D1 sedimentary sequence. This large age discrepancy in sediment layers close to each other in the rock stack means that a gap in time, an unconformity, exists here. The cause of this gap could have been a pause in uplift of the Rockies, resulting in less sediment delivered to the region; a change in climate, which increased weathering; or both. Either way, the rocks that sat at the surface during the long pause in sediment accumulation would have been subject to extensive weathering.

Given that the paleosol unit lies at the unconformity, geologists understandably assumed that it marks the weathered top of the D1 sedimentary sequence that lies below the unconformity. If so, that means the paleosols began forming in the early Paleocene, about 64 million years ago. However, when paleosol specialists looked more closely at the characteristics of these colorful beds, they realized that this unit doesn't consist of a single, continuous, thick paleosol created during a prolonged break in sedimentation. Rather, it contains a number of thinner paleosols that formed during a period of very slow sediment accumulation. As you walk amidst the paleosol-bearing unit, you can see for yourself that the pastel paleosols are patchy, with pods of white, stream-transported sandstone separating one colorful paleosol from the next.

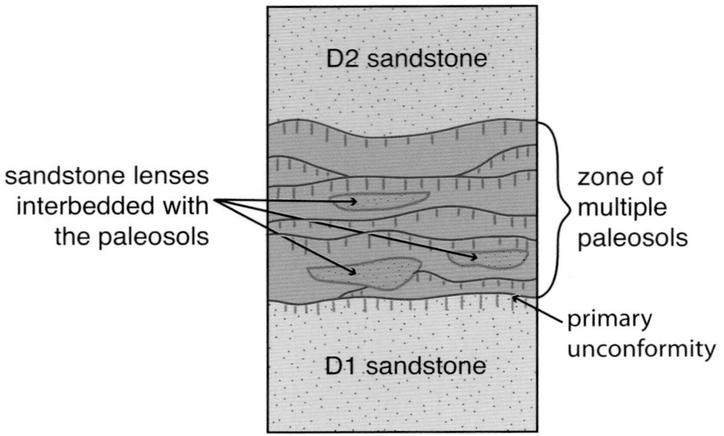

The Paint Mine paleosols are interspersed with channels of white sandstone, evidence that they form many small soil layers instead of one thick deposit.

Trivial though that distinction may sound, this revelation bears critically on when the paleosols formed. It means that they don't lie just *below* the time gap, at the top of the D1 sequence as previously thought, but rather just *above* the time gap, at the bottom of the Eocene-age D2 sequence. Pollen dating later confirmed this conclusion. That age places the paleosols squarely at the PETM, the single largest hyperthermal event of the last 65 million years. Intuitively, this age recasting makes abundant sense because the chemical reactions that turn sediment into soil double in speed with every 18°F increase in temperature. The PETM hothouse put soil formation into overdrive, and you can see the effects all around you.

From the details of the stacked paleosols, the same scientists were also able to glean what the climate was like in Colorado during the PETM. Unsurprisingly, Colorado was hotter back then. But more surprisingly, Colorado was considerably drier than it had been previously. The dark lignite layers you saw in the D1 sequence below the paleosols formed thanks to the growth, about 64 million years ago, of a forest that required abundant,

Shed off the young Rocky Mountains, the cliff-capping tan sandstones overlying the badlands have preserved the PETM paleosols. Both the sandstones and the colorful paleosols below them belong to the Eocene-age D2 sedimentary sequence.

continuous soil moisture in order to form. In contrast, the characteristics of the paleosols reveal that 9 million years later the Front Range had a tropical or subtropical climate marked by strongly seasonal precipitation, including witheringly parched dry seasons. The reason this is surprising is that most computer models used to determine ancient climates indicate that the world was, overall, wetter during the PETM. However, in the midst of a globally wetter climate there will inevitably be dry areas, and the Paint Mines evidence is consistent with evidence gathered in Wyoming and other PETM sites throughout the American West. This was a dry region during the PETM.

The differing pigmentation along the trail is firsthand evidence of the former moisture levels in the paleosols. The red pigments are due to an abundance of hematite, an iron oxide mineral. Because periodic soil desiccation oxidizes iron, turning it red, hematite forms in well-drained soils that lie in hot climates marked by strong seasonal precipitation extremes. The gray and yellowish brown splotches within these red paleosols were produced by chemical reactions that occurred during the wet season, when the soils became saturated with water. Other paleosols are a vivid purple. Chemical reactions with pooled water in poorly drained soils created this color. The downward percolation of stagnant surface water created bleached areas in the purple pigments. The bleached areas also host yellowish brown mottles that formed during the wet season. As you might imagine, the places where reds and purples blend are areas where drainage was intermediate, between that of poorly drained purple and well-drained red paleosols.

Researchers have excavated an impressive array of well-preserved leaf fossils from the lignite beds here at Paint Mines and numerous other locations. The fossils tell a fascinating tale of climatic and ecological change across the Front Range during the early Cenozoic. Of particular note was the discovery, in 1994, of an unusually rich trove of immaculately preserved, 64.1-million-year-old leaves in D1-sequence rocks during the construction of an interstate exit along I-25 in Castle Rock (a short distance south of Denver). The tremendously diverse leaves reveal that the Front Range foothills were covered by a rainforest reminiscent of today's Amazon. Over one hundred different species of trees thrived in this rainforest, one of the oldest known from anywhere on the planet. Of even greater interest is the fact that Colorado sported such impressive biotic diversity a mere 1.4 million years after the devastating Cretaceous-Tertiary asteroid impact (vignette 21). Over 70 percent of all Earth's species perished in that event. The Castle Rock rainforest fossils show that life rebounded and diversified after that catastrophe much more quickly than scientists had believed it could.

In contrast, the considerably less diverse, contemporaneous fossil floras recovered from locations east of the Front Range, at Paint Mines and elsewhere, reveal that the Great Plains, despite being continuously moist during the early Paleocene, were not nearly as wet as the foothills of the Rockies and did not support a full-fledged rainforest. This discovery strongly suggests that during the Paleocene, the Front Range was visited seasonally by moist monsoon air masses (vignette 4) that moved westward from the Gulf of Mexico across the Great Plains. These air masses brought abundant moisture to all of eastern Colorado, but as they tried to climb the mountains they unleashed especially large deluges on the eastern foothills, nourishing the thriving rainforest. Today's upslope snowstorms that bring abundant snowfall to the Front Range foothills are reminiscent of those earlier storms, though the Paleocene storms were considerably warmer and wetter.

In contrast to the evidence for abundant moisture contained in the D1 rocks below the PETM paleosols, the fossils found in the overlying D2 rocks at Paint Mines and elsewhere reveal that by the early Eocene, 55 to 53 million years ago, the Front Range climate was warmer and drier. The lush rainforests were, by then, already a distant memory.

By piecing together the clues embedded in ancient sediments, geologists have been able to reconstruct how the area's climate changed with the onset of the PETM. But how much did it change and why? The most important evidence comes from the chemical analyses of marine seashells, which retain a chemical fingerprint from which scientists can glean past climate information. The varying composition of oxygen isotopes (atoms of oxygen that contain different numbers of neutrons) recorded in the seashells shows that global ocean and air temperatures rose dramatically during the PETM—by as much as 9 to 18°F in the geologically miniscule span of ten thousand years.

The seashells also retain information about past carbon levels in the atmosphere. Seashells of different ages have different carbon isotopic concentrations that together suggest the PETM warming was due to the rapid injection of methane into the atmosphere. The methane was quickly converted into carbon dioxide, approximately 2,000 billion tons of it. Although that seems like a gargantuan amount, at current carbon emissions rates we will have introduced an equal amount into the atmosphere—beginning with the industrial revolution—sometime between the years 2100 and

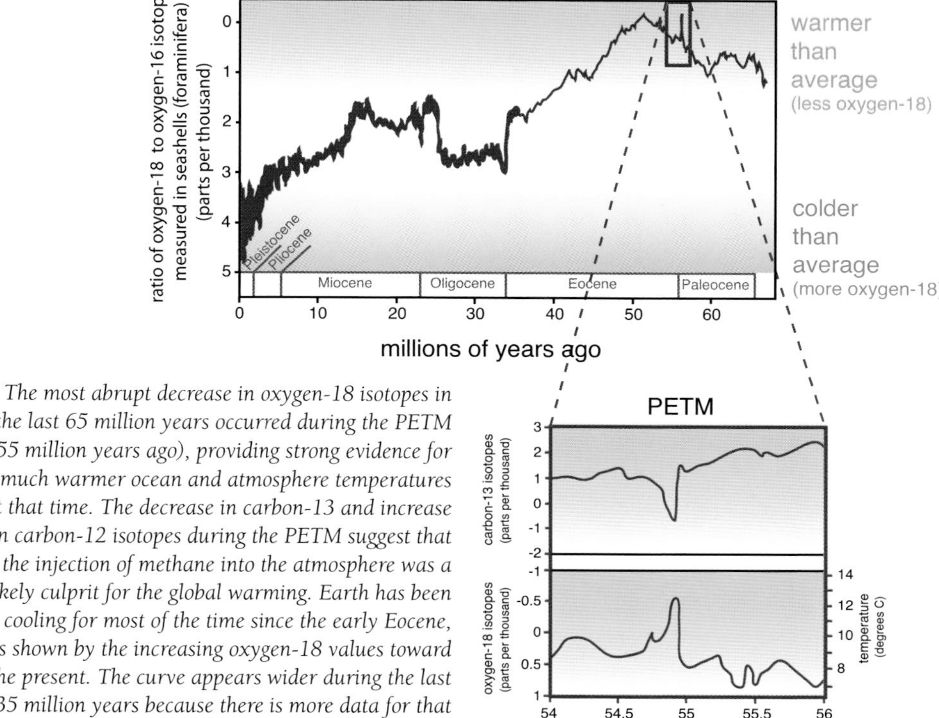

The most abrupt decrease in oxygen-18 isotopes in the last 65 million years occurred during the PETM (55 million years ago), providing strong evidence for much warmer ocean and atmosphere temperatures at that time. The decrease in carbon-13 and increase in carbon-12 isotopes during the PETM suggest that the injection of methane into the atmosphere was a likely culprit for the global warming. Earth has been cooling for most of the time since the early Eocene, as shown by the increasing oxygen-18 values toward the present. The curve appears wider during the last 35 million years because there is more data for that time interval. (Based on Zachos et al., 2008.)

2200. The PETM thus represents the closest geologic analogue for the amount and the rate of warming, as well as the consequent global effects, that we are likely to witness in the near future.

The concern that in the immediate future Earth might witness a global warming event of comparable magnitude and even greater speed than the PETM has spurred scientists to explore, in detail, the consequences of the PETM both for water supplies and for life. A warmer planet should enhance water evaporation and lead to more global rainfall. Computer models predict that the PETM was especially moist, and the rock evidence from many regions corroborates this inference. But rainfall did not increase everywhere and in all seasons. On the south slopes of the Pyrenees Mountains in Spain, the PETM was marked by tremendous floods that swept out of the mountains, triggered by intense storms the likes of which did not occur prior to the warming. The entire region from North Dakota to Colorado to Utah—including Paint Mines—became much drier. These results seem to mirror the pattern of increased regional drought and more intense storms that computer models predict in response to current climate change.

The consequences of the PETM for life in the deep sea were catastrophic. Forty percent of the shelled deep-sea microorganisms went extinct. The dying was most severe at high latitudes, probably because the oceans there warmed more than anywhere else. Well-understood chemical processes require that, inevitably, the excess atmospheric carbon dioxide would diffuse into the oceans, where it would combine with water to form carbonic acid. Such elevated oceanic acidity is corrosive to the carbonate shells secreted by most marine invertebrates. Indeed, marine sediment cores reveal that the typical, steady accumulation of tiny shells on the seafloor abruptly ceased during the PETM and didn't rebound to normal levels for several hundred thousand years. Modern trends bear similarities to those documented for the PETM, though none have yet achieved the same magnitude. The current atmospheric and oceanic warming is magnified at the poles, just as it was during the PETM. And marine scientists are alarmed at the rapid rate of ocean acidification, leading many to wonder whether we are in the earliest stages of a PETM-like collapse of the oceanic ecosystem.

The ecological effects of the PETM on terrestrial ecosystems were equally profound. One of the world's best records of Paleocene and Eocene life exists not far from Colorado, in northern Wyoming's Bighorn Basin. There sediment layers and paleosols overflow with an abundance of fossil plants and animals. The fossils reveal that during the PETM, warmth-loving invaders from southern North America and even Asia rapidly overwhelmed endemic plant species. Plants were under assault both from invasive species and from insects. Almost every fossil leaf reveals extensive damage from foraging insects. The rate of insect damage peaked with the maximum heat and waned as the heat subsided. Scientists are concerned that what happened during the PETM will happen again as Earth warms in the near future. Crops could be wiped out by swarms of ravenous invading insects.

In North America, plants weren't the only ones facing an invasion from abroad. The PETM ushered in the continent's greatest-ever turnover of mammal species. Most of the new species arrived from Europe and Asia as northern land bridges that had been too cold to support migrating animals warmed up enough to become passable. This migration was a good thing from a human perspective, as the Paleocene assemblage was replaced with representatives of all modern mammal groups, including the ancestors of important modern groups such as horses, cows, sheep, and deer. Of particular relevance to us was the evolution at that time of the primate order, the taxonomic order to which we belong. Primates arose in Asia and within a scant 25,000 years had migrated through a continuous belt of evergreen forest to Europe and then North America. The PETM appears to have been cruel to many organisms, but we humans owe our very existence to it!

Wyoming's Bighorn fossils showcase one additional oddity worth contemplating. Species of several mammal groups that lived during the PETM were nearly identical in almost every respect to their kin who lived both before and after the hothouse event, with one important exception: they were about 50 percent smaller. Scientists are not completely certain what caused this dwarfism, but they suspect that a combination of high temperatures and high atmospheric carbon dioxide levels are to blame. Modern animals tend to be smaller in hotter climates, and vegetation grown in artificially high atmospheric carbon dioxide is less nutritious than the same plants grown under normal conditions. This combination of fossil and experimental evidence triggers a concern that one result of the modern increase in carbon dioxide will be less nutritious plants, leading to slower growth of animals, including those raised to feed people.

As you drink in the view of the Paint Mines, Colorado's most colorful piece of the Great Plains, it is sobering to piece together what these vibrant pigments reveal about the hothouse climate that engulfed Colorado in the geologic blink of an eye 55 million years ago, and what this could mean with regard to the modern global warming event that is accelerating with each passing decade.

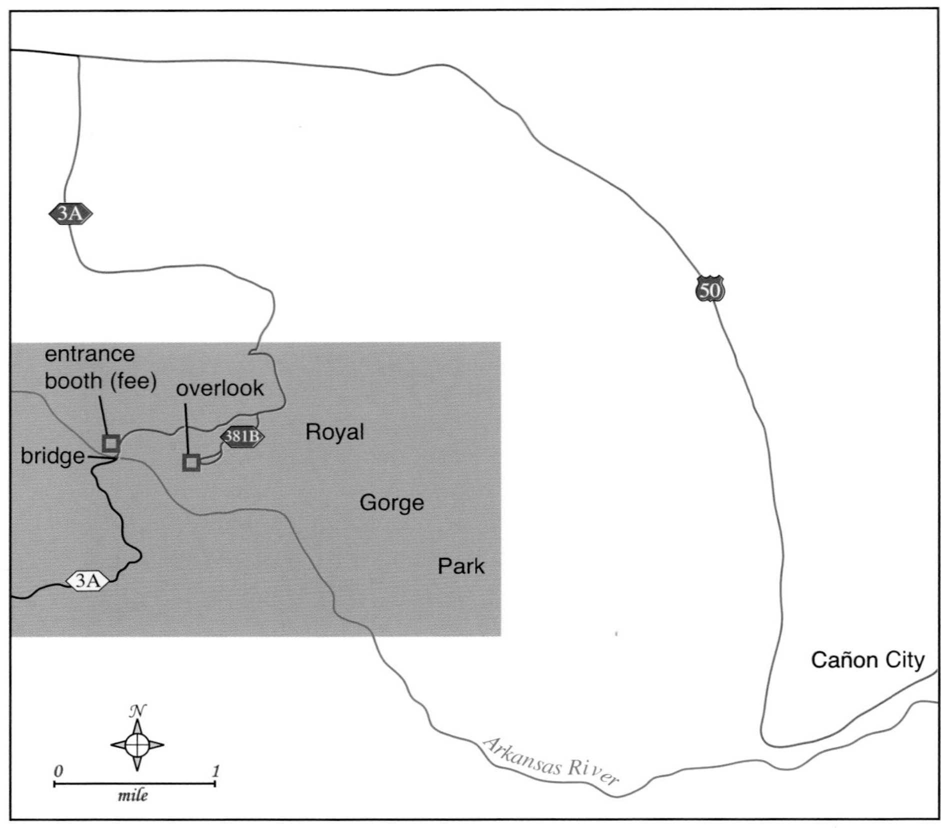

GETTING THERE: From Cañon City travel west 8 miles on US 50 to the clearly marked left turn onto Royal Gorge Road (County Road 3A). Drive 4.4 miles to the entrance booth. This is a Cañon City park (www.royalgorgebridge.com), and there is an entrance fee, which covers rides on the incline railway and aerial tram, and also provides access to the suspension bridge and other attractions. Good views of the gorge are also available for free from the Elk Horn picnic area. To reach it, turn left onto County Road 381B, a dirt road that branches off County Road 3A 3.6 miles from US 50. The road, which is marked by a "picnic area" sign, forms a lollipop-shaped loop. The best views of the gorge are from the western end of the loop. If you hike one of the several small trails that descend the slope south of the road for about five minutes, you will be able to see the entire suspension bridge across the gorge and the river at the bottom.

18

A WOUND IN THE SKIN OF THE EARTH
The Royal Gorge

We all live on Earth's crust, the planet's thin skin. The crust is so thin relative to the planet's girth that if you compare it to the crust on a slice of bread, the bread crust is, proportionally, about six times thicker. Yet despite the fact that our entire lives unfold on this slim surface, we rarely get the opportunity to examine it. Most of it hides beneath a veneer of loose sediments and sedimentary rock layers. Even where it's exposed, we can usually only glimpse its uppermost surface.

The Royal Gorge is a 1,200-foot-deep wound in Earth's skin that provides us with a wonderful cross-sectional view of the crust. It is the deepest and grandest of the many steep, narrow canyons that crease the Front Range's eastern flank. Because it has been developed as a tourist attraction, there are a large number of ways that you can examine this chasm. One of the world's highest suspension bridges and longest single-span aerial trams span the gorge. You can examine its depths aboard a rubber raft while challenging the Arkansas River's wild rapids or riding a train along the historic rails clinging precariously to the sheer walls. A particularly good way to examine the entire thickness of the exposed crust up close is to descend from rim to river on one of the world's steepest incline cog railways.

A particularly good vantage point of the gorge, and one that is sure to make your heart race a bit, is the center of the suspension bridge. From here you can scan the entire height of both canyon walls and gaze straight down to the raging Arkansas River, a dizzying 1,053 feet below. The vertical walls consist of dark rock with a distinct vertical fabric interspersed with pink and white rock ribbons that generally run along the same grain. The dark rocks are metamorphic, mainly amphibolite and gneiss. The pink and white rocks are igneous, mostly granite.

The rocks of the gorge's walls are largely inaccessible for close inspection. But at Point Sublime, on the south side of the canyon, the same rocks visible from the bridge are exposed immediately below the viewing platform.

The Royal Gorge as seen from the slope below the Elk Horn picnic area.

The descent to the bottom of the Royal Gorge on the cog railway provides close-up looks at Earth's crust.

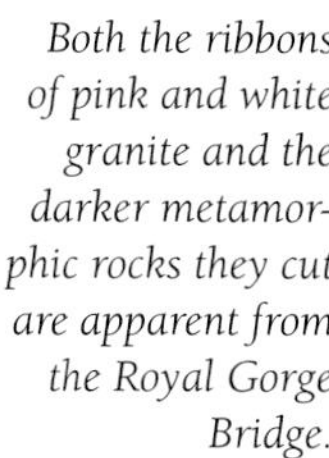

Both the ribbons of pink and white granite and the darker metamorphic rocks they cut are apparent from the Royal Gorge Bridge.

The granites are composed of visible crystals of white quartz and pink feldspar. The crystals' large size and interlocking texture both stem from the fact that they grew from slowly solidifying, water-rich magma deep beneath Earth's surface. Individual crystals are harder to discern in the dark brown metamorphic rocks, but the parallel alignment of crystals creates the rock's prominent banded appearance.

Like the granite, these metamorphic rocks formed deep beneath the surface, where high temperatures and pressures completely altered their original texture and mineral composition. Just as Franz Kafka's famous protagonist in *The Metamorphosis* went to bed one night a man and awoke as a beetle, these brown rocks were deposited as a pile of mud, only to be transformed into the smooth, hard rocks you see here. Nature's metamorphosis was accomplished after the mud had been buried 12 to 18 miles deep (middle crustal depths), exposed to extreme temperatures, and subjected to pressures six thousand to ten thousand times greater than those at Earth's surface. At such temperatures and pressures individual molecules are able to migrate, allowing them to reorganize into new minerals, in the process completely transforming the character of the rock. Importantly, this transformation was accomplished without the rock completely melting, otherwise the mud would have woken up as an igneous rock.

Under a microscope you would see the individual crystals, many of them consisting of the dark, needlelike mineral hornblende, and their parallel alignment. This alignment, and the layering it produces, is called foliation, which forms when a rock body is subjected to what is called differential pressure. Under these conditions, the rock body isn't subjected to uniform pressure from all sides. As mineral crystals undergo metamorphism in a tectonic setting with differential pressure, the newly formed crystals line up with their long axes perpendicular to the direction of greatest squeezing—the most stable possible configuration.

Though all the granites in the gorge look very similar, they formed via two different processes. The first involved a large magma chamber. As the chamber rose from deep in the crust, fingers of pressurized magma forced their way up along the path of least resistance. In foliated metamorphic rocks, that path is typically along the planes of foliation. The magma crystallized as tabular intrusions, or dikes, that parallel the foliation of the host rocks. The magma chamber that spawned these dikes is not visible from the bridge, but it is exposed just a couple of miles upstream, in the upper reaches of the gorge. If you ride the railroad or run the rapids, you will pass through the former chamber, which is now a mass of solidified granite recognizable by its light color and lack of vertical foliation. This granite is 1,705 million years old, making it one of the oldest rocks in the state.

The second process that formed the gorge's granite is partial melting. As you might imagine, the temperature at the depths at which granite forms is extremely hot, on the order of 1,100 to 1,300°F. When subjected to such high temperatures, metamorphic rocks begin to melt. Most crustal rocks are composed of just a handful of minerals, most of which contain silicon and oxygen. This is because silicon and oxygen are the two most abundant elements in the crust. Together, they form the chemical compound silica. Not all minerals melt at the same temperature. The more silica a mineral has, the lower its melting point and, generally, the lighter its color. As the brown metamorphic rock of the gorge was heating up, the minerals rich in silica (such as quartz and potassium feldspar) began to melt, while the minerals with less silica (like hornblende) remained unaffected. The resulting silica-rich magma then wiggled its way upward, also along the natural weaknesses presented by the metamorphic rock's foliation, before slowly crystallizing as light-colored granite pods embedded in the dark, hornblende-rich metamorphic rock that didn't melt. Such hybrid metamorphic-igneous rock is called a migmatite.

The rocks exposed along the cog railway down into the gorge are the same as those seen from Point Sublime. Such mixtures of metamorphic and

Close-up of the dark, foliated metamorphic rock and granite at Point Sublime.

igneous rock are typical of Earth's deep crust wherever nature has chosen to reveal it.

In what kind of tectonic environment does this rock combination form? One of the most telling clues is the foliation of the dark metamorphic rocks. The differential pressure that created this fabric is typically produced where two tectonic plates crash into one another, squeezing the rocks at their interface in a viselike grip. A second clue is the presence of the granite. The magma that eventually solidifies as granite begins forming in what geologists call subduction zones, tectonic margins that form where one tectonic plate is thrust hundreds of miles down beneath another plate and into Earth's mantle. At such depths the temperature easily exceeds the melting point of high-silica minerals, generating magma. Water dragged down with the plate infuses the surrounding mantle rock, triggering considerably more partial melting (water reduces the melting point of rock). The resulting silica-rich magma pods are less dense than the surrounding material, so like the blobs in a lava lamp they rise buoyantly up through the overlying material, then cool and solidify to form granitic rocks a few miles below the surface.

Many of these magma blobs feed a volcanic arc, a chain of volcanoes aligned parallel to the boundary where the plates are converging. Individual volcanoes typically live between one and two million years, so over tens of millions of years many generations of volcanoes are born and die. Over those time spans the accumulated pile of erupted ash and debris eroded from the volcanoes grows several miles thick—thick enough that its bottom layers are buried sufficiently to metamorphose and partially melt. The magma chambers that feed the younger generations of volcanoes intrude these metamorphosing rocks. In other words, the subduction process forms just the sort of mingling of dark metamorphic rocks and lighter granitic rocks that compose the Royal Gorge's soaring walls.

Because the ultimate source for all the rock of a volcanic arc, be it igneous or metamorphic, is magma enriched in silica via partial melting, the silica composition of the volcanic arc rock is higher than that of the rocks from which it was derived. This comparatively high silica content is the defining characteristic of continental crust. The arc, therefore, comprises a long, narrow strip of newly minted continental crust along the edge of an overriding plate, and subduction is the primary mechanism by which new continental crust forms. Because silica is less dense than the iron and magnesium that occur in abundance in oceanic crust, continental crust is inherently more buoyant than the denser oceanic crust that subducts. This difference keeps the continents generally above sea level, despite the fact that continental crust is much thicker (18 to 24 miles) than its oceanic counterpart (6 to 7 miles). Earth trying to subduct a plate veneered with continental crust is akin to a swimmer trying to submerge a log by pushing on it; because of its buoyancy it is nearly impossible.

Many of Earth's plates possess continental crust in some places and oceanic crust elsewhere. Commonly, the oceanic portion of one plate will begin to subduct beneath another plate, in the process dragging the continental portion of the subducting plate ever closer to the subduction zone. A volcanic arc forms atop the overriding tectonic plate, creating new continental crust in the process. Once the subducting plate's oceanic portion has been completely consumed in the subduction zone, continued plate convergence tries to drag the continental portion down after it. However, due to the buoyant nature of continental crust, it cannot be subducted. The continental crust collides with the continental material of the volcanic arc in what is called an arc-continent collision (see the illustrations on pages 100 and 101).

This exact scenario occurred repeatedly along the coast of the nascent North American continent between about 1,780 and 1,700 million years ago, in a mountain building episode called the Yavapai orogeny (and, locally, the Colorado orogeny). When the curtain rose on this protracted episode of arc-continent collision events, the edge of North America trended northeasterly, and in the Colorado area it was located near the Wyoming-Colorado border. One volcanic arc after another collided with the edge of

North America and was welded onto the continent (vignette 7), thereby extending the continental margin farther and farther to the southeast. The rocks of the Royal Gorge belong to the so-called Salida-Gunnison volcanic arc, the last of the volcanic arcs added to the continent during this series of collisions. When it was all over, a northeast-trending strip of land had been added to the continent that included much of Colorado and Nebraska, half of Utah and Arizona, and a portion of northwestern Mexico, and the edge of the continent had moved southeast by about 250 miles, from near

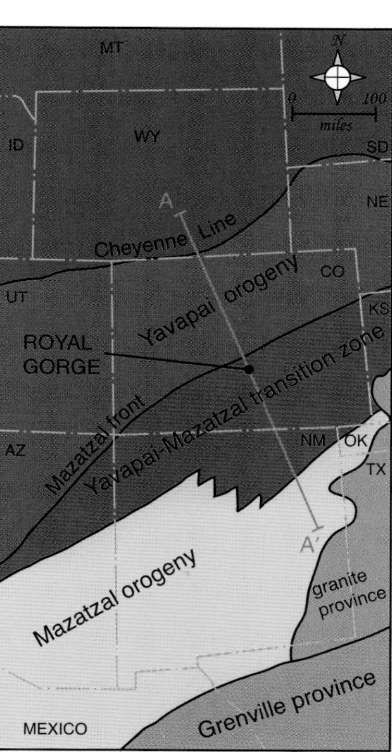

The crust exposed in the Royal Gorge formed in the Salida-Gunnison volcanic arc, which was added to the North American continent in the last major arc-continent collision of the Yavapai orogeny. The rocks were further deformed about 50 million years later, when another set of volcanic arcs was added to the continent during the Mazatzal orogeny. Arrows in the cross section denote relative direction of movement. (Modified from Karlstrom et al., 2002.)

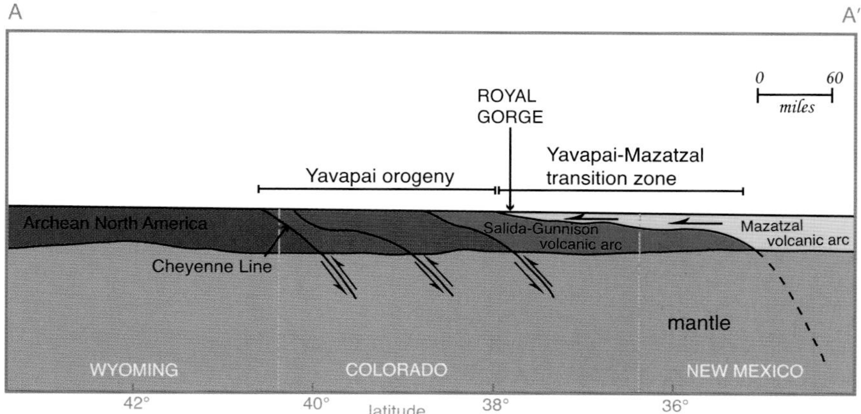

Laramie, Wyoming, to Cañon City, Colorado. After a pause of about 50 million years, a new series of collisions ensued, during what is known as the Mazatzal orogeny. These collisions moved the continental margin far to the south of the Royal Gorge, adding to the continent the rest of Colorado, Arizona, most of New Mexico, and other territory.

The trip on the cog railway gives you a tangible appreciation for the considerable depth of the gorge. If you consulted an elevation map of the area, you may have noticed a curious fact. The Arkansas River slices through the apex of a broad, uplifted dome of Proterozoic-age crustal rock—the rock of the Royal Gorge's walls. If the river had flowed just 3 miles farther south, through South Webster Park, it would have been able to make an end run around the dome, saving itself considerable effort. Not only is the South Webster Park terrain lower, but the rocks that compose it are considerably softer and easier to erode. Why, then, did the river choose this particularly arduous route out of the mountains and onto the plains?

At Parkdale, the small town where the Royal Gorge begins, the river flows across a gentle valley floor that lies at an elevation of 5,800 feet. Downstream the river cuts through the dome, whose summit elevation is more than 1,400 feet higher. The laws of gravity weren't suspended for the river's benefit; water always flows downhill, and the Arkansas River is no exception. The river didn't climb up and over the dome to carve the Royal Gorge, so the inescapable conclusion is that Parkdale lay higher than the crest of the dome before the gorge was cut.

So how did the dome come to straddle the river's course? Many geologists believe the Arkansas established its course in softer, more easily eroded sedimentary rocks that were stacked above the rocks of the modern gorge. After it cut down through those rocks, it encountered the hard metamorphic and igneous rocks of the dome. The Arkansas managed to carve a small canyon through the hard rocks and then, like a crosscut saw that has established a groove while cutting a piece of lumber, the river was trapped. It continued to carve a deeper and deeper canyon. The presence of river-deposited gravel on the Royal Gorge's south rim shows that the river once stood at the same elevation as the dome's top, lending further credence to this hypothesis. Meanwhile, tributaries excavated the softer rock to either side of the dome, chiseling away the rock around it like a sculptor revealing her masterpiece.

Any explanation for how the Arkansas River was superimposed onto the crustal dome must also explain the river's unusual course across the state. At its headwaters, the river flows southeast from Leadville, though Buena Vista, and on to Salida. This upper Arkansas River valley forms the northern reaches of one of the world's great rift systems, the Rio Grande Rift. The rift began forming in New Mexico between 35 and 30 million years ago, as the crust was stretched, and had propagated into Colorado by about 28 million years ago. South of the upper Arkansas, the Rio Grande River flows along the rift through the San Luis Valley and on into central New Mexico. Based on similarities between their Tertiary-era sedimentary records, many geologists suspect that the upper Arkansas River valley was connected to the San Luis Valley during the early stages of Rio Grand Rift development. Today, however, the Arkansas River doesn't flow into the San Luis Valley but instead bends sharply to the east at Salida, where it flows through a series of canyons, including the Royal Gorge, on its way down to the Great Plains at Cañon City and on to Kansas. Evidence suggests this course shift occurred early in the Pliocene, approximately 5 million years ago.

What caused the Arkansas to abandon its southerly course and turn east instead? Geologists have proposed two viable hypotheses. The first is that tectonic and volcanic activity in the Poncha Pass area dammed the upper Arkansas River, creating a lake in the Salida area. Eventually, the lake overflowed its banks and spilled eastward, carving a canyon into the softer rocks atop the dome. Now superimposed on the dome, the river carved an ever-deeper gorge through it, aided tremendously by the snowmelt that flowed into the river (and still does) as it passed the state's highest peaks.

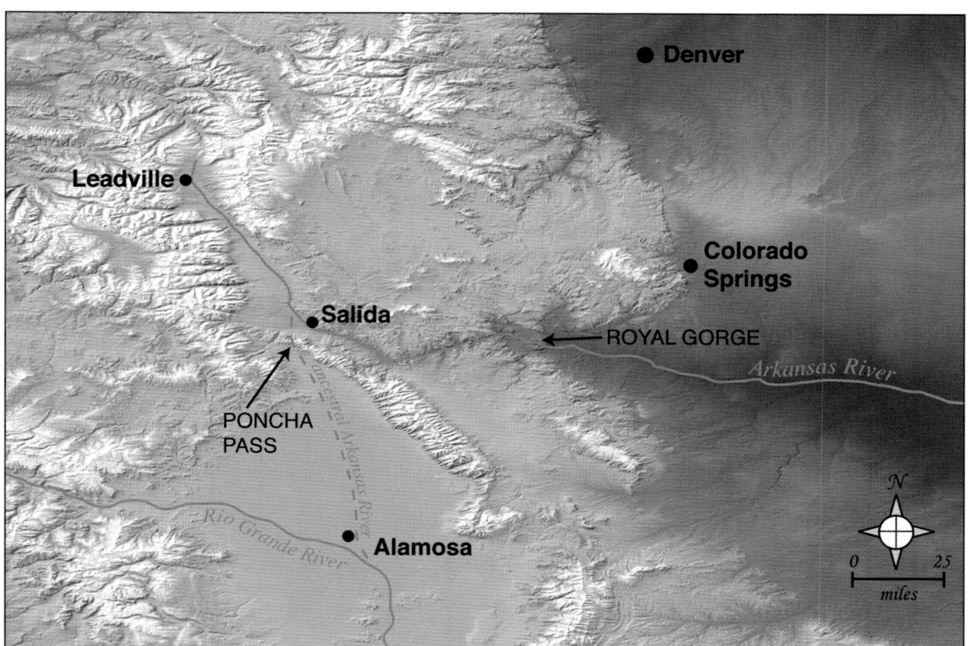

Color relief map of south-central Colorado. The modern, lower Arkansas River likely became linked to the upper river course during the Pliocene because of stream piracy or lake spillover near present-day Salida.

Rivers are always steepest at their headwaters, and where rivers are steep, they efficiently dissect the landscape. For this reason, rivers tend to erode toward their headwaters over time, becoming progressively longer, in a process known as headward erosion. The second idea, which goes by the colorful name of stream piracy, is that a short, steep stream flowing eastward off the Royal Gorge dome slowly ate its way headward, shifting its headwaters ever closer to the upper Arkansas River valley. This process could have been aided by uplift of the Rocky Mountains or by climate changes that produced more flash floods during that time, both of which would have led to more vigorous erosion along this and other local streams (see vignette 2 for a discussion of these ideas). Eventually, through headward erosion the stream breached the final ridge separating it from the upper Arkansas, causing the two to meet. Basic physics dictates that a river will always choose the steepest way to the sea. The small, steep, east-flowing stream pirated away the upper Arkansas, carrying away its water spoils and establishing the river's modern course. As with the lake spillover idea, the addition of so much water from the upper Arkansas would have led to relatively rapid erosion of the riverbed, carving the Royal Gorge in the process.

Geologists continue to search for clues that will allow them to tease out which of these processes superimposed the Arkansas River onto the Royal Gorge dome, and when it occurred. Whichever way this extraordinary cross section through the continental crust formed, we are the beneficiaries of the scenic grandeur provided by this wound in the skin of the Earth.

19

JURASSIC PARK
Dinosaurs of the Cañon City Area

The history of our planet is like a tattered scroll, and each rock or fossil is a scrap. If you could but locate and reassemble all the scroll's fragments, Earth's 4.6-billion-year history would be revealed. But plate tectonics, weathering, and erosion continuously resurface the planet, erasing whole chapters from the rock record and effectively shredding other parts into fragments too small to reassemble with confidence. These same geologic processes recycle other rock units into new rocks—secondhand pieces of parchment upon which more recent chapters are writ. Geologists and paleontologists gain their greatest insights about Earth history from the few rock units that have serendipitously survived the ravages of time with their stories nearly intact.

Rocks are thus like time capsules. For a glimpse of what life on land was like during the Late Jurassic period 150 million years ago, no capsule is more evocative than the Morrison Formation. Thanks to the abundance, diversity, and exquisite preservation of its fossils, Garden Park, north of Cañon City, has earned its reputation among paleontologists as North America's real Jurassic Park.

Although Dinosaur National Monument is far more famous and more bones have been unearthed at Wyoming's Como Bluff fossil area, Garden Park is the type area—the place where a fossil was first or best recognized and described—for eight different dinosaur species, including very famous ones belonging to genera such as *Allosaurus*, *Camarasaurus*, *Diplodocus*, and *Stegosaurus*. Garden Park has produced an exceptionally large number of nearly complete skeletons, which are especially valuable to paleontologists and help fuel public imagination in a way individual bones never could. For this reason, skeletons from Garden Park are unusually well represented in the world's most prestigious museums, including the Smithsonian, the American Museum of Natural History, and the Denver Museum of Nature and Science.

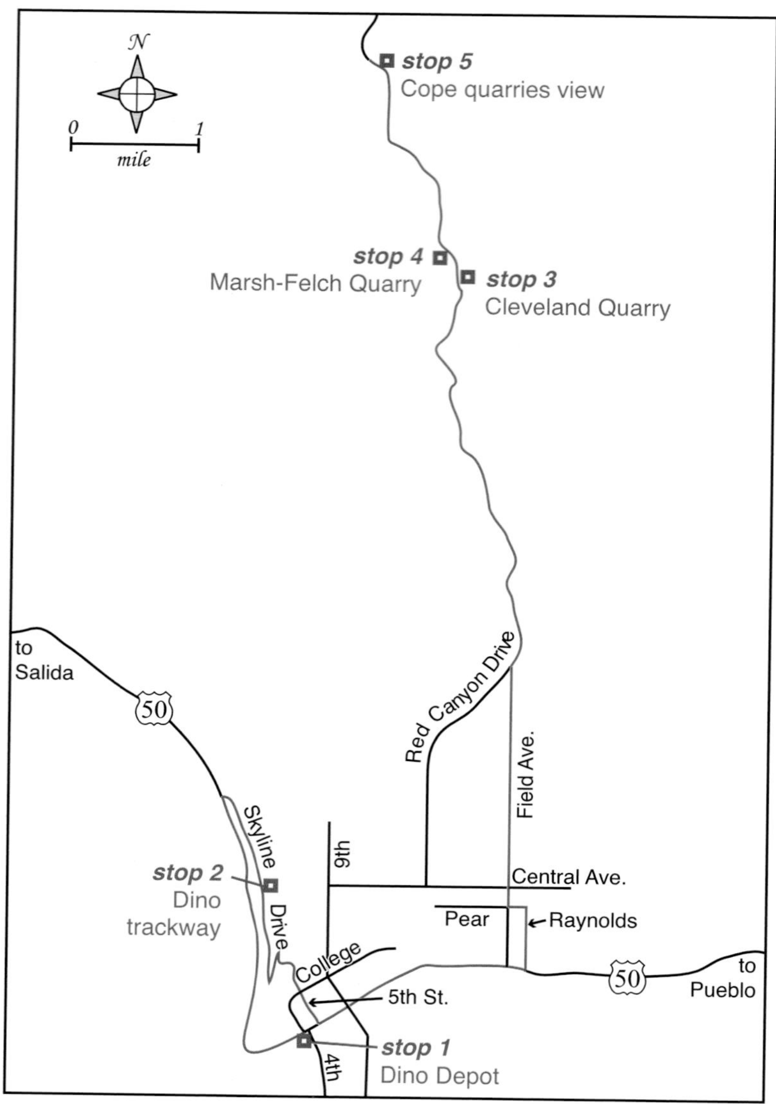

GETTING THERE: Stop 1 is Cañon City's Dinosaur Depot Museum (www.dinosaurdepot.com), which is located on the southwest corner of the junction of US 50 (the main street through town) and 4th Street. To reach stop 2, the Skyline Drive dinosaur trackway, from the Dinosaur Depot turn left (west) onto US 50 and follow it 3.4 miles to the marked right turn onto Skyline Drive. Despite steep drops, this narrow, winding, paved one-way road lacks guardrails. It is not suitable for recreational vehicles, people afraid of heights, or driving during foul weather (it closes when the weather is bad). The road climbs up the west side of a hogback and traverses its crest. From the road's entrance gate drive 0.8 mile and park in the next pullout on the right side of the road. Walk back down the road (north) about 0.1 mile to the trackway, which is marked with an interpretive sign entitled "Skyline Drive Dinosaur Tracks."

Garden Park has also yielded more specimens of the animals that shared the land with these dinosaurs than any other Morrison location. A total of twenty new genera of vertebrates have been discovered here, including fishes, turtles, lizards, crocodiles, and the first Jurassic-age mammals found in North America. Invertebrate and plant fossils are also abundant; Garden Park is the type area for thirteen species of clams and three species of freshwater shrimp. This count is impressive, but of even more significance for paleontologists tracking evolutionary changes is the fact that Garden Park yields abundant fossil material throughout the entire thickness of the Morrison Formation, which ranges in age between about 156 and 146 million years. The other major Morrison fossil beds have yielded many specimens, but they were confined to a stack of layers near the middle of the formation, providing no information on the species that came before or after this narrow slice of time.

Before exploring the Garden Park bone quarries, we'll examine some of their important fossils at the small but excellent Dinosaur Depot Museum. If the fossil preparation laboratory is open, you can see the painstaking process of revealing, cleaning, and reassembling ancient bones. The museum's entrance hallway features detailed interpretive panels describing the early history of the Garden Park quarries. They make for fascinating reading even before you learn the drama lying beneath what is presented here. Garden Park played a starring role in the Bone Wars, one of the most colorful, productive, and acrimonious rivalries in the annals of nineteenth-century science, waged between Othniel C. Marsh and Edward Drinker Cope.

The next three stops are views of historic Garden Park bone quarries. To reach stop 3, the Cleveland Quarry, continue 1.8 miles to the end of Skyline Drive, which delivers you to 5th Street in downtown Cañon City. Head right (south) on 5th Street for 0.7 mile to US 50 (Royal Gorge Boulevard) and turn left (east). Follow US 50 for 1.8 miles and turn left (north) at a light onto Raynolds Avenue. After 0.6 mile Raynolds jogs left, becoming Pear Street, then immediately right, becoming Field Avenue, which is signed as the Gold Belt Byway. Follow Field Avenue for 2.5 miles until it merges with Red Canyon Drive, then head north on Red Canyon another 3.2 miles to a roadside pullout on the right overlooking the Cleveland Quarry. The Bureau of Land Management has placed interpretive signs and a toilet at the quarry overlook. To reach stop 4, the Marsh-Felch Quarry, continue north along Red Canyon Drive for 0.2 mile to a pullout on the left, marked by more interpretive signs. The 0.25-mile hike to the overlook begins at the north end of the parking lot. This path is not handicap accessible. To reach stop 5, a distant view of the Cope quarries, drive another 1.1 miles north on Red Canyon Road to a prominent sign for the Cooper Mountain subdivision/ranch. There is an ample pullout on the right. The quarries lie at the base of the distinctive butte Cope called the Nipple, which you see on the western skyline.

Marsh, of Yale University, and Cope, from the Philadelphia Academy of Natural Sciences, spent almost three decades trying to outdo one another in the size, scope, and evolutionary significance of their fossil finds. They bore each other intense animosity, leading them to sabotage one another's efforts. The rivalry was already a decade old when, in March of 1877, Arthur Lakes discovered the bones of the largest dinosaurs then known in beds of the Morrison Formation at Dinosaur Ridge, near Golden (vignette 10). Not being a professional paleontologist, Lakes was unaware of the intensely personal nature of the Marsh-Cope feud, so he wrote to both renowned fossil experts for help in assessing the importance of his discovery. This innocent act was like lighting a fuse, focusing the rivals' full attention on the Morrison Formation as the new front line in their ongoing war. Marsh barely edged out Cope for control of the rich Dinosaur Ridge quarries, but Cope had a fallback position: Garden Park.

Also in March of 1877, a young Cañon City schoolteacher and amateur naturalist named Oramel W. Lucas discovered bones at Oil Creek in Garden Park. He sent specimens to Cope who, with his usual alacrity, published a scientific paper on the find by August. In the paper, Cope crowed that his newly named dinosaur, *Camarasaurus*, "exceeds in its proportions any other land animal hitherto discovered, including the one found near Golden City by Professor Lakes," referring to the Dinosaur Ridge specimens. Soon thereafter, another shipment of bones from Lucas allowed Cope to name and describe an even larger animal, *Amphicoelias*. Cope's coup incensed Marsh, who immediately dispatched one of his most trusted aides, Benjamin Mudge, to Cañon City to both snoop into Cope's activities and see if he could secure diggings for Marsh. He succeeded on both counts, including securing rights to prospect bones discovered by local rancher Marshall Felch.

Lucas had been selling bones to Cope for ten cents a pound, but after seeing the stir they were causing, he began to doubt his bargaining skills. Though Lucas honored his agreement with Cope, Mudge was able to convince him that the deal with Cope applied only to the bones of giant dinosaurs, so any other bones could be honorably sold to Marsh. In this way Mudge obtained the skeleton of a diminutive, birdlike dinosaur that Marsh named *Nanosaurus agilis*. This species is a crucial link in the evolutionary chain between dinosaurs and birds and became one of Marsh's greatest claims to fame.

But Marsh was not satisfied with Cope's leftovers. In September 1877 he sent a telegram to another trusted assistant, Samuel Williston, directing him to work the quarry at Felch's discovery site along with Felch and Mudge. There Williston discovered bones that Marsh used to fortify his description of the new dinosaur stegosaurus, which Lakes had first discovered a short time earlier at Dinosaur Ridge. These bones presaged the riches still to come from the so-called Marsh-Felch Quarry (stop 4).

Among Dinosaur Depot's displays you will see several skulls, a gigantic vertebra belonging to *Camarasaurus*, the nearly complete skeleton of a juvenile *Othnielia rex*, and Tony's Tree, a 20-foot-long petrified tree discovered in 1998 by a Colorado Springs high school student on a Dinosaur Depot paleontology tour. This 155-million-year-old conifer is so exquisitely preserved that some of its fragile upper branches extend up to 30 inches from the trunk. This is the only known Jurassic-age tree found east of the Continental Divide, and it is the first major Garden Park fossil that went on display locally instead of being shipped to a distant museum.

Pride of place among the museum's exhibits, though, goes to the massive cast of Ms. Spike, the most complete stegosaurus skeleton ever discovered. It was found in 1992, a decade after a campaign by Colorado schoolchildren immortalized stegosaurus as the state fossil. The campaign itself had been inspired by the 1937 discovery of another nearly complete Garden Park stegosaurus.

Ms. Spike's head is only the second complete stegosaurus skull ever found; the first was found in the Marsh-Felch Quarry in the 1880s. This recent find has therefore added considerably to our understanding of the species, including putting to rest an on-again, off-again controversy regarding whether the species' armored plates ran down its back single file or in two rows of alternating plates. Ms. Spike's skeleton showed conclusively that the plates were arranged in two rows.

The discoloration of one of Ms. Spike's tail spikes (lowermost) likely resulted from an infection that began here and then spread throughout her body.

As more dinosaur specimens are unearthed, paleontologists are able to ask increasingly sophisticated questions about how dinosaurs lived and died. One burgeoning subfield is paleopathology, which investigates how dinosaurs died. As you examine Ms. Spike's four intact tail spikes, notice how the lower one is short, stubby, and discolored. Scientists believe that the spike was damaged, possibly in combat, and became infected. There is also a large patch of discoloration on an armored plate near the head. This suggests that Ms. Spike's infection became systemic, eventually killing her.

The bones of specimens like Ms. Spike reveal dinosaur size, anatomy, and structure and allow paleontologists to construct dinosaur family trees that trace their evolution over time. But in addition to bones, dinosaurs left another important set of clues for paleontologists to study: their tracks. Both tracks and trackways—a series of fossilized prints made by a moving animal—supply important information that bones alone cannot, including the total mass of the animal (via the depth the tracks were impressed into the earth), how fast the animal moved (from the track spacing), and whether a given species was solitary or gregarious (from the grouping of trackways). This information can, in turn, help resolve fundamental questions of dinosaur anatomy. For instance, a long-running debate revolves around whether dinosaurs were warm- or cold-blooded animals. The discussions continue, but most paleontologists believe that at least some species were warm-blooded, in large part because trackways reveal that some dinosaurs moved quickly and were able to maintain high speeds over a relatively long distance (implying a fast metabolism). Trackways also reveal that some species traveled in herds (vignette 10), which today is most common in warm-blooded mammals and birds, not in cold-blooded reptiles.

Before you leave, look in the yard adjacent to the museum's west wall. There stands the cement cast of a trackway from the Picket Wire Canyonlands, the largest dinosaur track-site in North America. Located along the Purgatoire River, about 60 miles southeast of here in the Comanche National Grassland, the site can be visited on a guided tour; you can get up-to-date information at Dinosaur Depot. The Picket Wire trackway contains over 1,300 tracks belonging to one hundred individual dinosaurs. It, too, is located in the Jurassic-age Morrison Formation, and the tracks belong to many of the dinosaur species whose bones are found at Garden Park.

About 40 percent of the Picket Wire tracks, including those reproduced at Dinosaur Depot, belong to enormous plant-eating dinosaurs of the brontosaur group. This group includes apatosaurus (formerly known as brontosaurus) and diplodocus, which were first discovered at Dinosaur Ridge, as well as Cope's *Camarasaurus*, discovered here. The spacing of these tracks indicates that the apatosaurs were plodding along at a leisurely 2 to 4 miles per hour. Several of the Picket Wire trackways run parallel to one another, suggesting that at least some apatosaurs traveled in herds. The rest of the

The authors' kids stand in the cast at Dinosaur Depot of a brontosaur trackway from the Picket Wire Canyonlands. The large, plant-eating dinosaur that made this trackway was moving slowly, at just 2 to 4 miles per hour.

Picket Wire trackways consist of several different sizes and types of three-toed tracks, which are characteristic of meat-eating dinosaurs. The bigger ones may belong to allosaurs or other, less-famous Jurassic predators. The track spacing reveals that the carnivores were moving swiftly, at about 4 to 6 miles per hour, and there is no evidence that they traveled in herds.

On the way to stop 2, the spectacular Skyline Drive climbs up and over the hogback formed by the erosion-resistant Dakota Group rocks. As you ascend the hogback's west side, you cross the soft, multicolored mudstones of the Morrison Formation. The crest of the ridge consists of hard, tan, Cretaceous-age Dakota Group sandstones and black, organic-rich shales. The Skyline Drive trackway is hidden on the underside of a 107-million-year-old, eastward-tilting, brown sandstone bed that overhangs the softer, more easily eroded shale.

Because of this configuration you get a "worm's-eye view" of the tracks, which manifest as bulges studding the underside of the bed. The majority of more than fifty individual footprints are oblong blobs with four indistinct protrusions that mark the dinosaur's toes. The tracks belong to ankylosaurs, the low-slung, club-tailed dinosaurs that somewhat resembled overgrown armadillos. (Keep your eye out for three-toed tracks made by predators.) This is the largest ankylosaur trackway in the western United

The Skyline Drive trackway consists mostly of ankylosaur tracks, which are the round bulges. Four stubby toes are visible on the best-preserved ones, such as the one in the lower right. A few three-toed carnivore tracks are also present. One is visible immediately left of the large ankylosaur track in the center of the photo.

States. Several of these trackways run parallel to each other. Like the brontosaur trackways at the Picket Wire Canyonlands, these suggest that at least some ankylosaurs traveled together in a group.

Dinosaur trackways have been discovered at over sixty different sites in Dakota Group rocks along the east side of the Rockies and adjacent plains, with Dinosaur Ridge being one of the largest and most significant. All of those trackways are about 100 million years old, a few million years younger than these at Skyline Drive, and all of them are dominated by the tracks of hadrosaurs (duckbilled dinosaurs). As was the case for the Garden Park fossil beds, the presence here of dinosaur remains from an underrepresented time period has great significance for the study of dinosaur evolution. Scientists have used this wholesale change in track-making species to suggest that there was a major turnover in the dinosaur population between 107 and 100 million years ago. However, the 2006 discovery of two small ankylosaur trackways in southeastern Colorado in 100-million-year-old rocks indicates that ankylosaurs were still present at that time. The track-bearing rock at stop 2 is sandstone deposited along a riverbed, whereas the younger hadrosaur tracks are typically found in beach sandstones. This has led some scientists to propose an alternative hypothesis:

that hadrosaurs and ankylosaurs may have lived at the same time, but in different habitats.

As you walk back to your car, look for small, tubular protrusions on the undersides of rock layers higher up in the stack. These are burrows made by worms and shrimp that occupied a shallow sea that crept slowly over the area shortly (geologically speaking) after the ankylosaurs passed this way.

Garden Park got its name from the produce grown in the valley to supply the miners of Cripple Creek and Victor, the booming gold camps high in the mountains just to the north (vignette 13). The valley's famous bone quarries all lie in the Morrison Formation on public land belonging to the Bureau of Land Management (BLM), and the area has been designated both a National Natural Landmark and a Special Research Area. Fossil collecting without a permit is against the law. Very significant fossil discoveries continue to be made in this exceptionally rich bone bed. If you would like to participate in a dig, inquire with the staff at the Dinosaur Depot. If while visiting the quarries you stumble across what appears to be a fossil, as happens from time to time, please inform the museum staff so that your discovery can be evaluated by a trained paleontologist. Since paleontologists sometimes name significant finds after their discoverers, you just might become immortalized as a part of dinosaur history!

The first quarry on this tour is the Cleveland (stop 3). It lies on the far side of the creek, an overgrown scar in the hillside. The BLM has placed interpretive signs here discussing the quarry's history. Edwin Delfs of the Cleveland Museum of Natural History worked the quarry from 1954 to 1957. He and his team were rewarded for their hard work when they uncovered a nearly complete skeleton of a new species of long-necked sauropod, *Haplocanthosaurus delfsi*. This specimen is one of the main attractions at the Cleveland museum. Another exciting discovery here was a clutch of dinosaur eggs thought to belong to the diminutive *Othnielia*, which you saw at the Dinosaur Depot. These are the oldest dinosaur eggs yet found in North America.

Stop 4, the famous Marsh-Felch Quarry, is where many of the significant discoveries we discussed at the Dinosaur Depot were made. The 0.25-mile-long trail begins with a gentle walk north to a small wash. It then turns west and climbs moderately to a viewing platform on the southwest side of the wash. Tony's Tree was discovered left of the trail just in front of the third small wooden bridge the trail crosses. Interpretive signs along the trail discuss the area's history and the dinosaurs found here, including several at trail's end at the quarry overlook. The quarry was situated on the flat bench atop the prominent cliff band on the far side of the wash. During the Jurassic this spot lay in the bed of a river whose channel meandered across a broad floodplain. The lens-shaped sandstone layer in the cliff was once the river channel (seen in cross section) before it eventually filled with

The Marsh-Felch Quarry was located on the topographic bench, next to the juniper trees. The river that deposited these sediments, and the dinosaurs it fossilized, were active about 155 million years ago, when the Cañon City area was a semiarid savanna crisscrossed by meandering rivers and associated marshlands.

sand. The green-tinted, crumbly mudstones that lie below it accumulated on the river's floodplain, as did the gray and red mudstones above. The bones piled up in a deep pool in the channel a bit later in time, after the river had shifted its position slightly. This pool filled with sand and is now preserved as the smaller sandstone body sitting above the bench.

The bones of sixty-five individual dinosaurs were excavated from this quarry. Most of the bones are disarticulated, meaning they were not connected to other bones. This scattering is typical of the river-deposited Morrison Formation fossil sites. Floods carried the bones downstream, jumbling them in the process, and then deposited them in especially deep pools at river bends when floodwaters waned. Surprisingly, three almost complete skeletons—an allosaurus, *Ceratosaurus*, and stegosaurus—were included in the hodgepodge at this quarry. Thanks to the wealth of information they provide and their rarity, intact skeletons are the most coveted type of find in paleontology. All three are now on display at the Smithsonian. Significantly, these are the only skeletons in the entire dinosaur hall whose bones all came from the same individual; all the other displays are composite skeletons with bones from multiple individuals. Ms. Spike was discovered a mere 1.5

miles east of here. The skeletons' intact nature has caused paleontologists to speculate that these individuals died on the banks of a dwindling water hole that occupied the deepest part of the river channel during an extreme drought. When the rains returned, a flood quickly buried and preserved the specimens, preventing scavengers from scattering their bones.

The quarry also yielded enough scattered but high-quality bones to make it the type locality for seven different dinosaur species, including species belonging to the famous *Allosaurus*, *Diplodocus*, and *Stegosaurus* genera. Of equal importance, the Marsh-Felch Quarry also yielded the first Jurassic mammals ever discovered in North America.

The Cope quarries, which started the whole Garden Park bone rivalry, are not easily accessible, but they are visible in the distance at stop 5. A small, pointy butte that Lucas and Cope called the Nipple graces the skyline between two massive sandstone abutments they called the Forts. Lucas worked a series of quarries in the soft, red mudstones from the base of the Nipple toward the left Fort. Among the many beautifully preserved bones extracted here, the most famous is *Camarasaurus supremus*, the gigantic creature that allowed Cope to gleefully top Marsh as discoverer of the largest known land animal. A full-size drawing of the behemoth was displayed in a Philadelphia park in 1877, causing a sensation and drawing widespread attention to the seemingly otherworldly fauna that roamed the Cañon City area 150 million years ago, in North America's real-life Jurassic Park.

Cope's original Garden Park quarries lay along the topographic bench along the skyline between the Nipple (center) and the left Fort.

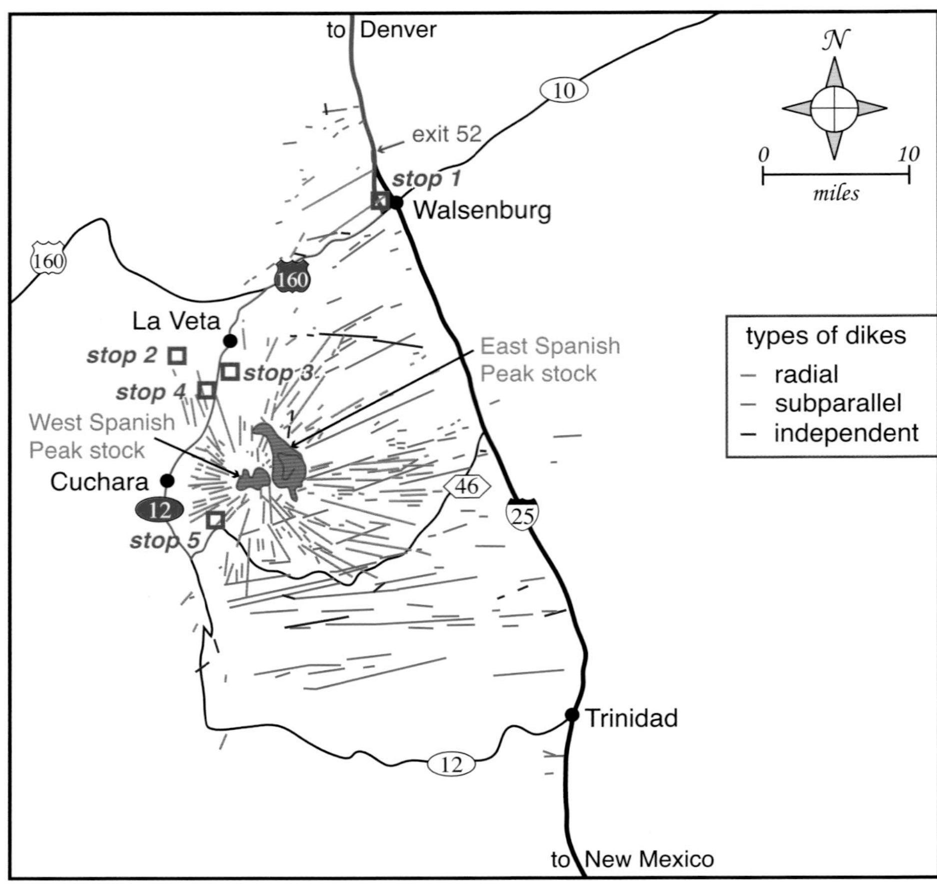

GETTING THERE: From Denver, head south on I-25 toward Walsenburg—about 160 miles. To reach stop 1, take exit 52 and travel 1.6 miles south on Business I-25 (Walsen Avenue), where the road slices through the hill formed by the Walsen Dike. Try to park on the reasonably wide shoulder, or, if that proves problematic, view the dike as you drive by.

To reach stop 2, continue south 0.5 mile on Business I-25 to the junction with US 160 in the center of Walsenburg. Turn west on US 160 and follow it 11 miles to the junction with CO 12, the Highway of Legends Scenic Byway. Turn left (south) onto CO 12, reaching the town of La Veta after 5 miles. CO 12 winds through town, going south on Main Street, turning right (west) on Grand Street, left (south) on Oak Street, then right (west) again at the Grandote Golf Course. Set your odometer to zero at this turn. CO 12 crosses the Cucharas River and then turns left (south) after 0.6 mile. Continue south for 0.5 mile and turn right (west) onto Indian Creek Road (County Road 420). Follow this good gravel road 2.9 miles and park on the roadside for a panoramic view south to West Spanish Peak, with the small knob of Goemmer Butte in the foreground.

For stop 3, retrace your route back to CO 12 and turn right (south). Continue south for 2.4 miles to a pullout on the left just before crossing the Cucharas River. To reach

20

LEGENDARY DIKES
The Spanish Peaks

Southern Colorado's Spanish Peaks are spectacular anomalies. Along with the better-known Pikes Peak, they share the distinction of being the first Rocky Mountain peaks encountered by westbound Great Plains travelers. Unobstructed by foothills, their shapely summits tower a breathtaking 6,500 and 7,500 feet above the plains. They are anomalous because, although geographically the first bastions of the Rockies, geologically they are vestiges of the much lower Great Plains.

Unlike Pikes Peak (vignette 14), a typical Rocky Mountain peak heaved up along a thrust fault about 54 million years ago, during the Laramide orogeny, the Spanish Peaks owe their existence to twin magma pods (called stocks) injected into the shallow crust a mere 24 million years ago, during a major episode of crustal stretching. The stocks are exposed at the summit of each peak, with the bulk of both mountains consisting of altered sedimentary rock that was rendered unusually resistant to erosion by the heat imparted by the intrusions. Hundreds of dikes, tabular sheets of magma, were injected along with the two stocks, and today many of them are precipitous rock walls rising up to 100 feet above the surrounding

stop 4, continue south on CO 12 for another 2.2 miles to a turnout on the right that has a Highway of Legends interpretive sign labeled "The Devils Stairsteps."

To reach stop 5, again continue south on CO 12. You pass a hogback 3.1 miles after leaving stop 4. Continue through the village of Cuchara to the top of Cucharas Pass, 10.9 miles beyond stop 4. Turn left (east) onto County Road 46, a gravel road leading to Aguilar. This road is rough and is closed during the winter. Follow this 6.3 miles to the summit of Cordova Pass. Park here and, weather permitting, follow Trail 1390, which heads north to West Spanish Peak. After about 0.5 mile of gentle uphill hiking the trail crosses a prominent clearing, then bends east, up the southwest ridge of West Spanish Peak. Stop 5 is at the top of the low knob 200 yards to the north.

The stunning Spanish Peaks rise on the western edge of the Great Plains

countryside. No finer example of igneous dikes exists in the world, making the area legendary among igneous geologists. Numerous, less-scientific legends explaining the striking landscape have sprung up over the centuries among the many cultures that have called this area home. In honor of those legends, the main road passing through the area is known as the Highway of Legends Scenic Byway. In this vignette we travel the highway and examine these world-class igneous intrusions while contemplating the puzzle of how the Spanish Peaks came to more closely resemble the Rocky Mountains than the rest of the Great Plains.

The hundreds of dikes surrounding the Spanish Peaks can be divided into three distinct groups. More than five hundred dikes, by far the most numerous group, radiate away from West Spanish Peak like spokes on a wheel. These are called radial dikes. A smaller group trends approximately east-west, with individual dikes running nearly parallel to one another—the subparallel group. The final group, the independent dikes, shares one geographic commonality: none of them belong to the other two groups.

At stop 1, on the northern edge of Walsenburg, you can examine the Walsen Dike. It stretches 12 miles—one of the longest of the subparallel dikes. Engineers blasted the road right through the dike and surrounding rock, providing us with an excellent cross-sectional view. The dike consists of the dark rock in the center of the road cut with vertical cracks, which formed as the once-molten magma cooled and contracted. The greenish rock to both sides of the dike is the Pierre shale, a sedimentary rock with thin, nearly horizontal layering.

The Pierre shale is normally a crumbly, easily eroded formation that rarely forms hills. In fact, the space to the left, right, and above the Walsen

The Walsen Dike belongs to the subparallel group of dikes.

Dike used to be filled with crumbly Pierre shale, but erosion has stripped it away. The igneous dike, which was intruded beneath the ground surface, is hard and erosion resistant, so as erosion removed the surrounding sedimentary rock, it stayed put, slowly emerging as the hill we see today. The small scraps of Pierre shale adjacent to the dike still exist because they are a bit more erosion resistant than the rest of the Pierre. They owe their relative strength to the contact metamorphism that occurred as the dike's magma intruded the shale. Based on the degree of alteration to wood fragments found in the Pierre, geologists have determined that the rock closest to the dike was heated above 930°F. The heating caused new crystals to grow in the shale's pores, strengthening the rock, creating what's called a contact aureole. Radiometric dating of the Walsen Dike reveals that it was emplaced 21.3 million years ago, making it one of the area's youngest intrusions.

Unlike the Walsen Dike, the majority of the Spanish Peaks dikes are arranged radially (like spokes) around West Spanish Peak. This pattern is most easily appreciated from the air, but stop 2 provides a good ground-level glimpse. West Spanish Peak is the large mountain rising in splendid isolation 6,300 feet above you. Below the peak stand three long, narrow walls of light-colored rock. Thanks to their height these three dikes are especially prominent, but a number of other radial dikes are also present

The view south from stop 2 encompasses Goemmer Butte, West Spanish Peak, and three radial dikes. Portions of each dike have eroded away, but by mentally extending each dike toward the south or east, you can see that they all meet at the peak, confirming their membership in the radial dike group.

in this panorama. They range in width from less than 1 foot to over 100 feet, and some run across the landscape for several miles. Interestingly, each radial dike has a uniform composition, indicating that it was injected in a single episode, but the composition of one dike is often quite different from its neighbor just a few feet away. This variation suggests that multiple magma bodies were tapped and/or the processes that affected each pod of magma during its ascent through the crust varied from dike to dike.

The Spanish Peaks stocks and their associated dikes were injected over a 5.3-million-year period. This episode was short enough that we can reasonably assume, as did earlier geologists, that all of the magma was created in response to the same geologic event. But until recently, dating techniques lacked the precision to determine if there was any kind of orderly age progression between the various families of dikes. Recent work has shown that indeed there is. The oldest intrusions, which are some 26.6 million years old, are the subparallel dikes that lie south of the Spanish Peaks. The West Spanish Peak stock was intruded next, 24.6 million years ago, followed soon thereafter by the East Spanish Peak stock 23.9 million years ago. The swarm of radial dikes was injected between about 23.3 and 21.9 million years ago. Finally, the set of subparallel dikes north of the Spanish Peaks (including the Walsen Dike) lodged themselves into the crust at the end of the igneous activity, about 21.3 million years ago. The independent dikes have not been dated.

The generation of magma at the Spanish Peaks coincided with the formation of the nearby Rio Grande Rift (vignettes 13, 18), and the two events are almost surely related. The rift consists of north-south-trending valleys that formed when Earth's crust was stretched and thinned, like pulled taffy, in an east-west direction. The rift is named for the southward-flowing Rio Grande River, which flows down the main rift valley from Colorado's San Luis Valley all the way to El Paso, Texas.

The east-west stretching required to form the Colorado portion of the rift began between 30 and 25 million years ago, some 15 to 20 million years after the east-west compression (the Laramide orogeny) that formed the Rocky Mountains had ended. Such a pronounced reversal of stress from compression to extension is, at face value, surprising. But it turns out to be a common feature of many mountain belts. Geologists debate the cause of the stretching here in Colorado, but the two most plausible explanations are either that the Rocky Mountains grew so high they collapsed under their own weight due to the tug of gravity, thereby extending the crust along normal faults, or that a blister of hot mantle material rose beneath Colorado and New Mexico, lifting and extending the crust above it.

However it was accomplished, the thinning of the crust allowed hot mantle material unusually close to Earth's surface. As the mantle rock rose it decompressed, triggering melting. The resulting dark, basaltic magma erupted throughout the floor of the rift, including in Colorado's San Luis Valley and throughout northern New Mexico, where the Rio Grande River has carved impressive gorges through it. The heat emanating from the rising basaltic magma melted some of the continental crust through which the magma passed, forming granitic magma bodies. It is typical for light-colored, high-silica granitic magmas to rise some distance outside the main valley of a rift. For example, in the modern East African Rift, the world's largest modern-day rift, such off-axis magma chambers have fed the mighty Kilimanjaro and Mt. Kenya volcanoes. The Spanish Peaks, which lie a short distance east of the San Luis Valley, the axis of the Rio Grande Rift, consist of analogous off-axis granitic magma chambers. Twenty-four million years ago they likely occupied a niche similar to the magma chambers feeding Africa's Mount Kenya and Kilimanjaro today.

The east-west stretching of the crust in this region therefore explains the location of both the Rio Grande Rift and the off-axis location of the Spanish Peaks stocks. Can it also explain the variations we have seen in the families of dikes? Recall that the oldest, subparallel dikes south of the peaks have east-west orientations. This trend can be most easily explained if the area retained some residual east-west compressional stress from the earlier Laramide orogeny at the time those first magmas rose. If so, the area could stretch most easily to the north and south. The resulting east-west-oriented cracks provided conduits through which the rising magma could intrude to create the first family of dikes.

The radial dikes narrate the next chapter of the area's tectonic development. As the regional east-west Laramide-style compression waned, it was overwhelmed by stress generated by another process: the intrusion of the West Spanish Peak stock and the weight of the mountain that formed above this intrusion. This produced a radial stress field. The radial cracks that formed in response to this stress field provided the path of least resistance for the upward movement of magma, resulting in the intrusion of the radial dikes soon after the stock was emplaced.

Why then is there not a similar set of radial dikes centered on East Spanish Peak? The absence of such dikes indicates that, due to its smaller volume or some other cause, the intrusion-induced radial stress field was insufficient to overcome the regional east-west stress field of the waning Laramide compression. As the magma of the West Spanish Peak stock cooled and began to solidify, the localized radial stress field it had been creating waned, meaning that during this final stage of magma emplacement, the regional, east-west stress field dominated. The result was a return to subparallel, east-west-oriented dikes, including the Walsen Dike. So the variation in the dikes had little to do with the east-west extension of the crust; rather it had more to do with localized doming of the crust caused by the intruding Spanish Peaks magma bodies and the last gasps of compression related to the earlier uplift of the Rockies.

The Spanish Peaks were merely the two largest of a host of magma bodies injected into the Great Plains' sedimentary rock along the eastern edge of the Rio Grande Rift. Goemmer Butte, the mass of dark rock visible in the foreground, is another, along with the White Peaks, Mt. Mestas, Silver Mountain, and several other nearby hills and mountains. Goemmer Butte is unique, though, in being the only one that shows clear signs of having fed a volcano. Although it is difficult to discern from this distance, the butte's west flank consists of volcanic breccia. Breccia forms when a violent eruption fractures a volcano's rocks. Some of these fractured, jagged fragments collapse back into the volcano's throat, where they are cemented together by more magma. Such breccias are a sure sign of volcanic activity, although the volcano that used to sit atop the butte has been eroded away. The butte is what geologists call a volcanic plug—the solidified remnants of the throat of a former volcano.

The absence of similar breccias in the area's other intrusions, like the Spanish Peaks, suggests that those magma bodies lacked sufficient buoyancy to rise all the way through the stack of sedimentary layers forming the Great Plains at the time. Instead, the other intrusions parked themselves a few hundred to a few thousand feet below the surface, where they slowly cooled and solidified, though it is still possible that these magma bodies fed volcanoes at the surface. The Goemmer Butte magma body was far from the biggest, but it was the most buoyant, allowing it to feed a volcano

At stop 3 the dark gray contact aureole of the altered sedimentary Cuchara Formation surrounds white granite of the Profile Rock radial dike.

that stood above this spot at the time. Bigger volcanoes might once have risen above the stocks of the Spanish Peaks, but if they did, all traces of them have been obliterated by extensive erosion.

Proceed now to stop 3. Directly across the road from the pullout rises a low road cut consisting of dark gray rock on the left and very light gray, almost white rock on the right. The light-colored rock is granite of the Profile Rock radial dike. Up close you can see numerous rectangular feldspar crystals embedded in a finer matrix. This texture speaks to the shallow depth of intrusion for this portion of the dike, which caused the magma to cool slowly enough that some mineral crystals grew reasonably large but quickly enough that others didn't grow beyond microscopic size. Magma that cools deep in the Earth does so slowly, allowing large mineral crystals to develop, whereas magma erupted onto the surface cools quickly, resulting in much smaller mineral crystals. The fine-grained, dark gray rock comprises the contact aureole of baked Cuchara Formation, the Eocene-age sedimentary rock the dike intruded.

Profile Rock is the impressive rock spine rising to your south, on the far side of the Cucharas River. Its name comes from the fact that many travelers, when viewing it from the west, see the profile of a person. The profile is most easily viewed from a wide pullout on the right side of the highway a 0.5 mile farther west at a Highway of Legends interpretive sign.

Profile Rock lines up with West Spanish Peak behind it, revealing that it is one of the radial dikes. East Spanish Peak is visible to the left.

The biggest and most impressive of the three radial dikes at stop 4 is the Devils Stairsteps (also known as the Stairway to Heaven). Erosion along a series of planar fractures, known as joints, has broken the dike into a series of three massive blocks, each one lower than the next, making it look like a giant's staircase. Most of the Stairsteps's rock is granite, explaining its light color. But there is a thin veneer of white sandstone and pebble conglomerate on the east side of the lowest step. This is a bit of the contact aureole still attached to the dike. As at the Profile Rock dike, the aureole here also consists of Cuchara Formation, baked and hardened by heat from the dike. At stop 3 the aureole consisted of mudstone and fine-grained sandstone baked nearly black, but here the rocks are much coarser, and the heat bleached them almost white.

To the left (east) of the Devils Stairsteps rises a second, light-colored radial dike. It is thinner than the Stairsteps but resembles it in all other respects. Forty yards to the left, ending just above the road, are what at first glance appear to be two more thin granitic dikes. But in this case, looks are deceiving. Instead of igneous rocks, the "dikes" consist of bleached, metamorphosed Cuchara sandstone similar to that which clings to the east side of the Stairsteps. The true dike is actually the depression between the resistant fins of sandstone. The difference stems from the fact that this dike is lamprophyre, a close relative of basalt that contains more potassium and even less silica. Lamprophyre consists of minerals that are highly susceptible to chemical weathering. Exposure to rain through the years has caused the dike's minerals to chemically transform into soft, easily eroded clay minerals.

En route to stop 5, about 3.1 miles farther southwest along CO 12, the highway passes through what appears to be another granitic Spanish Peaks dike. Despite the resemblance, this feature isn't a dike or a contact aureole. It is a fin of Dakota sandstone. As it does elsewhere along the Front Range (vignettes 10, 19), the Cretaceous-age Dakota Group here forms a hogback

The Devils Stairsteps is another granite radial dike that intruded the Cuchara Formation. The lower-left portion of the lowest step shows the contact aureole, as revealed by the faint horizontal layers consisting of white pebbles. A smaller radial dike protrudes from the vegetated hillside left of the Stairsteps.

Left of the Devils Stairsteps and a smaller granitic dike rise two rock fins. They are contact aureoles, composed of altered sandstone, that flank a lamprophyre dike, the depression covered by dark soil between the fins.

because it is very well cemented, making it far more resistant to erosion than the rocks that lie to either side of it. This and similar hogbacks are the gateway to the Rocky Mountains. To its west stand the Rockies, and to the east lie the Great Plains. The Spanish Peaks, in your rearview mirror, rise east of this hogback, highlighting the fact that despite their mountainous shape and stature, they belong to the Great Plains, not the Rockies.

About 55 million years ago the crust buckled just west of here due to tectonic compression during the Laramide orogeny, and a huge block of rock was thrust up along a fault to form the Sangre de Cristo Mountains. The stack of sedimentary rocks adjacent to the uplift, including this sandstone rib, was bent steeply upward. To the east the layers sagged down, creating the Raton Basin adjacent to the rising mountains. The great bowl of the basin was subsequently filled with a thick stack of Cuchara Formation sediments. We are examining rocks in a portion of the basin called the La Veta syncline, which is a concave-upward warp in rock strata. When, 30 million years later, the rift-related Spanish Peaks magma began to well up through the crust, the path of least resistance lay along the axis of the syncline. For this reason, the Spanish Peaks and many of their neighboring intrusions are located in the bottom of the syncline, where the stack of sedimentary rocks is the thickest.

This hogback, which looks like yet another dike, is actually a steeply tilted fin of Dakota sandstone, the legacy of a beach that once existed along the shore of a vast inland seaway.

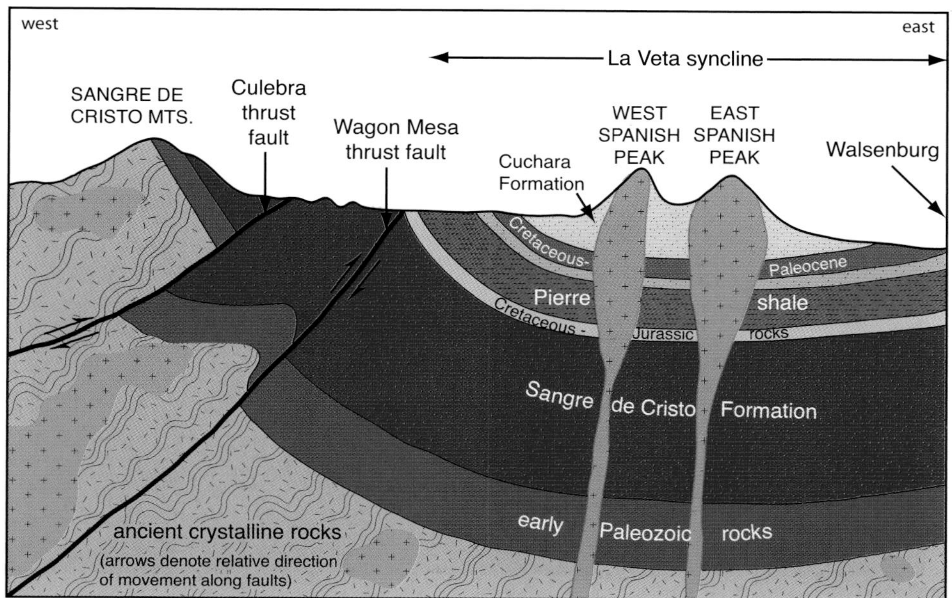

This west-east cross section shows the faults along which the Sangre de Cristo Mountains rose during the Laramide orogeny. To the east the land sagged down, forming the La Veta syncline, part of the larger Raton Basin. The Spanish Peaks magmas (brown with plus symbols) intruded crustal weaknesses at the bottom of the syncline. (Modified from Penn and Lindsey, 1996.)

From the Dakota sandstone hogback the road climbs up to Cordova Pass. A pleasant, 0.5-mile walk amidst beautiful scenery brings you to stop 5. Here, at an elevation of 11,412 feet, dozens of erosion-resistant dikes slash across the countryside below you, forming a series of long, narrow, rugged rock walls, the majority of which fan away from West Spanish Peak like spokes.

One of those dikes cuts through your perch. The rock north of the light-colored dike is the Cuchara Formation. The coarsening trend you observed in the sediment of the Cuchara between stops 3 and 4 continues in spectacular fashion; here the formation consists of boulder conglomerate. Relatively round boulders of gneiss, red sandstone, and quartz litter the ground, having weathered out of the formation's soft sedimentary matrix. The biggest boulders are over 3 feet across; their enormous size testifies to the power of the massive floods necessary to transport them here. The boulders are composed of the same rock types exposed along the crest of the Sangre de Cristo Mountains 7 miles west of here. As the mountains rose, the Cuchara Formation here was deposited on an alluvial fan that grew between the rising range and the Raton Basin to the east. The Cuchara Formation sediments we saw at stops 3 and 4 were finer grained, indicating they were deposited farther from the rising mountains by less powerful river flows.

The rock fins visible from stop 5 are some of the five hundred radial dikes emanating from the West Spanish Peak stock.

The horizontal layers visible on the flanks of West Spanish Peak are beds of Cuchara Formation that were metamorphosed when the magma of the West Spanish Peak stock came into contact with them and igneous sills that intruded parallel to the sedimentary layering. The light-colored rock in the foreground belongs to one of the radial dikes. The darker material on the left, with boulders sprinkled throughout it, is the Cuchara boulder conglomerate, deposited on an ancient alluvial fan.

At stop 5 you stand 5,200 feet higher than you did in Walsenburg, at stop 1. West Spanish Peak rises another 2,200 feet above you, so its summit stands 7,500 feet above the average height of the Great Plains. From here you can see that West Spanish Peak is composed of numerous, nearly horizontal rock layers. Although the peak's core is a granitic stock, its slopes are part of a contact aureole and consist of metamorphosed layers of the Cuchara Formation. Recall that the West Spanish Peak stock formed underground; it isn't a volcano that formed at Earth's surface. This straightforward statement has profound implications for the history of the Great Plains. It tells us that today's Great Plains land surface was buried deep beneath sedimentary layers when the magma chambers and associated dikes intruded the region 24 million years ago. How far underground? The answer is a minimum of 7,500 feet, the modern height difference between Walsenburg and the summit of West Spanish Peak.

That brings us back to our original question: Why do the Spanish Peaks, which inherently belong to the Great Plains, form such majestic, Rockies-like peaks? The answer is that 24 million years ago, thanks to many layers of sedimentary rock that no longer exist, the Great Plains stood at least

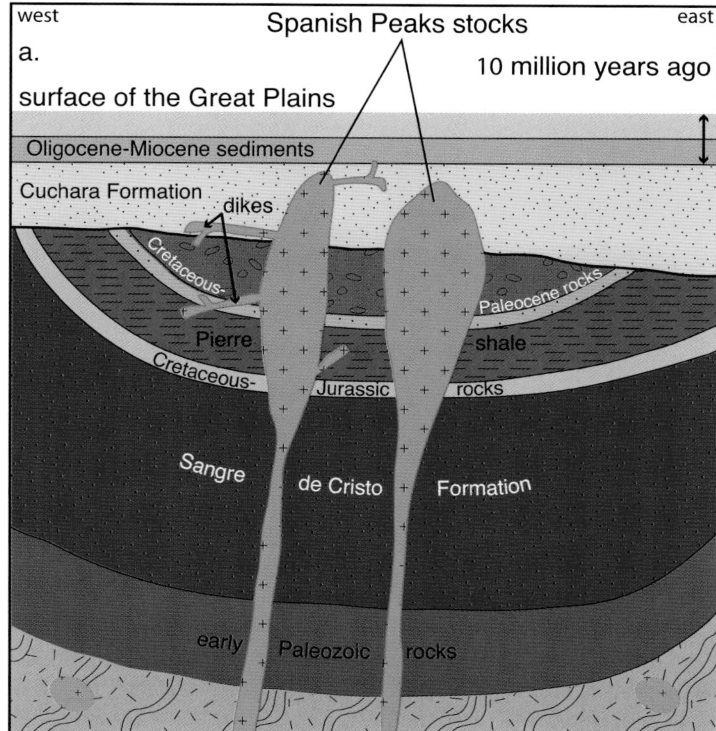

(a) Sediment layers accumulated on the Great Plains until at least 10 million years ago (vignette 2), burying the Spanish Peaks stocks and dikes farther beneath the flat, gently east-tilted surface.

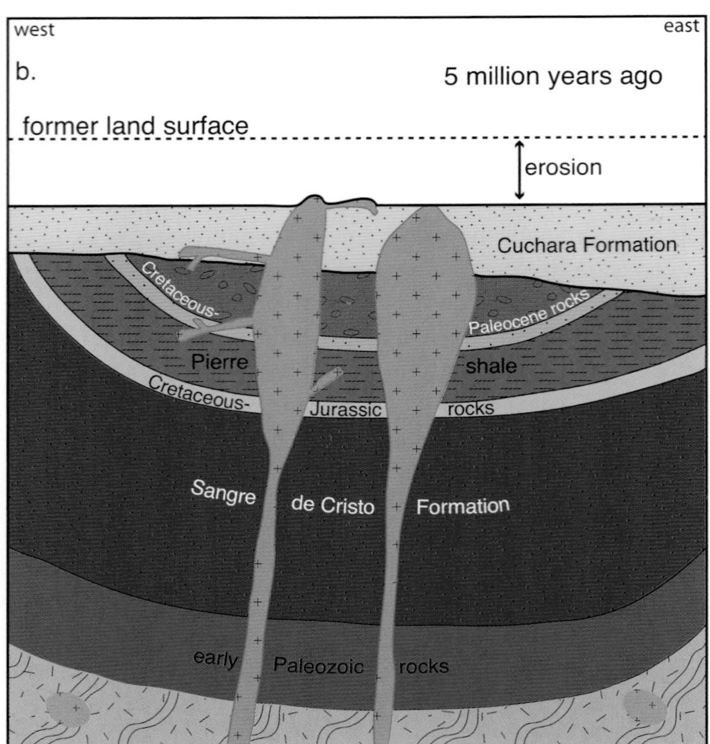

(b) Large-scale erosion began removing Great Plains sediment approximately 5 million years ago. The intrusive rock eroded more slowly than the surrounding sedimentary rock, so the Spanish Peaks formed small hills.

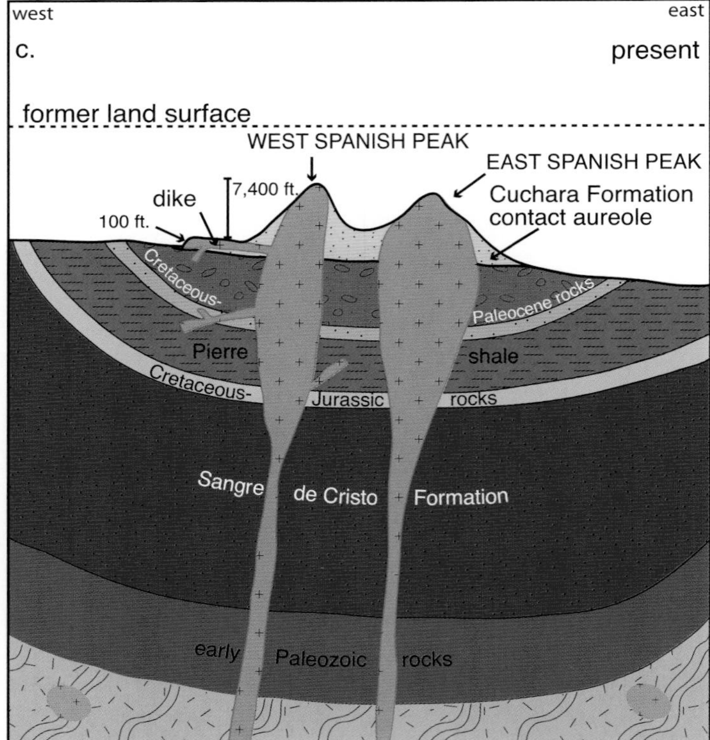

(c) As the Plains continued to erode, the resistant intrusions became today's very high peaks.

7,500 feet higher than they do today. It is almost certain that additional sediment accumulated on top of the 24-million-year-old land surface after the intrusions arrived, so the Great Plains may well have stood quite a bit higher.

Magma intruded these layers to form the Spanish Peaks stocks and associated dikes. Erosion later gnawed away at the sedimentary stack, lowering the entire Great Plains land surface by an average 3.7 inches every thousand years. The Spanish Peaks intrusive rocks, though, were too hard to be removed. Over the millennia, the Great Plains got progressively lower while the Spanish Peaks intrusions maintained their height. So despite the fact that the Spanish Peaks area was never heaved skyward along a Laramide thrust fault in the way that almost all other Colorado mountains were, their total vertical relief rivals that of any peak in the Colorado Rockies.

The Highway of Legends is aptly named. It weaves its way through the world's most impressive collection of igneous dikes, and the story those dikes and the Spanish Peaks stocks tell, of massive, wholesale Great Plains erosion, is as astounding as the dikes and stocks themselves. The geology of this corner of Colorado is legendary indeed.

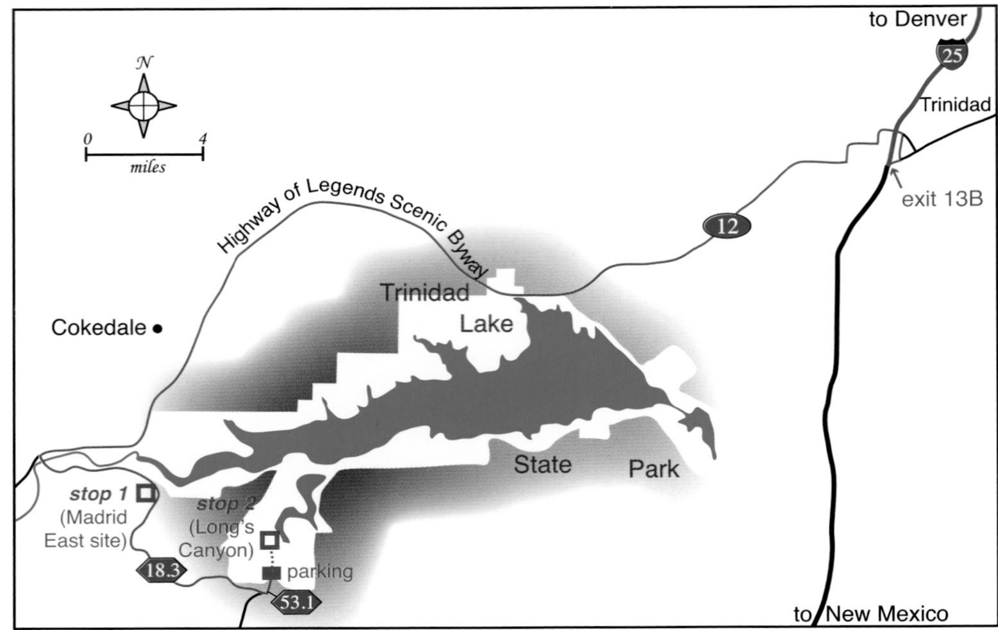

GETTING THERE: To reach Trinidad Lake State Park, exit I-25 at exit 13B (Main Street/Santa Fe Trail) in Trinidad. As you leave the interstate, reset your odometer and follow signs for CO 12. Turn left (east) onto Main Street and then take the first left onto Nevada Avenue. Turn left onto Animas Street just after you cross the Purgatoire River (this street becomes University Street as it passes under I-25), then turn left again onto Prospect Street. Where Prospect ends the road turns right and becomes Stonewall Avenue. Take the first left onto San Juan Street, then a right onto Robinson Avenue where San Juan ends. Robinson is CO 12. This all sounds complex, but each turn is clearly marked by signs for CO 12. At 3.6 miles from I-25 you will pass the left turn to Trinidad Lake State Park. Continue west on CO 12, passing the town of Cokedale. Turn left (south) onto County Road 18.3 at 9.7 miles. You immediately cross the Purgatoire River. After 0.7 mile the road turns to gravel. Stop 1 is what geologists call the Madrid East K-T boundary site. It is an outcrop on the right side of the road where County Road 18.3 executes a sharp right curve 1.3 miles after leaving CO 12. You can park along the road here to examine the outcrop. To reach stop 2, Long's Canyon, continue 1.9 miles farther down the road and turn left (north) onto County Road 53.1, which is marked to Long's Canyon. The road ends at a parking lot after 0.5 mile. Park here and walk 0.25 mile along the gentle trail to the first rock outcrop on the left. In order to examine closely the K-T boundary clay, it is helpful to bring a hand lens or magnifying glass.

21

THE DAY THE DINOSAURS DIED
The Infamous K-T Boundary at Trinidad Lake State Park

In contrast to the dinosaurs' long, multimillion-year reign at the top of the terrestrial food chain, their death was sudden and catastrophic. Although scientific consensus fingering the culprit is quite recent, the conclusion that a collision between Earth and a stray asteroid was to blame is so extraordinary, so made for Hollywood, that it has burst upon the public consciousness with an intensity that is rare for a scientific theory. In the geologic blink of an eye, 70 percent of all species inhabiting Earth, including all the dinosaurs, were completely wiped out. Even the few species that managed to survive were decimated. Life had absorbed a blow that left it staggering for many millennia and altered the course of evolution.

Presumably, the evidence for such a titanic catastrophe must be very pronounced in the geologic record. The signs of Earth's very bad day 65.5 million years ago, when the Cretaceous period gave way to the Tertiary period, or the K-T boundary (*K* for Cretaceous and *T* for Tertiary), must be blatantly obvious to experts and novices alike—right?

Although this assumption is reasonable, it is actually wrong. Geologic time is so vast, and the physical processes that reshape the planet are so pervasive, that most evidence of even this immense carnage has been efficiently erased. Luckily, though, for the modern rock detectives who evolved 65 million years later, unassuming stacks of rock have remained across the globe that contain the subtle clues used to piece together the compelling story of the dinosaurs' last days. At Trinidad Lake State Park we can follow in the footsteps of those crafty detectives and literally touch the fallout from a cosmic collision so large it set evolution on a completely different trajectory—one that eventually produced us.

At stop 1, immediately west of the road a 15-foot-tall cliff of tan sandstone caps a stack of crumbling gray mudstone and black coal beds. These

The energy released by an enormous asteroid impact 65.5 million years ago far exceeded the combined strength of all of Earth's nuclear arsenals and killed off 70 percent of the planet's species. In artist Cheryl McCutchan's rendering of Trinidad's Late Cretaceous landscape, a T. rex feasts on its last meal as the fireball approaches.

rocks all belong to the Raton Formation, which accumulated during the latest Cretaceous and early Tertiary periods. (The Tertiary is now called the Paleogene, so you sometimes see the K-T boundary referred to in modern publications as the K-P boundary.) Because deposition of the formation spanned the transition between the two periods, the cliff is an ideal place to look for the one rock layer that accumulated exactly at the K-T boundary. The Trinidad area at that time was part of a topographic depression known as the Raton Basin. The basin formed as the crust bowed down in response to the weight placed on it by the Rocky Mountains, newly risen to the west (vignette 20). The Raton Formation consists of some of the earliest sediments shed off of the young mountain range.

A few inches below the massive sandstone cap, in the midst of a thinly bedded stack of dark gray mudstone and black coal layers, you will find a 1-inch-thick stripe of light gray claystone. This layer is known as the K-T boundary clay. Once you've located it, try tracking it to the right (north) along the outcrop. Eventually it pinches out, or disappears, against the thick sandstone.

Modern rock sleuths have used evidence just like this to piece together what the environment was like in the Trinidad area when these rocks were deposited. The mudstone and coal seams show that this region was strongly reminiscent of a Louisiana bayou today, an immense, low-lying plain with lazy rivers slowly dropping their load of mud on floodplains. The abundant coal layers consist of the compacted remains of ancient deciduous forests, whose trees died and fell into the swamps. Mining of the area's rich coal reserves formed the economic lifeblood of the Trinidad region from the late 1800s until the 1950s, when the widespread replacement of railroad steam engines by diesel locomotives led to a precipitous drop in the demand for coal. The region's reserves were still used to fuel the steel furnaces in a Pueblo plant until the 1970s, but with the installation of electric furnaces the demand for Raton Formation coal evaporated almost completely, leading to the closing of all the mines. The area's economy has yet to fully rebound, but mines are beginning to reopen as foreign demand drives a growing U.S. coal export business.

At stop 1, a stack of thinly bedded, dark gray mudstone and coal underlies a thick, tan sandstone (dashed box shows location of inset photo). The infamous K-T boundary clay forms a light-colored stripe within the swamp deposits just a couple inches beneath the sandstone on the left side of the outcrop (inset, white arrow).

The thick sandstone cap formed when a flood coursing down a former, nearby river channel breached its natural levee and spilled sand-laden floodwater onto the adjacent coal swamp. Such levee breaches, also known as crevasses, are common during floods along modern meandering rivers in locations such as Louisiana. The breaching event leaves behind a cone-shaped pile of sand that eventually becomes cemented, forming a sandstone bed identical to the one you are looking at. Geologists call these deposits crevasse splays.

Because the sandstone overlies the K-T boundary clay, we know that this particular flood occurred shortly after 65.5 million years ago. When the torrent breached the levee, it obliterated the boundary clay on the right side of the outcrop, replacing it with the crevasse-splay sandstone. Although the flood erased part of the boundary clay, it is ultimately a very good thing that this and many other crevasse splays occurred along the Raton Basin's sluggish rivers in the early years of the Tertiary period. Without them and the resilient sandstone caps they formed, all of the soft clay would be long gone, along with the region's precious clues to what caused the dinosaurs' demise.

Since the earliest days of geological science, geologists have known from the fossil record that a major extinction occurred at the K-T boundary. It is for precisely this reason they selected it as the boundary between the Mesozoic and the Cenozoic eras of the geologic timescale. What they didn't know was why it occurred. When the father-and-son team of Luis and Walter Alvarez put their heads to this problem in the late 1970s, most

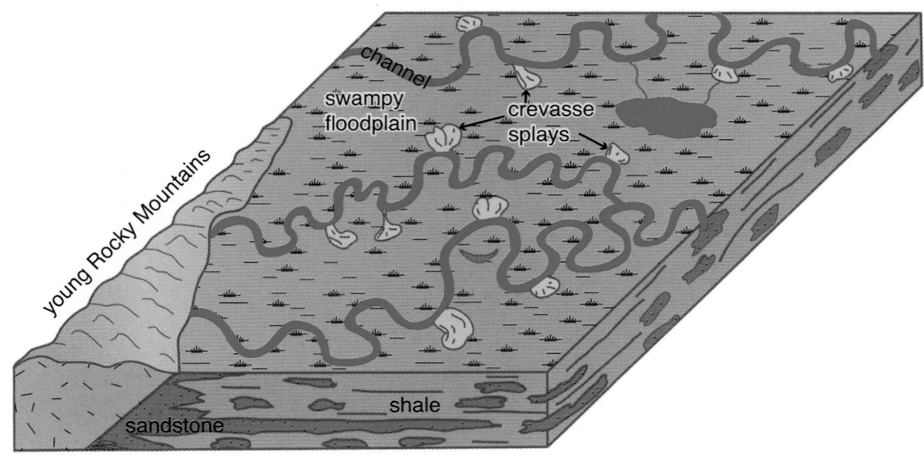

The Trinidad area 65.5 million years ago consisted of a broad, flat, swampy plain traversed by meandering rivers draining the young Rocky Mountains. During occasional floods, the rivers breached natural levees that separated the channels from the floodplains, spreading cones of sand (crevasse splays) across the floodplains.

geologists and paleontologists attributed the extinction to a gigantic volcanic event that occurred in India. This volcanism produced one of the biggest outpourings of lava (called the Deccan Traps) ever to occur on Earth, and it happened very closely in time to the K-T boundary.

But the Alvarezes, in a controversial 1980 paper, proposed a radically different idea. They posited that an asteroid impact triggered the mass extinction. The geologist son, Walter, had been studying a sequence of marine-deposited rocks in Gubbio, Italy, that straddle the K-T boundary. One day, when Walter was describing to his father, a Nobel-prize-winning physicist, the characteristics of a puzzling clay layer positioned exactly at the K-T boundary, the idea hit Luis to analyze the concentrations of various exotic elements in the rocks. While geologists rarely had a need to analyze these elements, it was common practice in Luis's branch of physics. To the surprise of both, the analyses revealed an abrupt spike in the concentration of the element iridium in the clay but nowhere else in the rock section. While iridium is exceedingly rare in Earth rocks, it is relatively enriched in meteorites, which are small asteroids that have fallen to Earth. This discovery set the Alvarezes on the path to their stunning proposal that a bolt from the blue felled the dinosaurs.

The Alvarez hypothesis was anything but popular with geologists, for whom this extraterrestrial mechanism sounded suspiciously like catastrophism, the nineteenth-century notion that the known laws of physics can be capriciously violated, and that these violations were primarily responsible for shaping Earth. The discipline of geology had battled this notion from the very inception of the science. In reality, the Alvarez hypothesis could not have been farther from the catastrophist views. They appealed to known physical laws governing the trajectories of extraterrestrial bodies and made compelling use of the observation that our planetary neighbors, such as the Moon, Mars, and Mercury, are all pockmarked with meteor craters. Geologists were accustomed to thinking about physical processes that occurred on Earth, not elsewhere in the solar system, so the idea at first hit them as beyond radical. But on further reflection they had to admit that Earth could not have avoided the bombardment that clearly befell our neighbors. In addition to providing a viable explanation for the K-T carnage, the Alvarezes' hypothesis forever expanded geologists' view of our planet; they began to look at Earth as one member of a larger solar system rather than as an isolated, self-contained body.

In their 1980 publication, the Alvarezes highlighted their discovery that additional sites around the world also contain the K-T boundary clay, as it became known, with iridium concentrations hundreds to thousands of times higher than had been previously measured in Earth rocks. Despite this astounding global evidence, other scientists remained skeptical. Some argued that because the rocks at every one of the Alvarezes' K-T sites had been deposited in shallow seas, some previously unknown process related to marine weathering could have caused the iridium anomaly. The only solution to this debate was to find a boundary clay deposited on land. The race was on.

Geologists locate the K-T boundary in marine rocks by identifying the horizon at which several key species of plankton go extinct and new species appear. But how then could geologists pinpoint the boundary on land? It soon became apparent that the K-T boundary also marked a wholesale change in pollen species, and hence the trees from which they came. Fossil pollen is commonly preserved in terrestrial (land-deposited) rocks, so the pollen marker was every bit as reliable in terrestrial rocks as the plankton marker was in marine rocks for locating the boundary.

Armed with this new knowledge, Charles Pillmore, a field geologist with the U.S. Geological Survey, located the first terrestrial K-T boundary in 1981, just a scant year after publication of the Alvarez hypothesis. He discovered the boundary clay, with elevated iridium levels, here in the Raton Basin, just a few miles south of Trinidad Lake, near New Mexico's York Canyon coal mine. The argument that marine weathering was the cause of the iridium anomaly was immediately retired. Since Pillmore's discovery, scientists have found twenty-five additional exposures of the K-T boundary clay in the Raton Basin, including the Madrid East exposure you have been examining. Of the one hundred terrestrial K-T rock exposures known worldwide, over a quarter were discovered in the Raton Basin, and over half are located in western North America.

At stop 2, Long's Canyon, proceed along the peaceful Long's Canyon Watchable Wildlife Trail. After 300 level yards, you will arrive at the southern end of a 200-foot-long K-T boundary outcrop. The stacked rocks are nearly identical to those you saw at stop 1: a hard, thick, crevasse splay sandstone cap protecting underlying coals and mudstones. As the crow flies, this site is less than 1 mile from stop 1, so the coal here likely formed in the same swamp. Not surprisingly, the 1-inch-thick, light gray boundary clay lies in the same position in the rock sequence, sandwiched between a thicker coal bed below and a thinner (2-inch) coal bed above, all just a few inches below the capping sandstone. Though the boundary clay is easy to trace along the entire length of this outcrop, the easiest place to examine the clay up close is at the southern end, where you can scramble up the small cone of coal debris above the trail.

The clay at Long's Canyon contains all of the key characteristics that scientists used to ferret out the culprit behind the mass extinction. These clues aren't readily apparent without a microscope or a mass spectrometer, but they are all here, making Long's Canyon and its neighboring Raton exposures one of the best places on Earth to study the K-T extinction event.

The K-T boundary outcrop at Long's Canyon.

Close-up of the K-T boundary clay, the prominent, light gray layer above the keys.

Chemical analysis of the clay has shown that it consists almost exclusively of kaolinite, a common by-product of the intense chemical weathering of many different minerals. Its presence, therefore, is not itself noteworthy. However, this particular kaolinite is indeed unusual. It is not the result of the typical breakdown of mineJrals, but rather of the weathering of microscopic, spherical glass beads, a few of which resisted alteration and are preserved in the clay.

Known as microtektites, the beads lack the regimented, crystalline atomic structure that is the hallmark of all minerals. Rather, they consist of a disordered solid, which we call glass. Such glass beads are highly unusual in the rock record. As seen during nuclear test explosions, they only form when rock is vaporized and hurled into the air. The molten debris cools almost instantly—much too quickly to form structured mineral crystals. As the glass droplets fall, air friction rounds them. The fact that these microtektites are found around the world in the K-T boundary clays has proved a significant argument in support of the their impact origin.

Here at Long's Canyon the peak iridium concentration is 10 parts per billion. Although that doesn't sound like much, it is about 1,400 times higher than the concentration of iridium in the surrounding rocks. At

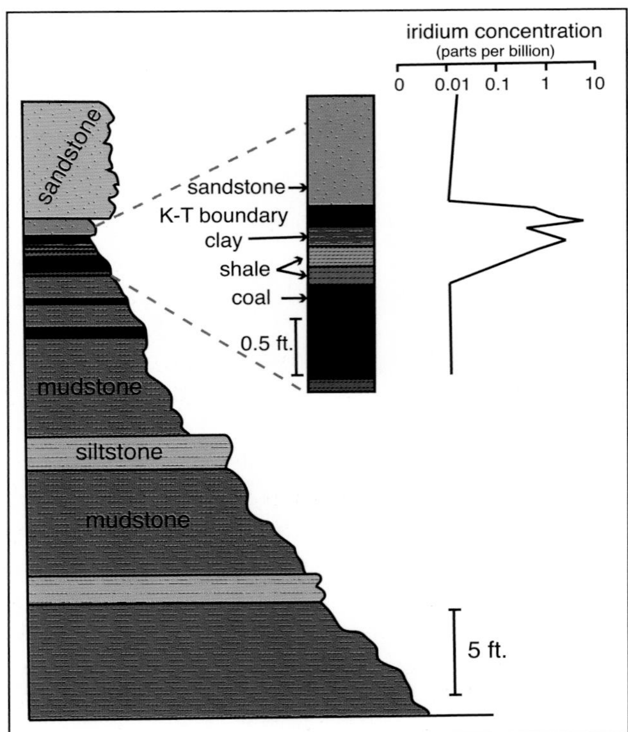

Typical of rocks deposited across the K-T boundary, the iridium concentration in the rock sequence at stop 2 peaks at 10 parts per billion in the K-T boundary clay and is negligible in surrounding rocks. (Redrawn from Pillmore et al., 1999.)

nearby Starkville, on I-25 immediately south of Trinidad, the concentration spikes to 56 parts per billion, a stunning 8,000 times higher than in surrounding layers and the highest iridium value ever measured in terrestrial rocks. The top of the clay in both locations also contains elevated concentrations of unusual metals such as titanium, scandium, vanadium, chromium, and antimony, further evidence of the clay's unusual origin.

Microscopic examination of the upper portion of the boundary clay revealed an abundance of mineral crystals, particularly quartz, with a series of parallel cracks running through them. These so-called shocked minerals are uncommon. In fact, prior to scientific scrutiny of the K-T boundary clay, shocked crystals had been seen only at ground zero after nuclear bomb tests. The pressure necessary to create shock-induced cracking is truly enormous, far greater than the forces generated during normal, Earth-based geologic events, even violent ones like explosive volcanic eruptions. The presence of shocked quartz in exposure after exposure of the K-T boundary clay was the final piece of evidence that caused many geologists to finally accept its impact origin.

After the Alvarezes proposed the impact hypothesis, geologists began looking for the crater or craters left behind by the asteroid. By 1990 two potential impact sites were on everyone's mind: the Chicxulub (pronounced "cheech-shoo-loob") Crater on Mexico's Yucatan Peninsula, or Iowa's Manson Crater. Both were approximately the right age. The Chicxulub Crater, at 110 miles in diameter, was caused by the impact of a 6-mile-wide asteroid, one that was big enough to trigger global devastation. The Manson Crater is "only" 23 miles across, meaning it was gouged out by a 1.5-mile-wide asteroid. While too small to wreak global havoc on its own, the Manson impact could have been one of a string of impacts that cumulatively devastated the planet. In 1994 scientists gained a better appreciation for how common such multiple impacts could be when they watched, in awe, as the gravity of Jupiter shattered an asteroid into twenty pieces, each of which collided with the planet within a week.

The presence of another shocked mineral in the Raton Basin boundary clay also sheds light on this puzzle. The second mineral is zircon, which has one important distinction: unlike quartz, it can be radiometrically dated. The ages of some zircon minerals were reset by the shock, confirming that it occurred 65.5 million years ago, precisely when the clays were deposited. But the shock event didn't reset the ages of other zircons, thereby allowing geologists to glean the age of the rocks the minerals were blasted from during the asteroid impact. The age evidence strongly suggested that all of the shocked zircons came from the same location. This was a significant clue in the search for the culprit crater. The zircons were much too young to have come from the rock in and around the Manson Crater, but the Chicxulub Crater, on the other hand, contains rocks of the correct age. Combined with other lines of evidence, these Raton Basin zircons have convinced most geologists that the asteroid that killed the dinosaurs smashed into Mexico's Yucatan Peninsula.

Recent detailed chemical analyses of K-T boundary microtektites show that the asteroid that killed the dinosaurs was carbonaceous chondrite, a rare type whose composition has remained unchanged since the birth of the solar system. Recently, scientists used the asteroid's rare composition in combination with computer modeling to suggest that the ultimate cause of Earth's encounter with this 6-mile-wide asteroid was a separate collision in the asteroid belt between Mars and Jupiter some 160 million years ago. A 37-mile-wide asteroid smashed into a 105-mile-wide object, shattering both into a thousand pieces bigger than 0.5 mile across. Many of these fragments remain today in a tightly clustered orbit in the asteroid belt. These carbonaceous chondrites reside in a particularly dangerous neighborhood for Earth, a region of the belt where gravitational tugs exerted by Jupiter and Mars increase the likelihood that an asteroid will be hurled out of the belt and into an Earth-crossing orbit.

These scientists believe this gravitational tug-of-war ejected the dinosaur-killing asteroid, as well as another asteroid that crashed into the moon 109 million years ago, forming the 53-mile-wide Tycho Crater. If this hypothesis proves correct, it is ironic that a collision in the asteroid belt during the early days of dinosaur domination on Earth destined them to extinction 94 million years later.

It is difficult to fathom that so much information can be gleaned from a mere 1 inch of rock, yet this clay can tell us even more. The number of microtektites and the iridium concentration both increase from bottom to top in the clay. These and other characteristics reveal that the clay was actually deposited in two stages. First, a rain of molten material deposited the lower clay as vaporized rock hurled out of the Chicxulub Crater pummeled the Raton Basin. A short time later the vaporized remains of the asteroid itself fell back to Earth, forming the upper clay, which scientists graphically refer to as the "fireball layer." This extraterrestrial material is what accounts for the elevated iridium concentration in the upper layer.

With a preponderance of evidence supporting the idea that a big asteroid did collide with Earth 65.5 million years ago, scientists turned their attention to learning more about how this and comparable impacts affected life on Earth. Could such a collision kill off 70 percent of its species?

Based on theory, scientists believe the impact of a 6-mile-wide asteroid would release the energy equivalent to about 100 *trillion* tons of TNT, which is comparable to the simultaneous detonation of 2 million atomic bombs! Scientists have developed a frightening scenario that may have unfolded after the asteroid impact. Creatures within a few hundred miles of the impact were killed instantly. Furthermore, because the asteroid smacked into the sea, it unleashed a tsunami hundreds of feet tall, which devastated coastal ecosystems around the globe. Dust and debris hurled into the atmosphere darkened the sky for years, creating an impact winter that likely caused the collapse of both the terrestrial and marine food chains. The shallow sea at ground zero was floored by limestone and gypsum rocks rich in carbon and sulfur. Vaporization of these rocks released massive quantities of carbon dioxide, a greenhouse gas, and sulfur dioxide, an icehouse gas, into the atmosphere. Along with the sun-obscuring dust, the more-potent but shorter-lived sulfur dioxide created temperatures likely well below freezing across the globe for decades, killing off still more organisms. Once the dust and sulfur dioxide had been scrubbed from the air, those creatures that survived the deep freeze then had to withstand a thousand years of vicious heat triggered by the lingering greenhouse effects of the carbon dioxide. In addition, both gases combined with water in the air to form acid rain, presenting another formidable challenge to many species. And if that weren't enough, the rain of glowing-hot rock from the crater likely set whole continents ablaze, with North America the most seriously affected.

Given this overwhelming scenario, it is easy to turn our original question on its head and ask not how the impact killed, but rather how any life survived. All these proposed mechanisms for the extinction event are strictly theoretical. But do the K-T boundary rocks in the Raton Basin provide any evidence about what caused the killing?

We know that in the Raton Basin the extinction was sudden. Between 30 and 40 percent of plant species identified by pollen in the K-T boundary clay died out simultaneously. Interestingly, a very thin layer of the clay is dominated not by pollen, but rather fern spores. This is a worldwide phenomenon that paleontologists call the "fern spike." The spike reveals that for a brief time ferns dominated terrestrial ecosystems around the globe. In the Raton Basin almost 100 percent of the flora shortly after the impact consisted of ferns, and 80 percent were a single species!

Ferns quickly colonize ravaged landscapes because their spores can be easily dispersed by wind, and once they are established in an area they can sprout from either spores or rootstocks. They grow quickly and tolerate poor soils exceptionally well. For these reasons scientists believe the fern spike is evidence that terrestrial ecosystems were devastated at the K-T boundary. The ferns formed the vanguard for recolonization, but in the Raton Basin and elsewhere a more diverse flora consisting of flowering plants and evergreens soon replaced them. Colorado's Castle Rock rainforest (vignette 17) reveals that 1.4 million years after the K-T catastrophe, a thriving rainforest populated by over one hundred different species of vegetation flourished in the foothills of the youthful Rocky Mountains. This fossil rainforest provides the world's best record of early plant diversification after the crisis.

One major reason terrestrial plant communities were decimated is that they endured a major temperature fluctuation. Leaf fossils from the nearby Denver Basin and North Dakota show an 80 percent turnover in plant species at the K-T boundary. Based on changes in leaf shape and size, the fossils indicate that the temperature plummeted at the K-T boundary and then rebounded, just as the impact theory would predict.

In the late 1980s scientists discovered boundary clays with up to 1,000 times more soot than that measured in surrounding rocks. This soot spike was almost surely produced by the burning of vegetation. The soot shows up in Raton Basin samples, but also in places as far-flung as Europe, New Zealand, and the deep Pacific Ocean. To produce such a spike, at least 10 percent of all the world's vegetation must have burned simultaneously—a sobering number for anyone who has witnessed the devastation wrought by a large, modern wildfire, which would be trivial compared to an entire continent ablaze.

It is extraordinary how subtle the evidence for a global catastrophe can be. Through painstaking scientific examination of a crumbly clay layer a mere 1 inch thick, scientists have developed an exquisitely detailed picture of an ancient event. It's mind-expanding to recognize that if the events that deposited this diminutive clay layer in Long's Canyon had not occurred 65.5 million years ago, we would likely not be present to contemplate them. Abundant paleontological evidence shows that dinosaurs were not slow, feeble-brained creatures whose shortcomings destined them to extinction, as they are sometimes portrayed in popular media. When the K-T asteroid hit they were thriving, as they had been for the preceding 130 million years. If fate had not dealt Earth a bolt from above, it is plausible that today this would be a dinosaur planet. We mammals benefited from the demise of the dinosaurs and the tenacity of our early ancestors, which allowed them to survive the K-T devastation, providing them with the space and the time to evolve into us.

Glossary

aggradation. An interval of time during which a river deposits alluvium.

Allosaurus. A genus of large, meat-eating dinosaurs that lived during the Late Jurassic period.

alluvial fan. A fan-shaped pile of sediment that forms at the base of a mountain range where swiftly flowing streams slow down as they reach the flatter valley floor.

alluvium. Loose sediment deposited by moving water, such as a river, in a nonmarine setting.

amphibole. A family of dark, relatively low-silica, rock-forming minerals.

amphibolite. A metamorphic rock containing a very high concentration of the dark mineral hornblende (a member of the amphibole family of minerals).

Ancestral Front Range. An ancient mountain range that formed during the Pennsylvanian period in approximately the same location as today's Front Range. It was one of several mountain ranges that comprised the Ancestral Rocky Mountains.

Ancestral Rocky Mountains. An ancient mountain range that formed during the Pennsylvanian period in Colorado and New Mexico.

andesite. A fine-grained, gray volcanic rock that contains more silica than basalt and less silica than rhyolite.

Ankylosaurus. A genus of armored dinosaurs that lived during the Late Cretaceous period.

anticline. A convex-upward (arch-shaped) fold whose core contains stratigraphically older rocks.

Apatosaurus. A genus of large, sauropod dinosaurs that lived during the Late Jurassic period.

aquifer. Sediment or rock with interconnected pore spaces that contains enough water to be pumped for human needs.

arête. A narrow, knife-edged mountain ridge most commonly formed by glacial erosion.

arkose. A sandstone that contains at least 25 percent feldspar grains.

ash. Fine-grained material erupted by volcanoes.

asteroid. A rocky or metallic object in the solar system that is much smaller than a planet.

asthenosphere. The layer in the mantle, below the lithosphere, that is hot enough to flow plastically. This flow drives tectonic plate movement.

badlands. Soft, heavily rilled hills formed of easily eroded mudstone bedrock that are nearly devoid of vegetation.

basalt. A fine-grained, dark volcanic rock rich in iron-bearing minerals.

batholith. A mass of intrusive igneous rock that covers an area larger than 40 square miles. It consists of numerous individual plutons that were injected into one another.

bed. The smallest sedimentary unit that is distinguishable from other beds above and below, generally ranging from about 0.375 inch to 6 feet thick.

bedding. The arrangement of a sedimentary rock in layers, or the general pattern of the beds within a rock.

bedrock. Solid rock underlying loose surficial sediments.

biotite. A dark, sheetlike silicate mineral.

boulder. A rock particle that is greater than 10 inches in diameter.

brachiopod. A two-shelled marine invertebrate commonly found fossilized in Paleozoic-age limestone.

braided river. A river in which water flows in a number of different channels simultaneously. These channels are separated by shifting islands of sediment, making the channel configuration resemble braided hair.

breccia. A sedimentary or volcanic rock composed of angular, pebble- to boulder-sized fragments in a matrix of finer-grained material.

brontosaur. A type of sauropod dinosaur that is the same as *Apatosaurus*. *See also Apatosaurus*.

calcite. A light-colored mineral composed of calcium carbonate. The primary component of limestone.

calcium carbonate. A white or colorless crystalline chemical compound. In its mineral form it is calcite, the primary component in limestone.

caldera. As used in this book, a silica-rich, very explosive volcano that collapses after an especially large, violent eruption. The term can also describe an especially large crater in a basalt volcano.

***Camarasaurus*.** A genus of large, sauropod dinosaurs that lived during the Late Jurassic period.

catastrophism. The hypothesis, popular during the nineteenth century, which posits that Earth's geologic record is largely the product of catastrophic events caused by God's suspension of the laws of physics as we know them. The main catastrophic event strongly advocated by proponents of the theory was the biblical flood. *See also* uniformitarianism.

chalcopyrite. A primary ore mineral for copper mining.

channel. The portion of a river in which water flows throughout the year. It is confined between raised banks that separate it from the floodplain, which is covered by water during large floods.

chemical weathering. The degradation of rocks by chemical processes such as dissolution. *See also* weathering.

chert. An exceptionally hard sedimentary rock composed of interlocking, microscopic quartz crystals.

cirque. An amphitheatre-like valley head formed by glacial erosion.

clast. A particle in sedimentary rock or a pile of loose sediment.

clay. The smallest sediment particles; those less than 0.00016 inch (0.004 millimeter) in diameter.

clay mineral. A mineral formed by the chemical weathering of preexisting rocks.

claystone. A sedimentary rock composed of clay-sized particles.

climate change. A change in climate at a global or regional scale.

coal. A black to brownish black sedimentary rock formed from the organic carbon of plant remains. It is a major fossil fuel.

cobble. A rock or mineral particle that is 2.5 to 10 inches in diameter. Found in conglomerate, breccia, or loose sediment.

Colorado Mineral Belt. A northeast-trending belt of igneous rocks and associated mineralization that developed during the Laramide orogeny (about 70 to 45 million years ago). Much of Colorado's mineral production has been from mines located in this belt.

Colorado orogeny. The local Colorado name for the mountain building event that occurred in the American Southwest between about 1,780 and 1,700 million years ago. *See also* Yavapai orogeny.

Colorado Plateau. A comparatively flat, elevated region in Colorado, Utah, Arizona, and New Mexico with sedimentary rocks that are only modestly deformed.

conglomerate. A sedimentary rock composed of rounded pebble- to boulder-sized particles in a finer-grained matrix.

contact aureole. A zone of metamorphism that surrounds an igneous intrusion. It develops because of elevated temperature.

contact metamorphism. Metamorphism of rock due to elevated temperature rather than elevated pressure. It most commonly occurs in a zone of rock in contact with an igneous intrusion.

continental crust. Buoyant crust composed of silica-rich rocks, such as granite, that forms the continents. *See also* oceanic crust.

core. The innermost section of Earth's interior. Composed of high-density, iron-rich compounds.

cosmogenic radionuclide dating. Dating of a rock or geologic event using radioactive elements produced in Earth's atmosphere or within the rock itself due to the collision of high-energy cosmic rays with terrestrial atoms.

crossbed. A layer of sedimentary rock deposited at an angle to the horizontal. Crossbeds usually mark the advancing crests of former windblown dunes or water-transported sediment. *See also* high-angle crossbedding.

crust. The outermost shell of Earth. *See also* continental crust; oceanic crust

deformation band. A narrow zone in rock in which strain accumulates during the early stages of faulting.

Denver Basin. A former topographic sag located in the Denver area in which a thick pile of sediments accumulated during the Late Cretaceous through the Eocene. It formed adjacent to the rising Rocky Mountains.

diatreme. A volcanic pipe filled with breccia that was formed by an explosive, gas-rich volcanic eruption.

differential pressure. When pressure is higher in one direction than in other directions as a rock is metamorphosed. *See also* foliation.

dike. A long, narrow igneous intrusion that cuts through massive nonlayered rocks or through layered rocks at a high angle.

***Diplodocus*.** A genus of large, sauropod dinosaurs that lived during the Late Jurassic period.

dolomite. A mineral composed of calcium, magnesium, and carbon. The term is also used to describe a sedimentary rock that consists dominantly of the mineral dolomite.

drift. Rock material transported and deposited by a glacier.

duckbilled dinosaur. A dinosaur belonging to the Hadrosauridae family. The hadrosaurs lived during the Late Cretaceous and possessed a bill that resembles that of a duck.

eon. The largest division of geologic time. An eon encompasses several eras.

era. A division of geologic time. Eras are composed of periods; eras compose eons.

erosion. The loosening and moving of soil and rock downhill or downwind. Erosion is accomplished by several agents (wind, water, ice) through a variety of processes.

erosion surface. A flat-topped land surface that has been beveled by erosion.

evaporite. Sedimentary rock composed mainly of minerals left behind when seawater or lake water evaporates. Also refers to the minerals themselves.

extension. Pulling apart of Earth's crust, usually along normal faults.

fault. A break in rocks along which movement has occurred. *See also* normal fault; reverse fault; strike-slip fault; thrust fault.

fault block. A body of rock on one side of a fault.

fault plane. The planar surface along which fault blocks slip.

fault zone. A zone up to thousands of yards wide comprised of many small fractures that accommodate tectonic motion.

feldspar. The most common rock-forming mineral. It is light colored and composed of aluminum, silicon, oxygen, and either potassium, sodium, or calcium.

flash flood. A flood that happens suddenly, usually because of very heavy rainfall.

floodplain. A level plain of stratified, unconsolidated sediment on either side of a stream or river that is submerged during floods.

foliation. The parallel alignment of minerals in metamorphosed rock. *See also* differential pressure.

formation. The primary rock unit used for formal rock description and mapping. A formation is a grouping of rock that possesses distinctive, recognizable physical characteristics that distinguishes it from surrounding rock layers.

fossil. A remnant or trace of an organism preserved from the geologic past.

gabbro. A dark intrusive igneous rock with the same chemical composition as basalt but with coarser crystals visible to the naked eye.

galena. An important ore mineral for lead.

Gangplank. A nearly flat-topped, eastward-tilting surface that connects the Great Plains with the crest of the Rockies on the Wyoming-Colorado state line.

geologic timescale. The division of geologic history into eons, eras, periods, and epochs.

glacial horn. A steep, jagged mountain peak shaped by glacial erosion.

glacier. A body of compacted ice that flows slowly in a downhill direction.

glauconite. A green mineral that forms on marine continental shelves where sediment accumulates slowly.

global warming. The warming of Earth. Many scientists attribute warming within the last few hundred years to human activities.

gneiss. A common metamorphic rock that possesses foliation consisting of alternating bands of dark and light minerals.

gradient. The steepness of a river channel as measured by the angle between the water surface and the horizontal.

granite. A light-colored, coarse-grained intrusive igneous rock with quartz, feldspar, hornblende, and mica as dominant minerals.

Great Unconformity. An unconformity in the American West that separates Paleozoic-age sedimentary rock from Proterozoic-age igneous and metamorphic rock.

Grenville orogeny. A long-lived mountain building event that occurred in what is today North America approximately 1,200 to 1,000 million years ago, during the Proterozoic eon. It formed a mountain range that stretched from Labrador to Mexico. Most geologists believe it was associated with the final assembly of the supercontinent Rodinia.

ground moraine. An accumulation of glacially deposited debris that was broadly distributed along the base of a former glacier. Ground moraines do not form prominent hills as do other types of moraines. *See also* lateral moraine; terminal moraine.

groundwater. Water that resides underground in the cracks and pore spaces of sediment and rocks.

hadrosaur. A dinosaur belonging to the Hadrosauridae family. Hadrosaurs lived during the Late Cretaceous period and possessed a bill that resembles that of a duck. For this reason they are also known as duckbilled dinosaurs.

hanging valley. A U-shaped valley that joins a main valley far above the floor of the main valley. Because the hanging valley was carved by a tributary glacier that contained less ice than the glacier of the main valley, the floor elevation of the hanging valley was higher than that of the main valley.

headwall. A steep cliff that stands at the head of a glacial cirque.

headward erosion. The process of a river extending its length through accelerated erosion toward its steep headwaters.

headwaters. The uppermost reaches of a stream, where it begins to flow.

hematite. A mineral that is red when its crystals are tiny and steel gray when larger. It forms when iron-bearing minerals in a rock are oxidized by exposure to air and water. It is the mineral that forms common rust.

high-angle crossbedding. Crossbeds in sandstone that intersect one another at an angle greater than about 20 degrees.

hogback. A ridge formed by a steeply tilted, highly erosion-resistant sedimentary layer.

hornblende. A dark amphibole mineral that is one of the major rock-forming minerals. Technically speaking, there is no one mineral called hornblende. Rather, this is a general field term for dark, iron- and magnesium-rich amphibole minerals.

hot spot. A volcanically active area that is fed by a portion of the underlying mantle that is unusually hot compared with the surrounding mantle.

hydrothermal fluids. Subsurface water, often hot, that dissolves minerals as it circulates. Commonly associated with volcanoes and magma.

hydrothermal metamorphism. Metamorphism of rock due to interaction with hot fluid.

hypersaline. Water with abnormally high concentrations of salt.

ice age. A prolonged period of unusually cold temperatures that is distinguished by the presence of periodic ice sheets that cover large portions of the continents.

igneous rock. Rock formed by the solidification of magma. Intrusive igneous rocks solidify underground, whereas extrusive igneous rocks solidify from magma erupted onto Earth's surface as lava.

Ignimbrite Flare-up. A period of intense, explosive volcanic activity in the western United States that occurred between about 37 and 24 million years ago, during the middle Tertiary period.

Iguanodon. A genus of herbivorous dinosaurs that lived during the Late Jurassic through Late Cretaceous periods.

incision. The process of a river eroding its bed to a lower elevation.

intrusion. A mass of igneous rock formed from the cooling and solidification of magma injected into preexisting rock below the surface.

invertebrate. An animal without a backbone.

iridium. A chemical element that is rare on Earth and more common in comets and meteorites. Elevated iridium levels in rocks on Earth may indicate a meteorite impacted the region.

isotope. A variety of a given chemical element that possesses a set number of neutrons. Different isotopes of the same element contain different numbers of neutrons.

joint. A fracture in rock along which no movement has occurred.

kettle. A shallow depression formed where ice blocks are stranded as glaciers melt back. The volume of the ice block reduces the amount of till that is deposited, resulting in the depression. Lakes commonly form in kettles.

kimberlite. A potassium-rich volcanic rock that commonly contains diamonds. Kimberlite solidifies as carrot-shaped intrusions from magma that rises rapidly from deep in the mantle.

K-T boundary. An abbreviation for the time boundary between the Cretaceous and Tertiary periods (also the Mesozoic and Cenozoic eras) of geologic time. A mass extinction, one of the five biggest in Earth's history, occurred at this time boundary.

Laramide orogeny. A mountain building episode that raised the Colorado Plateau and much of the Rocky Mountains between approximately 70 and 40 million years ago.

Laramide Rockies. The group of mountain ranges constructed during the Laramide orogeny.

large-scale crossbedding. Crossbeds in sandstone with a thickness greater than approximately 1.5 feet.

lateral moraine. A moraine that forms along the sides of a glacier and parallels the valley in which the glacier flowed. *See also* ground moraine; terminal moraine.

lava. Molten rock that erupts on Earth's surface.

lava flow. A flow of molten rock erupted by a volcano.

lens. A sedimentary deposit that is thick in the middle and tapers to nothing at its edges.

levee. A natural mound of sediment that separates a river channel from the floodplain. Levees form via sediment deposition during floods.

lignite. A soft brown coal that results from the shallow burial of plant material.

limestone. A sedimentary rock composed mostly of the mineral calcite and often containing marine fossils.

lithification. The compaction and cementation of loose sediments into sedimentary rock.

lithosphere. The planet's rigid outermost shell of rock that lies over the asthenosphere. It consists of all the crust and the uppermost portion of the mantle.

long profile. The graphical representation of the relationship between a river's elevation at a given point along its course and the distance that point lies upstream from the river's terminus.

magma. Molten rock below the surface from which igneous rock is derived.

magma body (magma pod). A general term for a subsurface pool of molten rock of any shape.

magma chamber. An approximately spherical pool of molten rock beneath the surface that feeds a volcano.

mantle. The section of Earth's interior between the crust and the core.

massif. A broad upland area commonly hosting multiple peaks.

massive. Rocks of any origin that are generally homogeneous in texture.

Mazatzal orogeny. A mountain building event that occurred in the American Southwest between about 1,650 and 1,600 million years ago, during the Proterozoic eon.

meandering river. A river with broad, semicircular curves that develop from erosion on the outside of bends and deposition on the inside of bends.

mesa. An elevated, steep-sided, flat-topped landscape feature that is much wider than it is tall.

metamorphic rock. Rock whose original mineralogy, texture, or composition has been changed by the effects of pressure and/or temperature.

mica. A group of silicate minerals that possesses a sheetlike structure.

Mid-Atlantic Ridge. A mountain chain on the seafloor in the middle of the Atlantic Ocean. It has developed as magma wells to the surface where the North American Plate and Eurasian Plate are diverging.

Mid-Continent Rift. An ancient rift zone that formed in North America about 1,100 million years ago. The rift ceased spreading before the continent was ripped apart, but large volumes of gabbro and basalt record the event.

migmatite. A rock that is partially igneous and partially metamorphic.

molybdenum. A metallic element that is used in many industrial processes.

monsoon. A seasonal switch in wind direction accompanied by changes in the amount of precipitation.

moraine. An accumulation of loose sediment deposited by a glacier. *See also* ground moraine; lateral moraine; terminal moraine.

mudstone. Fine-grained sedimentary rock formed from hardened clay and silt.

normal fault. A fault in which the fault block resting on top of the fault plane slides down relative to the fault block below the fault plane. It forms due to crustal extension. *See also* reverse fault; strike-slip fault; thrust fault.

North American Plate. The tectonic plate underlying most of the North American continent and the northwestern Atlantic Ocean. *See also* plate tectonics.

oceanic crust. Dense crust composed of basalt that forms ocean basins. *See also* continental crust.

ore. A rock unit in which a valuable material (for example, gold) is concentrated to such an extent that it is profitable to mine.

orogeny. A tectonic episode during which mountains are built.

paleo. A prefix meaning "old" or "ancient."

Paleocene-Eocene Thermal Maximum (PETM). A dramatic warming of the climate that occurred near the boundary between the Paleocene and Eocene epochs.

paleontology. The study of fossil organisms and the traces (such as tracks) of organisms in the rock record.

paleosol. An ancient soil layer in the rock record.

Pangaea. The supercontinent that developed between 300 and 200 million years ago.

pebble. Rock or mineral particles between roughly 0.08 and 2.5 inches (2 millimeters and 6.35 centimeters) in diameter.

pediment. A gently sloping erosion surface that develops at the foot of a mountain range and is veneered with a thin layer of gravel.

petrified wood. Ancient wood replaced, molecule by molecule, by minerals (usually chert). The texture of the original wood is still visible.

plankton. Small, drifting organisms that float in the uppermost water layers of an ocean or lake.

plate tectonics. The theory that posits the Earth's crust is broken into separate plates that move and interact with each other. *See also* tectonic plate.

pluton. A body of intrusive igneous rock that formed from the cooling and solidification of a former magma chamber beneath the surface.

plutonium. A radioactive element that is used in the construction of atomic bombs.

precipitate. The process of minerals solidifying out of a solution, or the resulting mineral.

pyrite. An iron sulfide mineral also known as fool's gold.

quartz. A very hard, clear or translucent mineral composed of silica.

quartzite. A metamorphic rock composed of sand-sized quartz grains fused by heat and pressure.

radiometric dating. The age dating of a rock by measuring the ratio between certain radioactive isotopes.

regional metamorphism. Metamorphism of a broad area of rocks due to tectonic activity, especially mountain building. Metamorphic rocks become foliated during regional metamorphism.

reverse fault. A high-angle fault in which the fault block above (resting on) the fault plane moves up relative to the fault block below the fault plane. It forms due to tectonic compression. *See also* normal fault; strike-slip fault; thrust fault.

rhyolite. A light-colored, fine-grained extrusive igneous rock with quartz, feldspar, and mica as dominant minerals.

rift. A place where the crust is being pulled apart due to tectonic extension and/or the depression or basin that forms as a result.

Rio Grande Rift. A rift extending northward from southern New Mexico to northern Colorado that has been active since the Neogene period.

ripple mark. A wavy texture formed on the bedding surface of sediment by moving water or wind.

Rodinia. An ancient supercontinent that assembled about 1,100 million years ago and broke up about 750 million years ago.

sand. Rock and mineral particles with a diameter between 0.0025 and 0.08 inch (0.0625 and 2 millimeters) in diameter.

sandstone. Sedimentary rock composed of cemented sand-sized grains.

saprolite. Deeply weathered bedrock that represents a transitional state between bedrock and soil.

sauropod. A suborder of herbivorous dinosaurs that possessed long necks and attained enormous size. Members of this group are the largest animals ever to have inhabited land.

schist. A foliated metamorphic rock that contains greater than 50 percent platy minerals, such as mica and hornblende, and splits along the planes of foliation.

sedimentary rock. Rock formed at Earth's surface from the sediment weathered from preexisting rocks or as the product of biological and/or chemical processes (for example, limestone).

shale. Fine-grained sedimentary rock formed from hardened clay and silt. It typically splits into thin layers.

shear zone. A region that has been severely deformed relative to adjacent areas. It is normally centered around a major fault that extends through most or all of the crust and, in some cases, into the upper mantle.

silica. A chemical compound of one silicon atom surrounded by four oxygen atoms that forms the basic building block of most rock-forming minerals.

silicate. A rock or compound that contains silica.

silt. Rock and mineral particles between 0.00016 and 0.0025 inch (0.004 and 0.0625 millimeter) in diameter.

sodic igneous rock. An igneous rock that contains considerably more sodium oxide than it does potassium oxide.

sphalerite. The primary ore mineral for zinc.

***Stegosaurus*.** A genus of herbivorous, armored dinosaurs that lived during the Late Jurassic period in what are now North America and Europe.

stock. A bulbous igneous intrusion that has a surface exposure of less than 40 square miles.

stratovolcano. A tall, steep-sided, highly explosive volcano built of alternating layers of lava and ejected debris.

strike-slip fault. A fault along which the fault block on one side slides horizontally relative to the fault block on the other side. *See also* normal fault; reverse fault; thrust fault.

subduction. A tectonic process in which a dense oceanic plate dives beneath another plate due to convergence.

subduction zone. The plate boundary where subduction occurs. It is marked by a chain of volcanoes. *See also* volcanic (island) arc.

supercontinent. An ancient continent that contained all or most of the world's existing continental area. *See also* Pangaea; Rodinia.

suture zone. The seam that developed where two tectonic plates are juxtaposed along an ancient collision zone.

syncline. A concave-upward (bowl-shaped) fold whose core contains stratigraphically younger rocks.

tailings. The pulverized material left over after the valuable metal has been extracted from ore.

tectonic. Pertaining to the large-scale processes that deform Earth's crust. It is mostly used in reference to plate tectonics.

tectonic plate. A rigid section of Earth's lithosphere that moves relative to and interacts with other rigid sections. *See also* plate tectonics.

tennantite. An important copper ore.

terminal moraine. The pile of glacially deposited sediment that forms at the terminus of a glacier. *See also* ground moraine; lateral moraine.

terrace. A pediment that stands above a modern river floodplain due to river incision.

theropod. A suborder of carnivorous dinosaurs that walked on two feet. Members of this suborder were the largest carnivores to ever inhabit land.

thrust fault. A low-angle fault in which the fault block above (resting on) the fault plane moves up relative to the fault block below the fault plane. It forms due to tectonic compression. *See also* normal fault; reverse fault; strike-slip fault.

till. Glacially deposited sediment composed of particles of all sizes.

trace fossil. A fossil that reveals the former presence of an organism but does not contain any part of the organism's body; for instance, a footprint.

track. A fossilized footprint.

trackway. A series of fossilized footprints made by a moving animal.

***Triceratops*.** A genus of herbivorous dinosaurs that lived during the Late Cretaceous period in what is now North America.

tuff. Rock composed of compacted volcanic fragments, mostly ash.

unconformity. A contact between two different rocks that represents a time gap in the geologic record during which rock layers were eroded or never deposited.

uniformitarianism. The assumption that the same natural laws and processes that operate today also operated in the past. The foundational principle of geology. *See also* catastrophism.

uplift. An event that topographically raises an area, or the structurally high area produced by this motion.

vein. A tabular body of crystallized minerals within a rock. Veins are deposited by the passage of hot fluids (water or magma) through a rock.

vertebrate. An animal that possesses a backbone.

volcanic field. An area in which volcanic activity is abundant over a specified period of time.

volcanic (island) arc. A chain of volcanoes associated with a subduction zone. When the plates involved in subduction are oceanic, the volcanoes form an arcuate chain of islands. When one plate is continental, the volcanoes form a coastal mountain range.

volcanic pipe. The vertical conduit below a volcano through which magma passes.

vug. A cavity inside a rock.

weathering. The disintegration and decomposition of rock at or near Earth's surface by chemical and physical means. *See also* erosion.

Western Interior Seaway. A shallow, interior seaway that existed in North America during the Cretaceous period. It stretched from the present-day Gulf of Mexico to Hudson Bay, inundating most of the Midwest.

Yavapai orogeny. A mountain building event that occurred in the American Southwest between about 1,780 and 1,700 million years ago. *See also* Colorado orogeny.

zircon. A very durable silicate mineral found in many rocks. Widely used in radiometric dating.

Sources of More Information

GENERAL

Dechesne, M., et al. 2011. *Notes on the Denver Basin geologic maps: Bedrock geology, structure, and isopach maps of the Upper Cretaceous to Paleogene strata between Greeley and Colorado Springs, Colorado*. Denver: Denver Museum of Nature and Science and Colorado Geological Survey.

Johnson, K. R., and R. G. Raynolds. 2003. *Ancient Denvers*. Denver: Denver Museum of Nature and Science.

Matthews, V. 2009. *Messages in stone: Colorado's colorful geology*. Denver: Colorado Geological Survey.

McGookey, D. P. 2009. *Geologic wonders of South Park, Colorado*. Midland, TX: Donald McGookey.

Raynolds, R. G., et al. 2007. Earth history along Colorado's Front Range: Salvaging geologic data in the suburbs and sharing it with the citizens. *GSA Today* 17 (12):4–10.

Taylor, A. M. 1999. *Guide to the geology of Colorado*. Golden, CO: Cataract Lode Mining Company.

1. DIAMONDS

Colorado Geological Survey. 1999. Diamonds. *Rocktalk* 2 (3):1–12.

Lester, A., et al. 2001. Neoproterozoic kimberlite emplacement in the Front Range, Colorado. *Rocky Mountain Geology* 36 (1):1–12.

Lester, A., and G. L. Farmer. 1998. Lower crustal and upper mantle xenoliths along the Cheyenne Belt and vicinity. *Rocky Mountain Geology* 33 (2):293–304.

Marshak, S., K. Karlstrom, and J. M. Timmons. 2000. Inversion of Proterozoic extensional faults: An explanation for the pattern of Laramide and Ancestral Rockies intracratonic deformation, United States. *Geology* 28 (8):735–38.

Sandweiss, M. A. 2009. *Passing strange: A Gilded Age tale of love and deception across the color line*. New York: Penguin.

2. SOAPSTONE PRAIRIE

Courtright, T. R., and W. Braddock. 1989. *Geologic map of the Table Mountain quadrangle and adjacent parts of the Round Butte and Buckeye quadrangles,*

Larimer County, Colorado, and Laramie County, Wyoming. U.S. Geological Survey miscellaneous investigations map I-1805, 1 sheet, scale 1:24,000.

McMillan, M. E., C. L. Angevine, and P. L. Heller. 2002. Postdepositional tilt of the Miocene-Pliocene Ogallala Group on the western Great Plains: Evidence of late Cenozoic uplift of the Rocky Mountains. *Geology* 30 (1):63–66.

Molnar, P., and P. England. 1990. Late Cenozoic uplift of mountain ranges and global climate change: Chicken or egg? *Nature* 346: 29–34.

Moore, F. E. 1960. Summary of Cenozoic history, southern Laramie Range, Wyoming and Colorado. In *Guide to the geology of Colorado*, eds. R. J. Weimer and J. D. Haun, 217–222. New York: Geological Society of America.

3. TRAIL RIDGE ROAD

Braddock, W., and J. Cole. 1990. *Geologic map of Rocky Mountain National Park and vicinity, Colorado.* U.S. Geological Survey miscellaneous investigations map I-1973, 1 sheet, scale 1:50,000.

Cole, J., and W. Braddock. 2009. *Geologic map of the Estes Park 30′ x 60′ quadrangle, north-central Colorado.* U.S. Geological Survey scientific investigations map 3039, 1 sheet, scale 1:100,000.

Raup, O. 1996. *Geology along Trail Ridge Road.* Helena, MT: Rocky Mountain Nature Association.

4. BIG THOMPSON FLOOD

Balog, J. D. 1978. Flooding in Big Thompson River, Colorado, tributaries: Controls on channel erosion and estimates of recurrence interval. *Geology* 6 (4):200–204.

Costa, J. E. 1978. Colorado Big Thompson flood: Geologic evidence of a rare hydrologic event. *Geology* 6 (10):617–20.

Jarrett, R. D., and J. E. Costa. 2006. *1976 Big Thompson Flood, Colorado—thirty years later.* U.S. Geological Survey fact sheet 2006-3095.

5. ELDORADO CANYON STATE PARK

Sweet, D. E., and G. S. Soreghan. 2010. Late Paleozoic tectonics and paleogeography of the ancestral Front Range: Structural, stratigraphic, and sedimentologic evidence from the Fountain Formation (Manitou Springs, Colorado). *Geological Society of America Bulletin* 122 (3–4):575–94.

Van de Kamp, P. C., and B. E. Leake. 1994. Petrology, geochemistry, and alteration of Pennsylvanian-Permian arkose, Colorado and Utah. *Geological Society of America Bulletin* 106 (12):1571–82.

Warnock, A. C., and P. C. Van de Kamp. 1999. Hump-shaped $^{40}Ar/^{39}Ar$ spectra in K-feldspar and evidence for Cretaceous authigenesis in the Fountain Formation near Eldorado Springs, Colorado. *Earth and Planetary Science Letters* 174 (1–2):99–111.

6. ROCKY FLATS

Colorado Department of Public Health and Environment. *Rocky Flats historical public exposures studies*, technical topic papers. www.cdphe.state.co.us/rf/contamin.htm.

Dünforth, M., et al. 2012. Unsteady late Pleistocene incision of streams bounding the Colorado Front Range from measurements of meteoric and in situ ^{10}Be. *Journal of Geophysical Research* 117, F01023, doi:10.1029/2011JF002232.

Johnson, C. J., R. R. Tidball, and R. C. Severson. 1976. Plutonium in respirable dust on the surface of soil. *Science* 193 (4252):488–90.

Knepper, D. H. 2008. Bedrock erosion surface beneath the Rocky Flats alluvial fan, Jefferson and Boulder counties, Colorado. *Mountain Geologist* 42 (1):1–9.

Krey, P. W., and E. P. Hardy. 1970. *Plutonium in soils around the Rocky Flats plant*. HASL 235, U.S. Atomic Energy Commission Health and Safety Laboratory.

Riihimaki, C. A., et al. 2006. Longevity and progressive abandonment of the Rocky Flats surface, Front Range, Colorado. *Geomorphology* 78 (3–4):265–78.

7. COLORADO MINERAL BELT

Aleinikoff, J. N., et al. 1993. The Mount Evans Batholith in the Colorado Front Range: Revision of its age and reinterpretation of its structure. *Geological Society of America Bulletin* 105 (6):791–806.

Budge, S., et al. 1987. Tertiary mineralization—Idaho Springs, Colorado. In *Centennial field guide*, vol. 2, ed. S. S. Beus, 311–14. Boulder, CO: Geological Society of America.

Caine, J. S., et al. 2006. Structural fabrics, mineralization, and Laramide kinematics of the Idaho Springs–Ralston shear zone, Colorado Mineral Belt, and central Front Range uplift. *Mountain Geologist* 43 (1):1–24.

Chapin, C. E. 2012. Origin of the Colorado Mineral Belt. *Geosphere* 8 (1): 28–43.

Colorado Department of Public Health and Environment. 2000. *Argo Water Treatment Plant, Idaho Springs, Idaho: History and overview*.

McCoy, A., et al. 2005. The Proterozoic ancestry of the Colorado Mineral Belt: 1.4 Ga shear zone system in central Colorado. In *The Rocky Mountain region: An evolving lithosphere*, geophysical monograph 154, eds. K. E. Karlstrom and R. G. Keller, 71–90. Washington, DC: American Geophysical Union.

8. THE RAISING AND THE RAZING OF THE ROCKIES

Drewes, H., and J. Townrow. 2005. *Trailwalkers guide to the Dinosaur Ridge, Red Rocks, and Green Mountain area*. Morrison, CO: Friends of Dinosaur Ridge.

Fair, E., et al. 2008. *A guide to Triceratops Trail*. Morrison, CO: Friends of Dinosaur Ridge.

Jones, C. H., et al. 2011. Hydrodynamic mechanism for the Laramide orogeny. *Geosphere* 7 (1):183–201.

Obradovich, J. D. 2002. Geochronology of Laramide synorogenic strata in the Denver Basin, Colorado. *Rocky Mountain Geology* 37 (2):165–71.

Raynolds, R. G. 2002. Upper Cretaceous and Tertiary stratigraphy of the Denver Basin, Colorado. *Rocky Mountain Geology* 37 (2):111–34.

Scott, G. R. 1972. *Geologic map of the Morrison quadrangle, Jefferson County, Colorado*. U.S. Geological Survey miscellaneous geologic investigations map I-790-A, 1 sheet, scale 1:24,000.

9. RED ROCKS TO GOLDEN

Johnson, K. R., and R. G. Raynolds. 2003. *Ancient Denvers*. Denver: Denver Museum of Nature and Science.

Weimer, R. J. 2004. *Lessons from the Mines Geology Trail*. Denver: Colorado School of Mines Geology Museum special publication 2.

Weimer, R. J., and L. W. LeRoy. 1987. Paleozoic-Mesozoic section: Red Rocks Park, I-70 road cut, and Rooney Road, Morrison area, Jefferson County, Colorado. In *Centennial field guide*, vol. 2, ed. S. S. Beus, 315–19. Boulder, CO: Geological Society of America.

10. DINOSAUR RIDGE

Friends of Dinosaur Ridge website. www.dinoridge.org.

Jaffe, M. 2000. *The gilded dinosaur: The fossil war between E .D. Cope and O. C. Marsh and the rise of American science*. New York: Crown.

Lockley, M. 2001. *A field guide to Dinosaur Ridge*. Denver: University of Colorado at Denver and Friends of Dinosaur Ridge.

Mountain Geologist. 2001. 38:87–164. Special edition with six articles dedicated to various studies of Dinosaur Ridge.

Wallace, D. R. 1999. *The bonehunters' revenge*. Boston: Houghton Mifflin.

11. WALL MOUNTAIN TUFF AND CASTLE ROCK CONGLOMERATE

Chapin, C. E., and W. C. McIntosh. 2004. Geochronology of the central Colorado volcanic field. In *Tectonics, geochronology, and volcanism in the southern Rocky Mountains and Rio Grande Rift*, eds. S. M. Cather, W. McIntosh, and S. A. Kelley, 205–37. New Mexico Bureau of Mines and Mineral Resources bulletin 160.

Johnson, K. R., and R. G. Raynolds. 2003. *Ancient Denvers*. Denver: Denver Museum of Nature and Science.

Leonard, E. M., et al. 2002. High Plains to Rio Grande Rift: Late Cenozoic evolution of central Colorado. In *Science at the highest level*, field guide 3, ed. D. Lageson, 59–93. Boulder, CO: Geological Society of America.

Morse, D. G. 1985. Oligocene paleogeography in the southern Denver Basin. In *Cenozoic paleogeography of the west-central United States*, eds. R. M. Flores and S. S. Kaplan, 272–92. Denver, CO: Rocky Mountain Section, Society of Economic Paleontologists and Mineralogists.

12. FLORISSANT FOSSIL BEDS NATIONAL MONUMENT

Barton, M. 2010. *Floral diversity and climate change in central Colorado during the Eocene and Oligocene*. Thesis, University of Colorado, Boulder.

Henry, T. W., et al. 2004. *Geologic guidebook to the Gold Belt Byway Colorado*. Gunnison, CO: Gold Belt Tour Historic and Scenic Byway Association.

MacGinitie, H. 1953. Fossil plants of the Florissant beds, Colorado. Washington, DC: Carnegie Institution of Washington.

Meyer, H. W., and D. M. Smith. 2008. *Paleontology of the upper Eocene Florissant Formation, Colorado*. Geological Society of America special papers 435.

Meyer, H. W., S. W. Veatch, and A. Cook. 2004. Field guide to the paleontology and volcanic setting of the Florissant fossil beds, Colorado. In *Field trips in the southern Rocky Mountains, USA*, field guide 5, eds. E. P. Nelson and E. A. Erslev, 151–66. Boulder, CO: Geological Society of America.

Prothero, D. R. 2008. Magnetic stratigraphy of the Eocene-Oligocene floral transition in western North America. In *Paleontology of the upper Eocene Florissant Formation, Colorado*, Geological Society of America special papers 435, eds. H. W. Meyer and D. M. Smith, 71–87. Boulder, CO: Geological Society of America.

13. CRIPPLE CREEK

Cappa, J. A. 1998. *Alkalic igneous rocks of Colorado and their associated ore deposits*. Colorado Geological Survey resource series 35.

Colorado Geological Survey. 2003. Gold! Gold! Gold! *Rocktalk* 6 (2):1–12.

Henry, T. W., et al. 2004. *Geologic guidebook to the Gold Belt Byway Colorado*. Gunnison, CO: Gold Belt Tour Historic and Scenic Byway Association.

Jensen, E. P., and M. D. Barton. 2008. Geology, petrochemistry, and time-space evolution of the Cripple Creek district, Colorado. In *Roaming the Rocky Mountains and environs: Geological field trips*, field guide 10, ed. R. G. Raynolds, 63–78. Boulder, CO: Geological Society of America.

14. PIKES PEAK

Hutchinson, R. M. 1987. Granite-tectonics of the Pikes Peak intrusive center of Pikes Peak composite batholith, Colorado. In *Centennial field guide*, vol. 2, ed. S. S. Beus, 331–34. Boulder, CO: Geological Society of America.

Noblett, J. B. 1994. *A guide to the geological history of the Pikes Peak region*. Colorado Springs, CO: Colorado College.

Raines, E. 2001. A brief summary of the mineral deposits of the Pikes Peak Batholith, Colorado. *Rocks and Minerals* 76 (5):298–303.

Smith, D. R., et al. 1999. A review of the Pikes Peak Batholith, Front Range, central Colorado: A "type example" of A-type granitic magmatism. *Rocky Mountain Geology* 34 (2):289–312.

Whitmeyer, S. J., and K. E. Karlstrom. 2007. Tectonic model for the Proterozoic growth of North America. *Geosphere* 3 (4):220–59. DOI: 10.1130/GES00055.1.

15. CAVE OF THE WINDS

Cave of the Winds website. www.caveofthewinds.com.

City of Manitou Springs website information on the city's mineral springs. www.manitousprings.org/mineral-springs.

Luiszer, F. G. 2009. Speleogenesis of Cave of the Winds, Manitou Springs, Colorado. In *Select field guides to cave and karst lands of the United States*, special publication 15, eds. A. S. Engel and S. A. Engel, 119–32. Leesburg, VA: Karst Waters Institute.

Luiszer, F. G. 1999. Field trip to Manitou Springs, Colorado, with specific emphasis on the sediments of Cave of the Winds and their relationship to nearby alluvial deposits and spring sediments. In *Colorado and adjacent areas*, field guide 1, eds. D. R. Lageson, A. P. Lester, and B. D. Trudgill, 61–70. Boulder, CO: Geological Society of America.

Myrow, P. M., et al. 2003. Fallen arches: Dispelling myths concerning Cambrian and Ordovician paleogeography of the Rocky Mountain region. *Geological Society of America Bulletin* 115 (6):695–713.

Myrow, P. M., et al. 1999. Stratigraphy, sedimentology, and paleontology of the Cambrian-Ordovician of Colorado. In *Colorado and adjacent areas*, field guide 1, eds. D. R. Lageson, A. P. Lester, and B. D. Trudgill, 157–76. Boulder, CO: Geological Society of America.

Noblett, J. B., et al. 1987. The Garden of the Gods and basal Phanerozoic nonconformity in and near Colorado Springs, Colorado. In *Centennial field guide*, vol. 2, ed. S. S. Beus, 335–38. Boulder, CO: Geological Society of America.

16. GARDEN OF THE GODS

Morgan, M. L., et al. 2003. *Geologic map of the Cascade quadrangle, El Paso County, Colorado*. Denver, CO: Colorado Geological Survey.

Milito, S. 2010. A survey of fossils and geology of Red Rock Canyon Open Space, Colorado Springs, Colorado. *Mountain Geologist* 47 (1):1–14.

Noblett, J. B. 1994. *A guide to the geological history of the Pikes Peak region*. Colorado Springs, CO: Colorado College.

Noblett, J. B., et al. 1987. The Garden of the Gods and basal Phanerozoic nonconformity in and near Colorado Springs, Colorado. In *Centennial field guide*, vol. 2, ed. S. S. Beus, 335–38. Boulder, CO: Geological Society of America.

Sweet, D. E., and G. S. Soreghan. 2010. Late Paleozoic tectonics and paleogeography of the Ancestral Front Range: Structural, stratigraphic, and sedimentologic evidence from the Fountain Formation (Manitou Springs, Colorado). *Geological Society of America Bulletin* 122 (3–4):575–94.

17. PAINT MINES INTERPRETIVE PARK

Denver Museum of Nature and Science Castle Rock Fossil Rainforest website: www.paleocurrents.com/castle_rock/docs/overview.html.

Ellis, B., K. R. Johnson, and R. E. Dunn. 2003. Evidence for an in situ early Paleocene rainforest from Castle Rock, Colorado. *Rocky Mountain Geology* 38 (1):73–100.

Farnham, T. M., and M. J. Kraus. 2002. The stratigraphic and climatic significance of the Paleogene alluvial paleosols in synorogenic strata of the Denver Basin, Colorado. *Rocky Mountain Geology* 37 (2):201–13.

Wing, S. L., et al. 2005. Transient floral change and rapid global warming at the Paleocene-Eocene boundary. *Science* 310 (5750):993–96.

Zachos, J. C., G. R. Dickens, and R. E. Zeebe. 2008. An early Cenozoic perspective on greenhouse warming and carbon-cycle dynamics. *Nature* 451:279–83.

18. ROYAL GORGE

Leonard, E. M., et al. 2002. High Plains to Rio Grande Rift: Late Cenozoic evolution of central Colorado. In *Science at the highest level*, field guide 3, ed. D. Lageson, 59–93. Boulder, CO: Geological Society of America.

Sak, P. B., et al. 2005. Late Cenozoic drainage reorganization of the Arkansas River, central Colorado, and history of the Royal Gorge. *Geological Society of America Abstracts with Programs* 37:295.

Wobus, R. A., et al. 2001. Geochemistry and tectonic setting of paleo-Proterozoic metavolcanic rocks of the southern Front Range, lower Arkansas River canyon, and northern Wet Mountains, central Colorado. *Rocky Mountain Geology* 36 (2):99–118.

19. JURASSIC PARK (CAÑON CITY AREA)

Bureau of Land Management. Garden Park Fossil Area website: www.handsontheland.org/garden-park.

Dinosaur Depot Museum website. www.dinosaurdepot.com.

Gorman, M. A., et al. 2008. Plants, fish, turtles, and insects from the Morrison Formation: A Late Jurassic ecosystem near Cañon City, Colorado. In *Roaming the Rocky Mountains and environs: Geologic field trips*, field guide 10, ed. R. G. Raynolds, 295–310. Boulder, CO: Geological Society of America.

Henry, T. W., et al. 2004. *Geologic guidebook to the Gold Belt Byway Colorado*. Gunnison, CO: Gold Belt Tour Historic and Scenic Byway Association.

Jaffe, M. 2000. *The gilded dinosaur: The fossil war between E. D. Cope and O. C. Marsh and the rise of American science*. New York: Crown.

Kurtz, W. J., M. G. Lockley, and D. J. Engard. 2001. Dinosaur tracks in the Plainview Formation, Dakota Group (Cretaceous, Albian) near Cañon City, Colorado: A preliminary report on another "Dinosaur Ridge." *Mountain Geologist* 38 (3):155–64.

Morgan, M. 2000. *A dash with the dinosaurs: A mountain bike trek to the Purgatoire River dinosaur trackway and the Cretaceous-Tertiary boundary impact layer of southeastern Colorado*. Denver: Colorado Geological Survey.

20. SPANISH PEAKS

Hutchinson, R. M., and J. D. Vine. 1987. Alteration zones related to igneous activity, Spanish Peaks area, Las Animas and Huerfano counties, Colorado. In *Centennial field guide*, vol. 2, ed. S. S. Beus, 357–60. Boulder, CO: Geological Society of America.

Penn, B. S. 1995–2012. *Igneous Petrology of the Spanish Peaks*. www.spanishpeakscolorado.com.

Penn, B. S., and D. A. Lindsey. 2009. $^{40}Ar/^{39}Ar$ dates for the Spanish Peaks intrusions in south-central Colorado. *Rocky Mountain Geology* 44 (1):17–32.

Penn, B. S., and D. A. Lindsey. 1996. *Tertiary igneous rocks and Laramide structure and stratigraphy of the Spanish Peaks region, south-central Colorado*. Colorado Geological Survey open-file report 96-4.

Smith, R. P. 1987. Alteration zones related to igneous activity, Spanish Peaks area, Las Animas and Huerfano counties, Colorado. In *Mafic dike swarms*, Geological Association of Canada special paper 34, eds. H. C. Halls and W. F. Fahrig, 47–54. Toronto: Geological Survey of Canada.

21. TRINIDAD LAKE STATE PARK

Alvarez, W. 1997. *T. rex and the crater of doom*. Princeton, NJ: Princeton University Press.

Izett, G. A. 1990. *The Cretaceous-Tertiary boundary interval, Raton Basin, Colorado and New Mexico, and its content of shock-metamorphosed minerals: Evidence relevant to the K-T boundary impact-extinction theory*. Geological Society of America special paper 249.

Krogh, T. E., et al. 1993. Fingerprinting the K-T impact site and determining the time of impact by U-Pb dating of single shocked zircons from distal ejecta. *Earth and Planetary Science Letters* 119 (3):425–29.

Morgan, M. 2000. *A dash with the dinosaurs: A mountain bike trek to the Purgatoire River dinosaur trackway and the Cretaceous-Tertiary boundary impact layer of southeastern Colorado*. Denver: Colorado Geological Survey.

Nichols, D. J. 2007. Selected plant microfossil records of the terminal Cretaceous event in terrestrial rocks, western North America. *Palaeogeography, Palaeoclimatology, Palaeoecology* 255 (1–2):22–34.

Pillmore, C. L., D. J. Nichols, and R. F. Fleming. 1999. Field guide to the continental Cretaceous-Tertiary boundary in the Raton Basin, Colorado and New Mexico. In *Colorado and adjacent areas*, field guide 1, eds. D. R. Lageson, A. P. Lester, and B. D. Trudgill, 135–56. Boulder, CO: Geological Society of America.

Powell, J. L. 1998. *Night comes to the Cretaceous: Dinosaur extinction and the transformation of modern geology*. San Diego: Harcourt Brace.

Index

Vignette images are referenced in the index in **bold font** with a letter following the page number as follows:

a—artistic renderings **d**—diagrams **m**—maps **p**—photographs

The same page number accompanying an image typically references a related caption.

Lon Abbott is a geology faculty member at the University of Colorado at Boulder whose recent research has focused on the cutting of the Grand Canyon and the formation of the Colorado Rockies. **Terri Cook** is a freelance science writer and member of the National Association of Science Writers. They are coauthors of *Geology Underfoot in Northern Arizona* and *Hiking the Grand Canyon's Geology*. Lon is also the author of an introductory geology lab manual and the rock climbing guidebook *Weekend Rock Arizona*.

Lon received a bachelor's degree in geology and geophysics from the University of Utah and a PhD in earth science from the University of California, Santa Cruz, where he specialized in the study of mountain building. Lon's research has taken him from remote mountain peaks in Papua New Guinea to a 15,000-foot-deep trench near Costa Rica.

Terri earned a master's degree in geology at the University of California, Santa Cruz, where she studied rocks from deep-sea hot springs. Terri's undergraduate degree in archaeology is from Tufts University, and her combined interests in geology, archaeology, and experiencing new cultures have led her across six continents.